RADAR TRANSMITTERS

GEORGE W. EWELL

Principal Research Engineer
Engineering Experiment Station
Georgia Institute of Technology
Atlanta, Georgia

McGRAW-HILL BOOK COMPANY

New York   St. Louis   San Francisco   Auckland
Bogotá   Hamburg   Johannesburg   London   Madrid   Mexico
Montreal   New Delhi   Panama   Paris   São Paulo
Singapore   Sydney   Tokyo   Toronto

ABOUT THE AUTHOR

George W. Ewell is Principal Research Engineer with the Engineering Experiment Station at Georgia Institute of Technology in Atlanta. He has been involved in radar-oriented research and development for over fifteen years. He has made important contributions in such diverse areas as clutter reflectivity, analysis of tracking system errors, and foreign technology, and he remains involved in numerous transmitter programs. He has been associated with transmitter developments using magnetrons, CFAs, EIOs, and TWTs at frequencies from below 1 GHz to above 100 GHz, with pulse lengths as short as 3 ns. Dr. Ewell, who has taught courses in the School of Electrical Engineering, lectures in numerous short courses through the Department of Continuing Education and serves as a consultant to government and private industry.

Library of Congress Cataloging in Publication Data

Ewell, George W
  Radar transmitters.

  Includes index.
  1. Radar transmitters. I. Title.
TK6587.E93   621.3848'3   80–29381

ISBN 0-07-019843-8

1 2 3 4 5 6 7 8 9 0 KPKP 8 9 8 7 6 5 4 3 2 1

The editors for this book were Tyler G. Hicks, Barry Richman, and Susan Thomas; the designer was Elliot Epstein; and the production supervisor was Thomas G. Kowalczyk. It was set in Baskerville by The Kingsport Press.

Printed and bound by The Kingsport Press.

CONTENTS

PREFACE

The material for this book was developed from presentations that were given at short courses on principles of radar, from internal notes and memoranda generated within the Experiment Station at Georgia Tech, and from the notes of a short course on the subject presented during July 1979. This earlier material has been substantially extended and augmented in order to provide a reasonably detailed and comprehensive coverage of high-power microwave radar transmitters.

The motivation for collecting this material was the observation over a number of years that knowledge of radar transmitter design techniques has not been widely disseminated, and that the lack of such knowledge continues to impact a number of radar research, development, and production programs. It has been my observation that design information for radar transmitters and components is not readily available from one source, but is widely scattered in a number of isolated locations, some of which are difficult to access even with the services of a large technical library. Therefore, the objective of this work is not to present a vast body of new knowledge or new and innovative techniques, but to collect from a number of diverse sources the basic design information for a radar transmitter and its components and to present such information in a reasonably uniform manner.

The emphasis is on the integrated design of the radar transmitter, beginning with the system requirements, which in turn generate the transmitter requirements, and on the continual interaction between these requirements and all aspects of transmitter design. The material begins, in Chapter 1, with a presentation of radar system requirements to indicate how the various transmitter requirements arise and to show how transmitter performance influences overall radar system operation. Chapter 2 discusses available microwave power tubes and some of their characteristics, and Chapter 3 is an introduction to radar modulators of various types and some of their principal characteristics. Chapter 4 begins the detailed analysis and design procedures for modulator components with the treatment of the pulse transformer. Chapter 5 presents pulse-forming network design, while the following two chapters discuss charging chokes and switching devices. Chapter 8 sets forth some observations on the specification of transmitters, while Chapter 9 discusses some sample designs to indicate the application of the procedures discussed earlier. Appendix A contains a discussion of measurement techniques unique to high-power microwave transmitters, while Appendix B provides conversions between a number of systems of units commonly in use.

In the event that additional detail is required in any of these areas, the references listed at the end of each chapter should be consulted. In particular, excellent references for microwave tubes include the articles by Skowron, Staprans, McGune, and Ruets, and the article by Mendel. The classical reference on modulators is, of course, Volume 5 of the Rad. Lab. series, and a copy should reside on every transmitter engineer's bookshelf. The most exhaustive reference on pulse-transformer design is undoubtedly the two-volume set by Fenoglio et al., and it certainly contains much additional useful information.

Because of the large number of different symbols which are required to express various concepts throughout the text, unique symbols could not reasonably be assigned to each variable; however, every attempt has been made to define all symbols used close to the point where they are employed and to be consistent in both symbols and units with common usage. Material directly extracted from references preserves the notation of the original source in most cases. A list of symbols and abbreviations used in this book may be found at the end of the front matter.

I would like to take this opportunity to acknowledge the support of a number of people who made this book possible. Mr. Ed Flynt and Dr. H. A. Ecker provided internal support to educate me in the mysteries of modulator design, and Mr. J. C. Butterworth provided invaluable support and practical knowledge during this continuing education. Mr. David Ladd prepared the original section on measurements, which formed the basis for the current Appendix A and designed the EIO modulator of Section IX. Dr. E. K. Reedy provided support for typing of the notes and encouragement to proceed with this endeavor, and Susan Fuller and Nancy Brown typed all of the text material. Finally, I would like to acknowledge the support and patience of my wife and children during the nights and weekends required for preparation of this volume.

I would also like to acknowledge my debt to the authors and publishers who have generously permitted me to reproduce figures and/or tables from their published work. The credit for each such piece of borrowed material is found in the form of a bracketed number, which refers the reader to a list of sources at the end of the chapter.

GEORGE W. EWELL

SYMBOLS AND ABBREVIATIONS USED IN THIS BOOK

a radius of PFN coil (p. 182); length of air gap in a magnetic circuit (p. 198)

A   amperes

A pulse amplitude (p. 15); gross core cross-sectional area (pp. 154, 198)

ac   alternating current

AWG   American wire gauge

B magnetic field strength; equivalent noise bandwidth (p. 3); receiver bandwidth (p. 15); a normalized variable used in PFN case size estimation (p. 190)

B_{dc} dc flux in core

B_m maximum allowable flux density

B_s saturation flux density

BWO   backward-wave oscillator

°C   temperature in degrees Celsius

C band   the radar band covering the 5-GHz region of the frequency spectrum

C_c value of coupling capacitor in a hard-tube modulator

C_d distributed capacitance of the high-voltage winding of a pulse transformer; distributed capacitance of the pulse transformer and load (p. 149)

CE   control electrode

CFA   crossed-field amplifier

C_l load capacitance

cm   centimeters

cmil   circular mil (wire cross-section)

C_n total pulse-forming-network capacitance

COHO   coherent oscillator

C_{out} total capacitance connected to the anode of a switch tube (p. 215)

C_s stray capacitance of hard-tube modulator load

CSV corona start voltage

C_{tot} total capacitance (C_n and stray) with which the charging choke resonates

CW continuous-wave

d PFN coil diameter

D strip width of a wound C core

dB decibels

dBm decibels referred to one milliwatt

dc direct current

DF capacitor dissipation factor

di/dt rate of change of current with respect to time

du duty cycle, the ratio of pulse width to interpulse period

dv/dt rate of change of voltage with respect to time

E electric field stress in solid insulator

E build of a wound C core

E_b plate-to-cathode voltage

E_{bb} dc plate-supply voltage

ec peak positive grid voltage

E_c grid-to-cathode voltage

E_{c1} control-grid voltage

E_{c2} screen-grid voltage

E_d magnetron equivalent diode voltage bias

E_{dc} dc supply voltage

E_f filament voltage

E_g electric field stress in an insulation void

eg grid voltage

EIA extended interaction amplifier

EIO extended interaction oscillator

EM (tuned) a voice-coil-actuated, reciprocation-tuned magnetron, also called a HI-FI tuned magnetron

E_o pulse transformer output voltage; peak output voltage in an SCR-magnetic modulator (p. 267)

e_p switch tube plate voltage during the output pulse

e_{py} peak thyratron anode voltage

E_{sg} screen-grid voltage

f frequency; PFN recharge frequency (p. 201); oscilloscope bandwidth (p. 296)

F C core window width (p. 156); ratio of number of PFN sections to pulse width (p. 194)

f_c filter bandwidth (p. 5); center frequency of pulse spectrum (p. 320)

f_D Doppler frequency

FET field-effect transistor

f_h upper edge of CFA operating frequency band

$F(H)$ PFN life factor (p. 190)

f_l lower edge of CFA operating frequency band

f_m middle of CFA operating frequency band

FM frequency modulation

FW	forward-wave (CFA)		resonant charging
G	C core window length	I_{dc}	direct current passing through a charging choke
GaAs	gallium arsenide		
$G(f)$	power response of MTI processor	IF	intermediate frequency
GHz	gigahertz	I_k	cathode current
$G(w)$	Doppler frequency response of an MTI processor	I_m	magnetizing current
		in	inches
H	henrys	I_o	load current
H	magnetic field strength	I_{op}	operating current
H_c	heat flux density (p. 162); critical magnetic-field intensity (p. 227)	i_p	plate current
		I_p	thyratron rms plate current
$H(f)$	receiver frequency response	I_s	diode saturation current
		J	joules
HI-FI (magnetron)	an E-M tuned magnetron	k	tube cathode perveance (pp. 60, 92); damping coefficient (pp. 145, 149); relative dielectric constant of insulation (p. 152); a core-loss constant (p. 201)
H_m	pulse magnetization force		
HV	high-voltage winding of a pulse transformer		
HVDC	high-voltage direct-current	K	Nagaoka's constant
Hz	hertz (cycles/second)	°K	temperature in degrees kelvin
I	MTI improvement factor	kA	kiloamperes
i_b	thyratron peak anode current	kG	kilogauss
I_b	thyratron average anode current	K_u band	the radar band covering the 16-GHz region of the frequency spectrum
I_b'	magnetic bias current of a saturating magnetic switch referred to the main winding	kV	kilovolts
		kW	kilowatts
i_{ce}	control electrode current	L	inductance per section of a PFN coil (p. 110); charging-choke inductance (p. 198)
$I_{c(av)}$	average charging current for resonant charging		
$I_{c(max)}$	peak charging current for resonant charging	l	length of coil of one PFN section (p. 110); length of magnetic circuit in a core (pp. 158, 198); coil length (p. 182)
$I_{c(rms)}$	rms charging current for		

L band — the radar band covering the l-GHz portion of the frequency spectrum

L_c — inductance of section of PFN on closed end (p. 110); charging inductance (p. 112)

l_c — average mean length of pulse transformer coil turn

L_l — leakage inductance of pulse transformer (p. 145); referred to the high-voltage winding (p. 151)

L_m — magnetizing inductance of a pulse transformer

L_n — total PFN inductance

L_n' — sum of leakage inductance and PFN inductance (p. 149)

L_r — viewing-resistor inductance

L_s — saturated inductance of a saturating magnetic switch; recharging inductance of a hard-tube modulator (p. 107)

$L_{2(s)}$ — saturated inductance of delay reactor L_2 (p. 126)

LV — low-voltage pulse-transformer winding

mA — milliamperes

MBWO — M-type backward-wave oscillator

mHz — megahertz

mil — one-thousandth of an inch

mm — millimeters

mmHg — absolute pressure in millimeters of mercury

MOPA — master-oscillator power amplifier

ms — milliseconds

MTI — moving-target indication

MW — megawatts (10^6 W)

n — transformer turns ratio; number of PFN sections (p. 110); designator for Darlington line sections (p. 183)

N — number of turns

NAND — a logic gate which performs the complement of the logical AND function

ns — nanoseconds

N_s — total number of high-voltage winding turns series-connected

OBWO — O-type backward-wave oscillator

Oe — oersteds

OFHC — oxygen-free, high-conductivity

oz — ounces

P — output power

P_b — thyratron plate-breakdown factor

pd — CFA drive power (p. 50)

P_d — switch-tube plate dissipation

pF — picofarads

PFN — pulse-forming network

PM — phase modulation

P_o — peak CFA power output (p. 55); thyratron power output (p. 211); peak SCR dissipation (p. 222)

PPM — periodic permanent magnet

PRF — pulse-repetition frequency

p_{rr} — pulse-repetition rate (p. 50)

Q the quality factor of a coil, the ratio of energy stored to energy dissipated per cycle

r' equivalent leakage resistance of a magnetron

RBDT   reverse-blocking diode thyristor

R_c recharging resistance of a hard-tube modulator (pp. 104, 106); equivalent charging-choke resistance (p. 112)

r_d magnetron dynamic impedance (p. 24)

R_e load resistance

R_{eff} effective wire resistance for high frequencies and pulses

R_{eq} equivalent resistance of a charging choke (p. 201)

RF   radio frequency

R_g pulse-source impedance (p. 145)

R_i load resistance during time shortly after the transformer output pulse (p. 149)

R_l load resistance

R_m equivalent magnetron resistance (p. 148); matching resistance (p. 312)

rms   root mean square

r_p equivalent plate resistance of a switch tube (p. 104)

R_p magnetron static resistance

RRV   rate of rise of voltage

R_s source resistance (p. 312)

RSR   reverse-switching rectifier

r_t insulation thermal resistivity

R_θ thermal impedance

S insulation pad thickness

SBV   self-breakdown voltage

SCR   silicon-controlled rectifier

$S(f)$ frequency spectrum of transmitted signal

SFD   a tube manufacturer, now a part of Varian, Inc.

STALO   stable local oscillator

T   teslas

T temperature; interpulse period; a normalized time variable (p. 146)

t wire traverse (p. 152); pulse length (p. 154); length of surface creep path (p. 164); insulation thickness (p. 186)

$T_{1(l)}$ leakage inductance of transformer T_1 (p. 126)

$T_{2(s)}$ saturated inductance of transformer T_2 (p. 126)

T_c case temperature

t_e core lamination thickness

TE   transverse electric

l_g insulation void thickness

T_j junction temperature

tp   pulse width (p. 122)

t_{pc} pulse width (p. 43)

t_{pd} pulse width of CFA drive pulse (p. 50)

t_{pf} CFA-output pulse width (p. 50)

t_q RBDT turnoff time

T_r time to charge PFN

t_r pulse rise time

$t_{r(\text{pulse})}$ pulse rise time

TWT   traveling-wave tube

V voltage

V_g pulse-generator source voltage (p. 145); voltage developed across insulation gap (p. 186)

VHF   very high frequency

V_n PFN voltage during resonant charging

V_o Twystron operating voltage (p. 72); initial transmission-line voltage (p. 109)

V_{op} magnetron operating voltage

VSWR   voltage standing-wave ratio

V_t total voltage across an insulation pad containing voids

V_x voltage across solid portion of an insulation pad containing voids

W   watts

Wb   webers

W_g air-gap loss in a gapped magnetic core

W_t total charging-choke losses

X band   the radar band covering the 9-GHz portion of the frequency spectrum

xfmr   transformer

Z_l transmission-line terminating impedance

Z_n equivalent PFN impedance (p. 116)

Z_o transmission-line characteristic impedance

$Z_\theta(t)$ transient thermal impedance

Z_r impedance of the rth network of a Darlington line

α_r pulse desensitization factor

β phase shift per unit length

Δ ratio of inductor current to load current

ΔA pulse-to-pulse voltage-amplitude change

ΔB induction change in magnetic core

ΔB_{AC} peak ac flux excursion in a magnetic core

ΔE_b change in anode-to-cathode voltage

Δf pulse-to-pulse frequency change

ΔI change in current

ΔI_d decrease in load current

ΔP change in power

Δpd change in drive power

ΔV change in voltage

η_c charging efficiency of a line-type modulator

θ temperature drop

θ_o klystron electrical length

λ operating wavelength; length of heat-flow path (p. 161); volt-time integral product for a magnetic core

μ amplification factor of a tube-control electrode (p. 59); triode amplification factor (p. 92)

μ_c cutoff amplification factor of a tube-control electrode (p. 59)

μ_d permeability during trailing edge of pulse (p. 148)

μ_Δ incremental permeability of core material under conditions of magnetization present in core

μ_e core permeability at end of pulse (p. 148); pulse permeability (pp. 155, 259)

μH microhenrys

μ_0 permeability of free space

μ_p plate voltage-amplification factor

μs microseconds

μ_s relative permeability of saturated core material; screen amplification factor (p. 93)

μ_{sg} screen-grid voltage-amplification factor

Σd total radial build of winding layers carrying pulse current in a pulse transformer

τ pulse width; interpulse period (p. 222)

ϕ magnetic flux

ω radian frequency, i.e. $\omega = 2\pi f$; network charging rate (p. 201)

Ω ohms

ω_0 undamped resonant frequency (p. 112)

1
RADAR TRANSMITTER REQUIREMENTS

One of the essential features of a representative radar system is some source of radiated energy. This energy may be continuous-wave (CW) or pulsed, and its amplitude and frequency structure may be designed to fulfill the specific requirements of the radar system. While radar transmitters cover a wide range of power levels and pulse lengths, this discussion will be largely confined to high-power pulsed transmitters of the type which would be commonly encountered in radar systems.

The characteristics of available transmitters may be an important factor in selecting operating frequency, transmitted waveform, duty cycle, or other important radar parameters. In addition, the transmitter is often a large, heavy, and expensive component of the radar system, and one which consumes considerable power and requires periodic maintenance and replacement. Thus, the proper choice of transmitter can strongly influence the size, operating cost, maintainability, reliability, and performance of the radar system. Therefore, a thorough knowledge of transmitter types and characteristics is essential to the practicing radar system engineer, and a thorough, professional transmitter design effort is necessary for a successful radar system.

Some of the factors to consider in radar transmitter selection and design include:

- Peak power
- Average power

- Spurious outputs
- Cost

- Pulse length
- Pulse-repetition frequency (PRF)
- Bandwidth
- Stability (amplitude and phase)
- Distortion
- Efficiency
- Size and weight

- Life
- Leakage (RF and X-ray)
- Tunability
- Arcing
- Gain
- Required dynamic range
- Reliability and maintainability

A simplified radar system block diagram is shown in Figure 1–1. The pulsed transmitter derives its power from the power source; its timing is established by a PRF generator; and its output is sent to a circulator or duplexer for transmission to the antenna. On reception, the received signal is routed through the receiver to the mixer, where it is mixed with the local oscillator output and amplified at intermediate frequencies before detection. The output of the detector may be directly displayed for the operator, or additional signal processing may be applied in order to emphasize particular characteristics of the received signal.

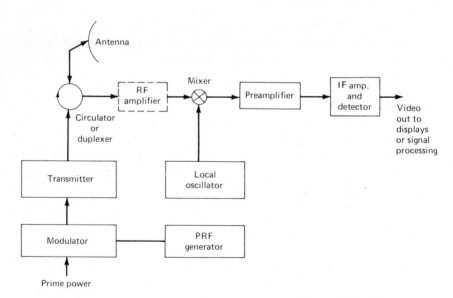

FIGURE 1–1 Simplified radar block diagram. PRF = pulse repetition frequency.

The range resolution of such a pulsed system is given by the equation

$$\frac{c\tau}{2}$$

where c is the velocity of light and τ is the transmitted pulse width. The unambiguous range is given by the equation

$$\frac{cT}{2}$$

where T is the interpulse period.

The power received by the radar system is given by the so-called radar equation,

$$P_r = \frac{P_t G_t G_r \lambda^2 \sigma}{(4\pi)^3 R^4} \tag{1-1}$$

where P_r = received power
$\quad\quad P_t$ = transmitted power
$\quad\quad G_t$ = transmitting antenna gain
$\quad\quad G_r$ = receiving antenna gain
$\quad\quad \lambda$ = operating wavelength
$\quad\quad \sigma$ = target radar cross section
$\quad\quad R$ = range to the target

in any consistent system of units (such as m, m², and w).

This received signal is received in the presence of receiver noise, which has an equivalent noise power given by

$$N_0 = kTB$$

where N_0 = noise power (W)
$\quad\quad k$ = Boltzmann's constant (1.38×10^{-23} J/°K)
$\quad\quad T$ = absolute temperature (°K)
$\quad\quad B$ = equivalent noise bandwidth (Hz)

Thus, the desired signal is never received alone; in all cases, it will be corrupted by the presence of thermal noise.

Decisions concerning the presence or absence of a target or the characteristics of that target require a probabilistic decision process. Historically, the concepts of false-alarm probability and detection probability have been developed to deal with this particular situation. It is not the intention of this book to deal at any length with the concepts of statistical detection theory, but it is important to note, and intuitively satisfying, that increased signal-to-noise ratios at the receiver output result in reduced false-alarm probability for a constant detection probability, or increased detection probability for a given false-alarm probability. Thus, maximization of the signal-to-noise ratio at the receiver output is a valid objective of a radar system design.

As shown by Equation 1–1, the signal-to-noise ratio at the output of the receiver may be increased by increasing transmitted power. However, dramatic increases in peak transmitted power are often made impossible by the characteristics of the available transmitting devices. Fortunately, there are a number of other ways to increase the signal-to-noise ratio at the receiver output; however, all of these require additional radar transmitter capabilities.

1–1 MATCHED FILTERING

The requirement for optimum detection of a signal of known characteristics in white gaussian noise gave rise to the concept of the *matched filter* [4]. The matched filter maximizes the peak signal-to-noise ratio for a known signal in additive white noise, and it is also optimum for a number of other detection strategies. The matched filter is a form of correlation receiver, and it requires that a particular relationship exist between the spectrum of the transmitted signal and the frequency response of the receiver system.

In particular, the matched filter requires that

$$H(f) = S^*(f)$$

where $H(f)$ is the receiver frequency response, $S(f)$ is the frequency spectrum of the transmitted signal, and * indicates the complex conjugate.

It is interesting to note that the signal-to-noise ratio for a matched filter is proportional to the total energy in the transmitted pulse; that is, to the product of the peak power and the pulse width for a rectangular pulse. Thus, the careful control of the spectrum of the transmitted signal and matching of the spectrum to the receiver bandpass is a requirement for matched filtering conditions to exist. For the case of a single-frequency, essentially rectangular or trapezoidal pulse, small deviations from the ideal matched condition produce little loss in signal-to-noise ratio at the receiver output. Schwartz has shown that for a rectangular pulse—with a $(\sin x)/x$ spectrum—and a gaussian receiver bandpass, the loss in peak signal-to-noise incurred in the nonideal matched filtering condition is as small as 1 dB, depending upon the receiver bandpass [4, p. 26]. A comparison of signal-to-noise ratio for various filters is given in Figure 1–2.

If matched filtering is to be successful, deviations from expected behavior must be carefully controlled, and this requirement usually gives

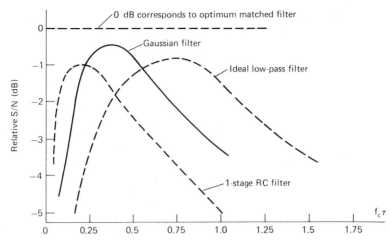

FIGURE 1–2 Signal-to-noise ratio as a function of bandwidth for various filters. The response is given relative to the output of a matched filter as a function of the product of the filter bandwidth and the pulse length. [4]

rise to specifications describing the width of the main transmitted frequency lobe and the peak amplitudes of the frequency side lobes. Figure 1–3 is a picture of the spectrum of a rectangular-envelope RF pulse. Important features that must be controlled include the width of the main frequency lobe, the peak amplitudes of the first and subsequent frequency lobes, and the symmetry of the output-signal spectra. Additional requirements may also be imposed to reduce mutual interference between radar systems [4].

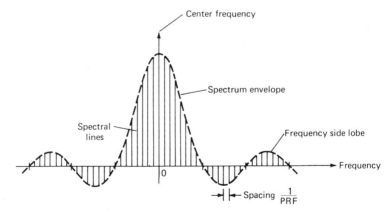

FIGURE 1–3 Spectrum of a train of rectangular RF pulses showing line spectra associated with a pulsed RF signal. [4]

1–2 PULSE COMPRESSION

The concept of matched filtering raises the possibility of using matched filtering in combination with more complex transmitted waveforms to achieve some significant advantage in overall system performance. There are a number of systems that utilize this concept, the simplest being the so-called *pulse-compression* systems. Pulse-compression systems were originally developed as an attempt to improve the signal-to-noise ratio for conditions where the peak power was limited by available transmitters but where the total energy per pulse could be increased by increasing pulse width. Since for a matched system the peak signal-to-noise ratio is related to the total energy in the pulse, increasing the pulse length was one approach to improving detectability. However, straightforward increases in pulse length result in a reduction of range resolution. In order to circumvent this difficulty, pulse compression (chirp) systems, also called linear FM pulse-compression systems, were developed.

In a linear FM pulse-compression system, the transmitted pulse is linearly swept over a band of frequencies and the chirped pulse is radiated. Received pulses are passed through a filter that is matched to the transmitted pulse characteristics, i.e., a filter that has an inverse delay with frequency. In such a system the resolution of the radar is related to the total frequency bandwidth of the transmitted pulse, and the detectability of targets in thermal noise is related to the total energy in the pulse (the product of the peak power and the pulse duration). Thus range resolution and pulse width have been decoupled.

There are a number of difficulties with linear FM pulse compression, not the least of these being the problem with so-called *range side lobes*. The output of a typical linear FM pulse-compression system is shown in Figure 1–4, which illustrates not only the presence of the main target output, but also spurious target responses, which are distributed in range. It may be the case for small targets in clutter, or small targets adjacent to large targets, that these range side lobes from unwanted targets may limit the detectability of the desired targets. In order to circumvent this difficulty a number of approaches have been developed.

In addition to linear FM, such techniques as nonlinear FM, the use of weighted waveforms, and phase or amplitude coding of the transmitted signal have been used in an attempt to maintain acceptable system resolution while reducing the amplitude of the range side lobes. One relatively effective means of reducing range side lobes involves the use of amplitude weighting of the various frequencies involved in generating the transmitted pulse. This may be achieved either before transmission or upon reception of the signal, and the reduction in range side lobes is achieved only at the expense of broadening the central response,

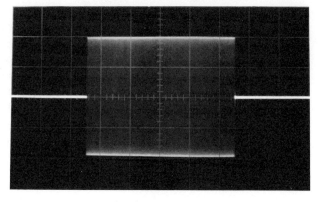

Expanded pulse
20μs/cm

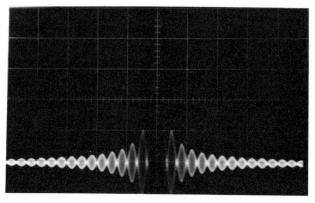

Compressed pulse
0.5μs/cm

FIGURE 1–4 Expanded and compressed pulses in a pulse-compression system, illustrating pulse compression from a pulse width of approximately 100 μs to a pulse width of less than 0.5 μs, and the range side lobes associated with the compressed pulse. (*Anderson Laboratories*)

with a consequent reduction in range resolution. The careful tradeoff between range resolution and range side-lobe levels is often the heart of a successful pulse-compression system. Weighting approaches that have been utilized include Tchebysheff, Butterworth, and Taylor weightings to achieve various levels and uniformity of side-lobe responses.

Whatever approach is taken, when range side-lobe levels below the 20- to 25-dB level are desired, careful control of the transmitted spectrum is vital. In general, the desired characteristics of the transmitted pulse may be achieved only by the generation of the complex signal at a low power level and the subsequent amplification of this signal to a usable level by a power amplifier. For example, the power-level variation ΔP during the pulse is related to the range side-lobe level SL (dB) by

$$SL = 20 \log \frac{\Delta P}{2} \qquad [2]$$

Achieving the required characteristics of the power amplifier for stability of phase, frequency, and amplitude required for small range side lobes may constitute a relatively difficult design problem.

1–3 TRACKING RADAR SYSTEMS

There are a number of different angle-tracking radar system concepts that involve the extraction of target angular information from the observation of the variations in received signal amplitude over a number of received pulses. These concepts include conical-scan radar systems and track-while-scan radar techniques. In each of these cases it is desirable that the source of transmitted energy be sufficiently stable that fluctuations in transmitted power do not limit the desired system accuracy. Random pulse-to-pulse fluctuations in the transmitted power output are, for many purposes, indistinguishable from fluctuations due to receiver noise, and requirements for amplitude stability of a few percent for time intervals of milliseconds are not an unusual requirement for such tracking systems.

1–4 FREQUENCY-SCANNING RADAR

There are a number of applications where it is desirable to rapidly reposition an antenna beam in space. One way of achieving such rapid beam scanning involves the utilization of frequency-scanning antennas, antennas whose beam direction in space is a function of the frequency of the radiated signal. Perhaps the most common utilization of frequency-scanning antennas involves a combination of frequency scan in elevation and mechanical scan in azimuth. The frequency scanning in elevation may be achieved by the transmission of sequential pulses on different frequencies, or by subdividing the transmitted pulse into a number of subpulses, each of which is radiated at a separate frequency corresponding to a separate antenna beam position. Since the desired frequencies are often quite closely spaced, the frequency-scanning radar systems often require a high degree of frequency accuracy and a capability for changing such a radiated frequency rapidly on a pulse-to-pulse basis, or even within a few microseconds. Such requirements often involve the use of lower-powered frequency synthesizers followed by higher-powered power-amplifier stages. Again the design of these power-amplifier stages must be such that they possess a high degree of frequency stability and fidelity in order to generate output pulses having the desired characteristics.

1–5 FREQUENCY AGILITY

It has been observed, and theoretically predicted, that a degree of improvement in a number of radar system performance measures, such as angle-tracking accuracy and target detectability in clutter, is provided by frequency-agile operation [1]. Frequency agility is the rapid shifting of transmitted frequency, often on a pulse-to-pulse basis. It has been observed that for randomly distributed clutter, the received signals decorrelate with a frequency change approximately equal to the bandwidth of the transmitted signal. Rapid frequency changes by at least this minimum amount tend to decorrelate, or smooth out, the clutter returns, or obtain a larger number of independent estimates of target position in a given observation time. Thus, a minimum pulse-to-pulse frequency separation of the reciprocal of the pulse width, and a frequency rate that results in the pattern of frequencies being repeated in an interval longer than the clutter or target decorrelation time, would often be required. This usually requires frequency steps of several megahertz and tuning rates of several hertz.

Frequency-agile systems often require that an appreciable bandwidth (as much as several percent) be scanned on a pulse-by-pulse basis, with adequate frequency-spectrum control and a sufficient knowledge of the transmitted frequency to permit local-oscillator tuning. The assessment of the increase in cost with frequency agility versus the anticipated performance improvement may represent an important radar system design tradeoff, and the size, cost, and complexity of the frequency-agile transmitter may be an important factor in such a decision.

1–6 MTI RADAR SYSTEMS

One of the problems that continually plague radar system designers is the detection of desired targets among a number of undesired targets. These undesired targets are often radar reflections from the surface of the earth or the sea or, in some cases, from cultural features. If the desired target is moving, it is possible to utilize the Doppler shift associated with such a moving target in order to differentiate between desired (moving) and undesired (stationary) returns.

One simple form of the system is the so-called moving-target indication (MTI) radar, shown in simplified form in Figure 1–5. A pulse with a known frequency is transmitted and reflected, and upon reception any Doppler shift is determined and this information used to differentiate between fixed and moving targets. A representative set of received signal

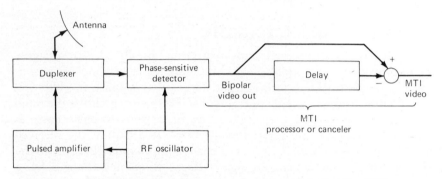

FIGURE 1–5 Simplified block diagram of a moving-target indication (MIT) system.

waveforms is shown in Figure 1-6 for such an MTI system, pulse-to-pulse subtraction being utilized to extract the desired moving targets. By the use of this concept, sequential received signals are subtracted, and returns from stationary targets, which do not change from pulse to pulse, are canceled, while those from moving targets, which fluctuate, produce a characteristic butterfly return. Such an MTI radar may use digital techniques, analog delay lines, or charge-storage tubes in order to achieve pulse-to-pulse subtraction. A number of pulses may be processed, and they may be weighted in order to provide the desired characteristics of the radar. The Doppler frequency response, $G(\omega)$, of such a system is given by the expression

$$G(\omega) = C_o + 2 \sum_{q=1}^{n-1} C_q \cos q\omega T$$

where

$$C_q = \sum_{j=1}^{n-q} x_j x_{j+q} \qquad 0 \le q \le n-1$$

and the x's are the weights of the various samples, n is the number of pulses processed, and $T = 1/\text{PRF}$.

A plot of the frequency response of a four-pulse canceler is given in Figure 1–7(a), where the plot is normalized as the ratio of the Doppler

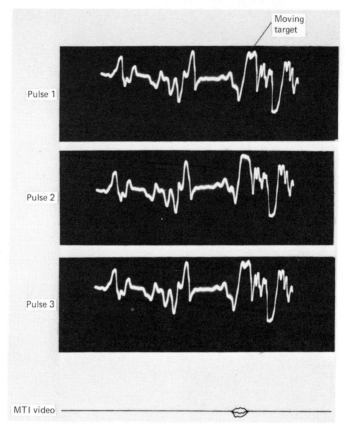

FIGURE 1–6 Waveforms in an MTI system, showing a set of received waveforms before MTI processing and the MTI video that results from successive subtraction of a number of such returns.

frequency $2V_r/\lambda$ to the system PRF. Note that there are radial velocities that result in zero response; these are called *blind speeds* V_b and are defined as follows:

$$\frac{2V_b}{\lambda} = k \times \text{PRF} \qquad (k = 1, 2, \ldots)$$

or

$$V_b \text{ (m/s)} = k\frac{\lambda \times \text{PRF}}{2} = k\frac{0.15 \times \text{PRF (Hz)}}{f(\text{GHz})}$$

Such MTI systems typically operate as search radar systems, utilizing a PRF that permits unambiguous range determination but ambiguous

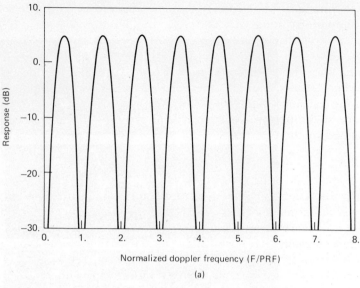

Normalized doppler frequency (F/PRF)

(a)

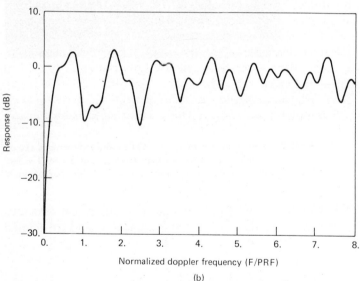

Normalized doppler frequency (F/PRF)

(b)

FIGURE 1–7 Doppler-frequency response for four-pulse cancelers, (a) without PRF stagger and (b) with PRF stagger and nonintegral weights. Frequency is expressed as the ratio of the Doppler frequency _F_ to the pulse-repetition frequency, PRF.

velocity determination. The effects of these blind speeds can be reduced by using nonuniform interpulse intervals, i.e., by *staggering* the PRF. The frequency response of a staggered PRF system is given in Figure 1–7(*b*).

Staggering the PRF of the system may constitute a severe design limitation when coupled with the other relatively stringent requirements for MTI-radar transmitter design.

A measure of the performance of an MTI system is the *improvement factor, I,* defined by the equation

$$I = \frac{S/C_o}{S/C_i}$$

where S/C_o is the target-to-clutter power ratio at the MTI system output, averaged over all target velocities, and S/C_i is the target-to-clutter ratio at the input to the receiver. This term replaces some earlier terms, such as *subclutter visibility* (SCV), which have been used in the past. Typical values of I are from 20 to 40 dB.

The required coherence between the transmitted signal and the reference signal for detection may be achieved in a number of different systems, including a master-oscillator power-amplifier system, a coherent-on-receive system, a clutter-referenced system, an incoherent Doppler system, or an externally coherent system.

The block diagram of a master-oscillator power-amplifier (MOPA) system is shown in Figure 1–8. The system provides for an accurate knowledge of the transmitted frequency and an accurate determination of the received Doppler shift. Unfortunately, such MOPA systems have

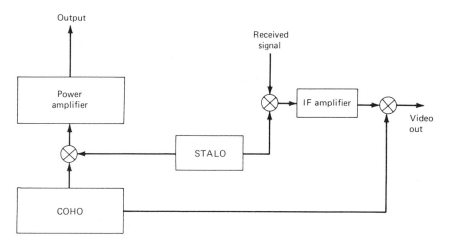

FIGURE 1–8   A master-oscillator power-amplifier (MOPA), MTI system block diagram. COHO = coherent local oscillator; STALO = stable local oscillator.

become available only in recent years and are often relatively large and expensive. For those applications where a reduced level of performance is satisfactory, so-called coherent-on-receive systems have been developed; a simplified block diagram of such a system is given in Figure 1–9.

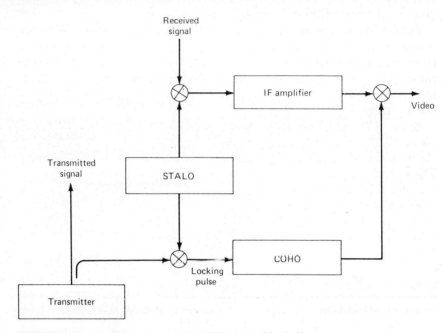

FIGURE 1–9   A coherent-on-receive MTI system block diagram.

The coherent-on-receive system mixes a sample of the transmitted pulse with the output of a stable local oscillator (STALO) and utilizes this signal to phase-lock a coherent local oscillator (COHO). This locking action provides a phase reference for the system, permitting the extraction of Doppler information from targets. It should be noted that it is not necessary to frequency-lock the COHO, but only to ensure an initial phase lock and a change in frequency with time that is repeatable from pulse to pulse. In order to achieve a reasonable phase lock, the magnetron pulse must be free from incidental frequency modulation or amplitude modulation.

For a situation where the radar platform is moving, the peak of the clutter spectral return may be extracted as a reference and utilized to provide the desired offset frequency for the system; the result is a clutter-referenced system.

An incoherent Doppler system relies on extracting the Doppler signal provided by the interference between the desired moving target and the approximately stationary clutter returns located in the same resolution cell. The operation of such a system requires that the clutter returns and the target returns be of comparable magnitude. The application of this concept has been largely confined to relatively small, lightweight, and inexpensive ground-based surveillance systems.

Finally, there are so-called externally coherent systems, which are similar to the coherent-on-receive systems, except that they utilize signals from strong external targets (such as clutter or chaff) to lock the COHO rather than utilizing the transmitter pulse. Externally coherent systems are particularly useful for viewing chaff clouds or large areas of nonstationary targets.

Since MTI radars are typically designed to achieve a value of I from 20 to 40 dB, relatively small amplitude, phase, or delay variations of the transmitted signal can significantly affect overall system performance. The specific impact of these factors depends upon the specific type of canceler involved. Table 1–1 summarizes a number of instability limitations on MTI performance for a two-pulse canceler. If the instabilities are independent of each other, they may be combined in an rms fashion to determine the total limitation on MTI performance.

TABLE 1–1   LIMITATIONS ON MTI PERFORMANCE [5]

Pulse-to-pulse instability	Limit on improvement factor
Transmitter frequency	$20 \log [1/(\pi \, \Delta f \, \tau)]$
STALO or COHO frequency	$20 \log [1/(2\pi \, \Delta f \, T)]$
Transmitter phase shift	$20 \log (1/\Delta\phi)$
COHO locking	$20 \log (1/\Delta\phi)$
Pulse timing	$20 \log [\tau/(\sqrt{2} \, \Delta t \, \sqrt{B\tau})]$
Pulse width	$20 \log [\tau/(\Delta PW \, \sqrt{B\tau})]$
Pulse amplitude	$20 \log (A/\Delta A)$

NOTATION:
Δf = frequency change
τ = transmitted-pulse length
T = time to and from target
$\Delta\phi$ = interpulse phase change
Δt = time jitter
$B\tau$ = time-bandwidth product of transmitted pulse
ΔPW = pulse-width jitter
A = pulse amplitude (V)
ΔA = pulse-to-pulse amplitude change (V)

It is worthwhile to note that for a given level of improvement, the frequency requirements are much less stringent for the transmitter than for the STALO or the COHO. For this reason, in coherent-on-receive systems the transmitter frequency is often governed by automatic frequency control (AFC) from the STALO.

In general, however, the various sources of limitation on I are not independent, or cannot be measured separately. For this reason, they are often lumped together and included in the description of the spectral spread of the transmitted signal. In this case, the power output from the MTI processor due to transmitter instabilities is given by

$$\int_{-B}^{B} S(f)G(f) \, df$$

where $S(f)$ = transmitter-power spectral density
$G(f)$ = power response of MTI processor
B = receiver bandwidth (assumed rectangular)

a laborious calculation to say the least.

Figure 1–10 shows the measured power spectrum of a coherent-on-

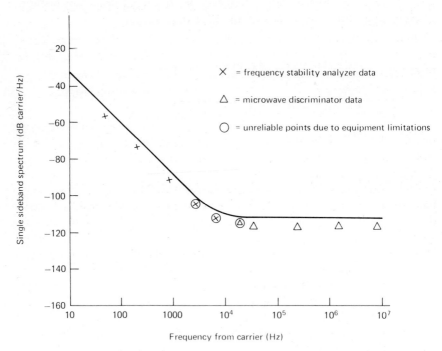

FIGURE 1–10 **Frequency spreading of the transmitted central line associated with phase and amplitude instabilities in a magnetron transmitter. [3]**

receive magnetron system. If it is assumed that a two-pulse canceler is used and if $S(\omega)$ is approximated by an analytical function, then the output power due to transmitter-spectrum broadening may be easily calculated.

If one assumes a PRF of 1800 Hz and a two-pulse canceler with response

$$\sin 2\pi f/1800$$

and approximates the frequency spectrum as

$$0.1/f^2$$

for

$$0 \le f \le 1800 \text{ Hz}$$

and -113 dB carrier for $f > 1800$ Hz, then one can write

$$\text{Total power} = 2\int_0^{1800} \frac{0.1}{f^2} \sin \frac{2\pi f}{1800} \, df$$

$$+ 2\int_{1800}^{B} 0.5 \times 10^{-11} \sin \frac{2\pi f}{1800} \, df \tag{1-2}$$

Numerical integration of Equation 1–2 results in an improvement limit of approximately 31 dB, which is due to the first term, the contribution of the second term being negligibly small in this case.

Thus, for many MTI systems, the characteristics of the transmitter may represent a limit on achievable system performance, and careful transmitter design is essential for good MTI system performance.

1–7 PULSE-DOPPLER SYSTEMS

There are a number of situations where an exact knowledge of target velocity is required, and for such applications the normal MTI with its ambiguous velocity measurement is not suitable. For that reason, so-called pulse-Doppler systems have been developed; these systems typically operate with an unambiguous velocity, and the resulting high PRF results in an ambiguous range measurement. A simplified block diagram of such a pulse-Doppler radar system is shown in Figure 1–11. The block diagram shows a master-oscillator power-amplifier system and a number of range-gated Doppler filters, which are utilized to estimate the Doppler frequency. Since the bandwidths of the individual Doppler filters are considerably narrower than the bandwidth of an MTI system, the clutter-improvement or clutter-rejection capability of a typical pulse-Doppler system is greater than that of a representative MTI system; values of 50 to 60 dB are often achieved with pulse-Doppler systems, values up to 40 dB greater than those typically achieved with MTI systems.

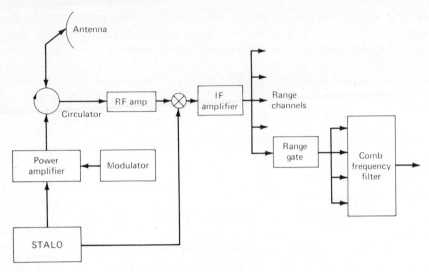

FIGURE 1–11 Simplified block diagram of a pulse-Doppler radar system.

The greater accuracy of velocity measurement and the higher value of clutter improvement place additional requirements on the spectral purity of the pulse-Doppler transmitter output. In addition, the high PRFs that are utilized often result in a relatively high transmitter duty cycle, approaching 10% in some instances, which represents a severe requirement for both the high-power tube and the modulator in the transmitter; in addition, the high duty cycle requires considerable flexibility in choice of interpulse period in order to prevent the masking of desired returns by the transmitted pulse.

Modulations of the carrier frequency, the amplitude of the output pulse, pulse position, pulse width, and pulse droop all affect overall system operation. The allowable levels of spurious modulation, or spectral spreading of the central transmitter line, are a function of the specific radar configuration, the widths of the filters utilized, and the amount of degradation in clutter rejection that is acceptable. A commonly used figure of merit is the ratio of the residual transmitter-produced signal to system noise at the output of the individual narrow-band Doppler filters, and it is usually desired that this ratio by considerably less than 1. In the most general case, this figure must be obtained by integration of the transmitter-power spectral density over the receiver Doppler-filter bandwidth. However, it should be noted that an extremely narrow transmitted line spectrum is generally required for satisfactory operation of a pulse-Doppler system, and that achieving adequate transmitter stability is often a most difficult part of the overall pulse-Doppler system design.

In this chapter we have attempted to show how such factors as

- Peak power
- Average power
- Pulse length
- PRF

- Bandwidth
- Stability
- Gain

are all important requirements which are placed on transmitters and which can have an important impact on overall radar system performance. In Chapter 2, the major types of microwave devices that are available for use in transmitters are introduced, and some of the principal characteristics of each major type are discussed.

REFERENCES

1. Barton, D. K., *Frequency Agility and Diversity,* vol. 6 of *Radars,* Artech House, Dedham, Mass., 1977.

2. Barnett, W. R., J. R. Luscombe, and C. R. White, "An Inverter Powered, One Megawatt Klystron Power Amplifier for a Radar Transmitter," in *Proc. Radar-77 Intern. Conf.,* IEE Conference Publication No. 155, 1977, pp. 349–353.

3. Scherer, E., Varian Associates, personal communication, Apr. 14, 1977.

4. Schwartz, M., *Information Transmission Modulation and Noise,* McGraw-Hill, New York, 1959.

5. Shrader, W. D., in M. I. Skolnik, ed., *Radar Handbook,* McGraw-Hill, New York, 1970, chap. 17, pp. 17–48.

2
MICROWAVE SOURCES

Microwave radar transmitters are usually of one of two types, either oscillators or amplifiers. The self-excited oscillator, as typified by the magnetron and the various semiconductor bulk-effect devices—Gunn-effect devices, impact avalanche and transit-time devices (IMPATTs), and limited space-charge accumulation (LSA) devices—are suitable for many radar applications. The amplifiers, which include crossed-field amplifiers (CFAs), klystrons, traveling-wave tubes (TWTs), and transistor amplifiers, are useful where the amplification of a low-power signal is required, as in a coherent MTI system, a pulse-compression radar, or a pulse-Doppler system. Many radar systems operate pulsed and require devices capable of considerable peak and average power. While there are exceptions, applications requiring high output powers usually use thermionic vacuum tubes for the transmitting device. The primary emphasis in this chapter will be on thermionic tubes, although for completeness, Section 2–3 briefly discusses solid-state sources as well.

High-power microwave tubes may be divided into two general categories: the crossed-field devices, characterized by orthogonal electric and magnetic fields, and the linear-beam devices, which have a continuous electron beam traversing an interaction region. The crossed-field devices are typified by the magnetron and the CFA, while the linear-beam devices include the cavity klystron, the TWT, the Twystron, and the extended-interaction oscillator. Each of these devices has its own peculiarities concerning arcing, voltage-current relationships at the terminals, RF performance, and the effects of terminal voltages on tunability and device stability.

There is an intimate relationship between the proper operation of the microwave tube and the device used to provide the appropriate voltages and currents for tube operation. The required pulse rise, fall, and flatness, the ability to withstand arcs, and changes in terminal characteristics with changes in frequency are all important characteristics of the tube that impact the design of the modulator or pulser. This chapter provides an introduction to the characteristics of each of the principal types of microwave power generators, and it will attempt to bring out some of the characteristics of these devices that are important both in system design and in modulator selection and specification.

2–1 CROSSED-FIELD DEVICES

Magnetrons [6,30,31]

The magnetron is an oscillator that is characterized by small size, light weight, reasonable operating voltages, good efficiency, rugged construction, and long life. The magnetron was the first practical high-power pulsed radar source used at microwave frequencies, and it is still rather widely utilized today. Its main disadvantage is that the magnetron, being an oscillator, is not suitable for use in many coherent systems. It is also not well suited for generating short (less than 50-ns), high-power pulses.

The magnetron converts energy extracted from a constant electric field to an RF field. A cutaway view of one possible magnetron configuration is shown in Figure 2–1. The principal parts of the magnetron are

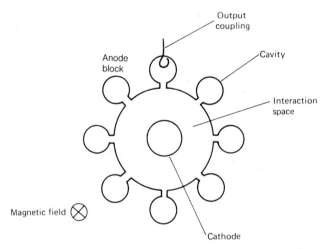

FIGURE 2–1   A cross-sectional schematic representation of the anode-cathode region of a microwave cavity magnetron.

identified: the cathode, the interaction region, cavities, and the output coupling. A magnetic field is applied perpendicular to the plane of the paper, and a constant potential is established between the anode block and the cathode; therefore, the electric and magnetic fields are crossed in the interaction region. If the proper electric and magnetic fields are applied, electrons travel from the cathode, coupling energy to the RF field, which is in turn coupled to the output.

The establishment of conditions that result in the coupling of energy from the constant (dc) anode-to-cathode field to the RF field requires a specific combination of applied magnetic field and applied potential difference for a given cavity configuration. One consequence of this is that appreciable current is not drawn by a conventional magnetron until a critical voltage, normally approximately 90% of the operating voltage, is reached. This voltage is called the *Hartree voltage;* it is illustrated together with the voltage/current relationships for a magnetron in Figure 2-2.

Because of the highly nonlinear relationship between the applied voltage and the current drawn by the magnetron, a magnetron is often represented by an equivalent circuit consisting of a biased diode, with the magnetron's associated stray capacitance represented by a capacitor connected in parallel. Thus, a reasonable cathode-equivalent circuit for a magnetron is as shown in Figure 2-3. While details of the voltage/current characteristics differ with tube type and power level, most magne-

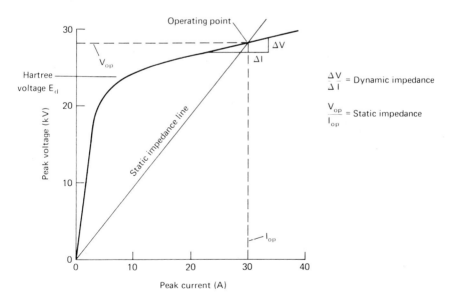

FIGURE 2-2 Voltage/current relationships for a microwave magnetron, including definition of magnetron static and dynamic impedance.

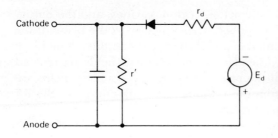

FIGURE 2–3 Biased-diode equivalent circuit for a magnetron oscillator, including effects of stray-capacity current and leakage current (r').

trons can be represented by an equivalent circuit of the general type shown in Figure 2–3, with a Hartree voltage given by approximately 80 to 90% of the normal operating cathode potential. It should be noted that low levels of RF output power may be generated by the tube even below the Hartree voltage. Therefore, care should be taken to ensure that voltage is promptly removed after the desired pulse and not reapplied, even at low levels.

As one might expect, magnetron operation is strongly influenced by the load characteristics and by the applied magnetic and electric fields. The change in frequency for a change in anode current with a fixed load is called the *pushing figure* (mHz/A). Another important parameter of magnetrons is the *pulling figure,* defined as the difference between the maximum and minimum frequencies of the magnetron oscillator when the phase angle of a load having a voltage/standing-wave ratio (VSWR) of 1.5 is varied through 360° of phase. These characteristics may be derived from graphical representations of magnetron performance, the most useful of which is the Rieke diagram. Figure 2–4 is a Rieke diagram for the 2J51 magnetron; it presents load VSWR and phase angle in polar coordinates, with lines of constant frequency and power output superimposed. This figure shows the pulling figure to be approximately 15 MHz.

A problem with magnetron oscillators is that the interaction space in a magnetron will support more than one possible mode of oscillation. In well-designed magnetrons, the various modes are well separated in both voltage and frequency and the magnetrons will operate stably in the desired mode. However, certain parameters, notably the characteristics of the modulator, such as the rate of rise of voltage (RRV), can strongly influence the mode selection in magnetrons. Operation in other than the normal mode (called *moding*) is usually undesirable, because oscillations are separated from the normal operating frequency and the power does not couple out of the tube in the proper fashion. Excessive applied voltages can also be an undesired result of moding; continued operation in the wrong mode can permanently damage the tube.

Another property of magnetrons, which is probably closely related

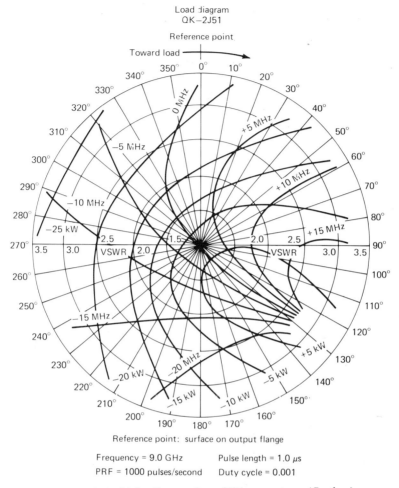

Load diagram
QK–2J51

Reference point

Toward load

Reference point: surface on output flange

Frequency = 9.0 GHz	Pulse length = 1.0 μs
PRF = 1000 pulses/second	Duty cycle = 0.001

FIGURE 2–4   Rieke diagram for a 2J51 magnetron. (*Raytheon*)

to moding, is the tendency of such tubes to produce an occasional RF output pulse of reduced amplitude, or to fail to produce any RF output pulse. In a well-designed tube, such missing pulses would typically occur less often than 1 in 10^4. As with any high-power tube, the possibility of internal tube arcing always exists, and in magnetrons arcing is one factor that must be considered in the design of the modulator or pulser to drive the tube.

In normal operation, as the electrons leave the cathode and energy is transferred to the RF field, an appreciable portion of these electrons do not couple to the RF field and fall back to the cathode, producing additional heating. If heater power is not reduced or other measures taken, this so-called *back heating* can result in excessive cathode temperature and damage to the tube. In practice, the tube-heater power is reduced as the average output power is increased, and for a number of high-power tubes operated at high duty cycles, the magnetron can be operated with no heater input power once operation has been started, all of the required cathode heating being produced by back bombardment of the cathode. The reduction of heater power in accordance with increases in tube output power, the so-called *heater schedule*, is normally part of the tube data provided by the magnetron tube manufacturer.

In order to achieve improved frequency stability, the coaxial magnetron has been developed. This tube, utilizing a resonant cavity as the frequency-determining element, can demonstrate improved frequency stability with load, current, and temperature changes when compared with a conventional magnetron. However, coaxial tubes are often less tolerant of high RRV and may mode quite easily, particularly for short-pulse operation. Cutaway views of two types of coaxial magnetrons are given in Figure 2–5.

The conventional magnetron can operate through X or K_u bands. Above this frequency, rising-sun or inverted coaxial magnetrons are often utilized. The voltage-current relationships of all of these magnetrons are quite similar, except that the rising-sun magnetron may sometimes exhibit a low-voltage mode, making a rapidly rising voltage pulse quite desirable for such tubes. Table 2–1 is a representative tabulation of some commercially available magnetrons.

As was pointed out in Chapter 1, there are a number of applications where frequency agility is desirable; in order to fill that need, a number of frequency-agile magnetrons have been developed. All of these frequency-agile magnetrons change output frequency by changing the resonant frequency of the magnetron cavity, and there are a number of means by which this may be accomplished. The first of these may be loosely called electronic tuning. While it is possible to build a true voltage-tuned magnetron, satisfactory operation has been achieved only at power levels of a few hundred watts. Electronic tuning using an electron beam to produce a variable reactance, tuning by the use of auxiliary magnetron diodes in each of the magnetron cavities, and tuning of a coaxial magnetron by loading the cavity with PIN diodes have all been attempted, but these have the drawback of a quite limited tuning range [32].

On the other hand, multipactor-tuned magnetrons have indicated some promise in producing a useful frequency-agile magnetron. The multipactor discharge is used as a variable capacitance to vary the frequency of an auxiliary coupled resonator. When the multipactor dis-

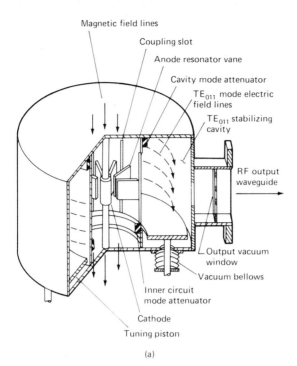

Magnetic field lines

Coupling slot

Anode resonator vane

Cavity mode attenuator

TE_{011} mode electric field lines

TE_{011} stabilizing cavity

RF output waveguide

Output vacuum window

Vacuum bellows

Inner circuit mode attenuator

Cathode

Tuning piston

(a)

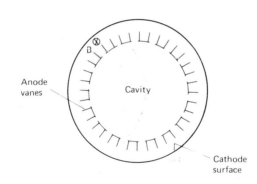

Anode vanes

Cavity

Cathode surface

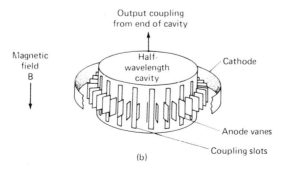

Output coupling from end of cavity

Magnetic field B

Half-wavelength cavity

Cathode

Anode vanes

Coupling slots

(b)

FIGURE 2–5   Schematic representations of (a) coaxial magnetron [5] and (b) inverted coaxial magnetron. [6]

TABLE 2-1   SOME COMMERCIALLY AVAILABLE HIGH-POWER PULSED
MAGNETRONS

Tube type	Center frequency (GHz)	Peak P_o	Maximum duty cycle	Peak Voltage (kV)	Peak Current (A)
M 545	1.290	25.0 MW	0.0025	52	260
3M901	2.765	4.7 MW	0.001	75	135
SFD344	5.60	1.0 MW	0.001	37.5	65
VF 11	9.250	1.0 MW	0.0015	30	70
7208 B	16.5	100 kW	0.001	22	20
VF 20	16.5	400 kW	0.0015	26	40
SFD326	24	120 kW	0.0005	14	30
SFD327	34.86	150 kW	0.0005	23	22
BL235	52.5	10 kW	0.0012	14.5	9.5
DX221	69.75	10 kW	0.00055		
M 5613	95.5	2 kW	0.0002	10	9
DX252	120	2.5 kW	0.0002	10	11

charge is initiated by the application of an appropriate bias voltage, the discharge varies the resonant frequency of the auxiliary cavity, which in turn changes the magnetron operating frequency. A number of cavities can be coupled to a given anode and each one turned on or off independently, so that if there are n cavities, there are 2^n combinations or frequencies of oscillation that may be selected. While showing some promise, such multipactor-tuned magnetrons remain laboratory devices at this time [32].

The second technique involves placing piezoelectric material within the cavity and applying a voltage across these crystals, thus resulting in a change in cavity dimensions and a change in cavity tuning. The third group of techniques may be classed as reciprocating techniques, and are usually implemented by incorporating a ring which moves along the axis of the cavity near the end of the resonant structure. Finally, insertion of dielectric structures within the cavity and rotation of these structures can result in tuning of the device. Most of the readily available devices that have found widespread system usage are either of the reciprocating or of the rotary type.

A simplified sketch of a reciprocating "voice-coil" tuned frequency-agile magnetron is given in Figure 2–6, which shows an electronic actua-

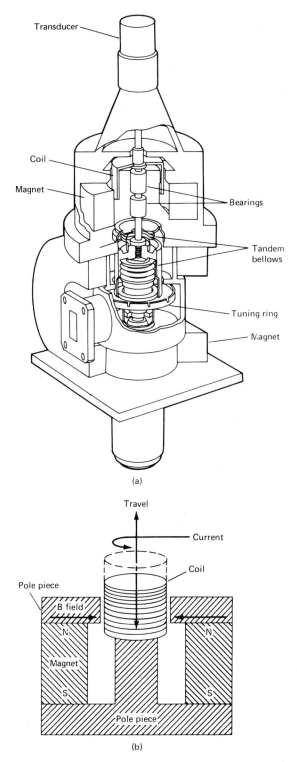

FIGURE 2–6   (*a*) Cutaway view of reciprocation-tuned
(also called a HI-FI- or EM-tuned) magnetron [22], and
(*b*) detail of the voice coil driver.

tor (which functions similarly to a speaker coil), the bellows used to drive through the high vacuum interface, and a position- and velocity-sensing transducer that is used to sense the tuning ring and thus give a measure of magnetron frequency.

Figure 2–7 shows a cross-sectional view of a motor-driven reciprocation-tuned magnetron. Rapid tuning is achieved by the use of a cam mounted on the motor shaft to actuate the tuning plunger. Rotation

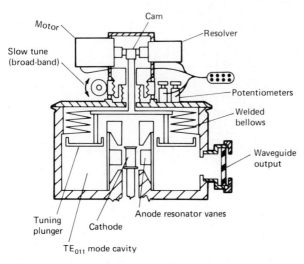

FIGURE 2–7 Motor-driven reciprocation-tuned magnetron cross-sectional view [23].

of the motor shaft is thereby converted to a linear motion of the tuning rod. Also connected to the motor shaft is a resolver to give a frequency readout. The motor may be either free-running or servo-controlled, depending upon system requirements.

In reciprocation-tuned magnetrons, frequency agility is accomplished by the movement of a particular mass. The rate at which a mass may be moved and the amount of the mass moved are not independent, if a constant source of driving energy is available. Figure 2–8 shows the relationship between frequency-tuning speed and tuning range for a particular K_u-band magnetron. If the amount of drive power is increased, increased tuning ranges or rates can be achieved.

The reciprocating type of magnetron has difficulties, including limited tuning rates, tuning nonlinearities, and susceptibility to vibration and fatigue. In order to circumvent some of these difficulties, a rotating type of structure has been developed. One early technique was based

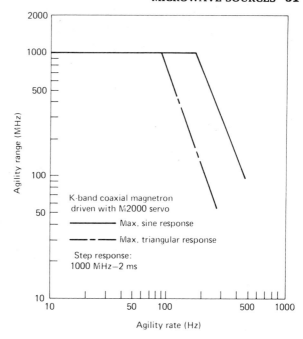

FIGURE 2–8 Tuning range as a function of agility rate for a reciprocation-tuned tube. (*Litton Industries*)

on the rotation of a notched tuning element in the back wall of the magnetron cavity. The passage of slots across the cavity openings resulted in changes in magnetron frequency. This rotary tuning method has a wide frequency excursion and a rapid tuning rate, but it is not readily adaptable to coaxial structures and does not readily yield an accurate measure of magnetron frequency.

The coaxial magnetron operates with a TE_{011} mode in the coaxial cavity, which results in an electric field as illustrated in Figure 2–9. It is possible to change the oscillating frequency of such a device by inserting a small dielectric vane at a region of appreciable electric field within the cavity. Rotating a symmetric vane causes a change in frequency as a function of vane position, as shown in Figure 2–10. In practice, several vanes are normally employed and distributed around the cavity so as to provide symmetrical field distortion and minimize the reduction in Q of the cavity, and an example of such a device is shown in Figure 2–11 (p. 36). Since such a device is continuously rotating, it is relatively easy to provide high agility rates, along with an accurate measure of magnetron frequency for controlling the local-oscillator function.

There are a number of design tradeoffs associated with frequency-

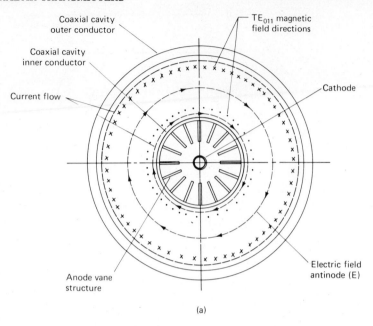

Coaxial cavity
outer conductor

Coaxial cavity
inner conductor

Current flow

TE$_{011}$ magnetic
field directions

Cathode

Anode vane
structure

Electric field
antinode (E)

(a)

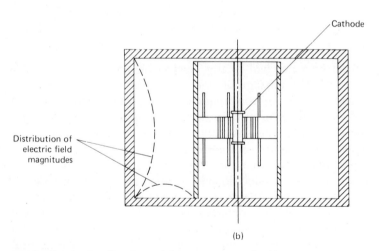

Cathode

Distribution of
electric field
magnitudes

(b)

FIGURE 2–9 Details of coaxial magnetron cavity [21]: (*a*) top view and (*b*) cutaway side view.

agile magnetrons, and a comparison of a number of different approaches for medium power K$_u$-band magnetrons is given in Table 2–2.

When tunable magnetrons that supply large amounts of peak and average power are considered, the transfer of heat from the cavity becomes important. Much of the heat conducted from the cavity passes

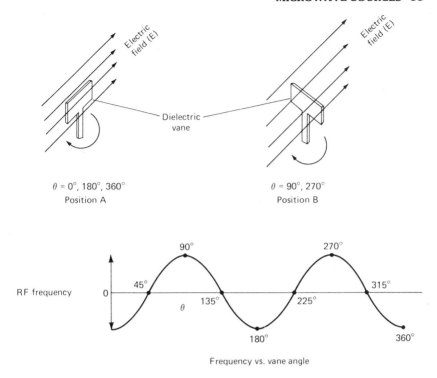

FIGURE 2–10 Rotating a dielectric vane in a coaxial cavity may be used to shift the frequency of oscillation of the cavity [21]. θ is angle of vane relative to electric field of TE_{011} mode in coaxial cavity.

through the tuning mechanism, and usually this heat path includes the actuator support bearing. For this reason, linear actuators, which use sleeve bearings having good heat-transfer properties, are often preferred for high-power tubes.

In any of the frequency-agile systems, the provision of a reasonably accurate local oscillator is a significant design problem. One means of providing such a signal is by a tracking local oscillator, which utilizes the transducer voltage output in order to set an approximate local oscillator frequency, which is then refined by a sample of the transmitted frequency. This process is repeated on a pulse-to-pulse basis.

The pulsed magnetron is undoubtedly the most widely used magnetron in radar systems, but it is also feasible to produce CW magnetrons. CW magnetrons have applications in Doppler and electronic countermeasure systems, and tubes producing from 100 to 500 W at frequencies as high as the X band have been produced for these purposes. Lately, however, CW magnetrons have been produced for heating purposes. These tubes normally operate in the 2450-MHz industrial heating band

TABLE 2–2 COMPARISON OF FREQUENCY-AGILITY METHODS FOR MEDIUM-POWER K_u-BAND MAGNETRONS (after Litton Industries)

Parameter	Method						
	Litton gyro	Litton E/M	Raytheon ring tuner	Varian Dither I	Varian Dither II	Amperex spin tune	EEV piezoelectric
Maximum rate (Hz)	600	400	200	200	200	200	Est. 100
Maximum range (MHz)	300	Total bandwidth of tube	300	Total bandwidth of tube	300	1000	Est. 50
Typical maximum rate–range combination	200 Hz 300 MHz	200 Hz 100 MHz	200 Hz 300 MHz	200 50	200 300	200 3000	Est. 100 50
Rapid-tune mode	Sine only	Sine and/or random	Sine only	Sine	Sine only	Sine only	Sine and/or random
Broadband-tunable	Yes	Built into E/M system	Yes	Yes	Yes	No	Yes
Readout accuracy (MHz, maximum rate–range)	±5	±10	±5	±1	±5	No readout	No data available
Nominal operating/ life (h)	750 min.	5000	650 min.	<500	<500	No data available	Est. 5000

Flexibility	Good	Excellent	Est. fair	Poor	Poor	Good	Excellent
Complexity	High	Low but requires servo amplifier	Moderate	Moderate	Moderate	Low	Low
Vibration	Good	Poor	Moderate	Good	Good	Moderate	Good off piezo resonance
Altitude	Good	Good	Moderate	Moderate	Moderate	Good	Good
Vacuum structure compromises	Complex vacuum sleeve	None	Mode-suppression Q's, additional vacuum seals	None	None	Vacuum bearings, Q's	Minor
Magnetron type	Coaxial	Conventional or coaxial	Coaxial	Coaxial	Coaxial	Conventional	Conventional

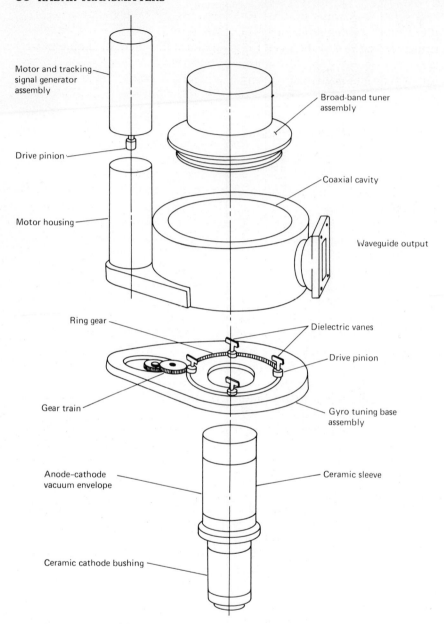

Motor and tracking
signal generator
assembly

Broad-band tuner
assembly

Drive pinion

Coaxial cavity

Motor housing

Waveguide output

Ring gear

Dielectric vanes

Drive pinion

Gear train

Gyro tuning base
assembly

Anode–cathode
vacuum envelope

Ceramic sleeve

Ceramic cathode bushing

FIGURE 2–11   Exploded view of a rotary, Gyro-Tuned magnetron. [21]

and produce outputs of 1 to 10 kW at this frequency. The design of these tubes differs somewhat from that of other CW magnetrons [31], primarily because of the need for economical production, simple power supplies, and an ability to operate into mismatched loads. The market for such devices is increasing, and heating magnetrons constitute a considerable portion of the output of many microwave-tube facilities.

Crossed-Field Amplifiers [30,31,36,37]

The crossed-field amplifier (CFA) is a microwave amplifier that is usually characterized by reasonable operating voltages, good efficiency, wide bandwidth, and long life, but low gain. The CFA is often utilized in Doppler systems, phased arrays, frequency-agile radars, and pulse-compression systems. The CFA derives its name from the fact that, as in magnetrons, the RF-dc interaction region is a region of crossed electric and magnetic fields.

There are two general types of CFAs: the injected-beam CFA and the distributed-emission CFA. The electrons are injected into the interaction region by an electron gun in the injected-beam CFA and are emitted by the cathode or *sole* in the distributed-emission CFA. The injected-beam CFA is generally not suited for high powers, and we will confine our discussion to distributed-emission CFAs. CFAs may be operated either CW or pulsed, depending upon the particular design. Unless otherwise specified, the following discussion will be directed toward tubes for pulsed operation, although much of the discussion is also applicable to continuous-wave CFAs.

The distributed-emission CFA may be constructed in either the linear or the circular format, both of which are illustrated schematically in Figure 2–12 and in detail in Figure 2–13. In the circular format, electrons from the output may be isolated from the input, forming the nonreentrant configuration. In the reentrant configuration, the feedback electrons may be bunched, forming RF feedback, or the electrons may be debunched, eliminating the RF feedback. The linear-format tubes are, of course, of a nonreentrant type. The interaction in the tube may be with either the forward or the backward wave. Each of these configurations has its own specific properties. CFAs of various types are manufactured under various trade names by different manufacturers: the Amplitron, a reentrant CFA utilizing the circular format, RF feedback, and backward wave interaction is manufactured by Raytheon; and the Dematron, most usually a linear-format, forward-wave-interaction tube, is manufactured by Litton Industries. Varian (SFD) also manufactures circular-format CFAs, which are reentrant and without RF feedback, employing either forward or backward wave interaction; Varian does not use any specific trade name for its CFAs.

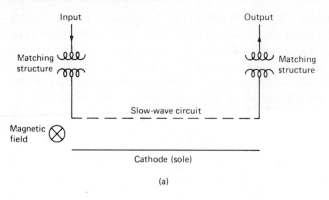

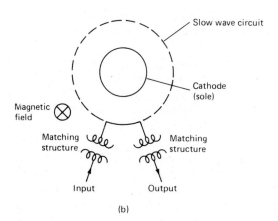

FIGURE 2–12 **Simplified schematic representations of principal portions of (*a*) linear-format and (*b*) circular-format CFAs.**

The backward-wave CFA derives its name from the characteristics of the slow-wave structures utilized in such tubes. The relationship of the phase velocity to the group velocity on the microwave circuit can be conveniently shown by a so-called omega-beta diagram, such as the one in Figure 2–14, which shows the phase shift per unit of length of a slow-wave structure plotted as a function of the operating frequency. When presented in such a manner, the slope of the curve is proportional to the group velocity on the circuit, and the slope of a line from the origin to an operating point is a measure of the phase velocity of the electrons in the interaction region. The terminal characteristics with changing frequency are substantially different for the backward-wave and forward-wave crossed-field amplifiers.

The backward-wave structure was the first CFA structure to be devel-

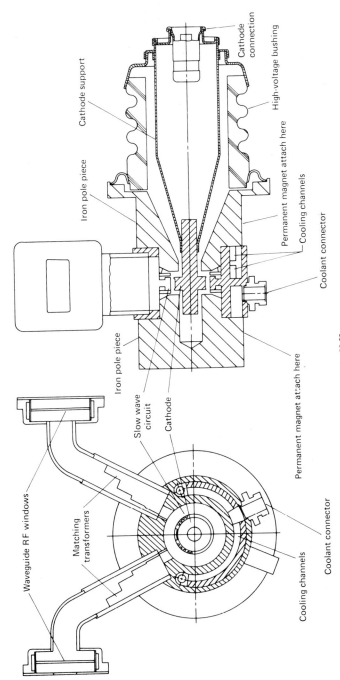

FIGURE 2-13   Cross-sectional view of a circular-format CFA. [36]

Cathode support

Cathode connection

High-voltage bushing

Iron pole piece

Permanent magnet attach here

Cooling channels

Coolant connector

Iron pole piece

Permanent magnet attach here

Slow wave circuit

Cathode

Waveguide RF windows

Matching transformers

Cooling channels

Coolant connector

39

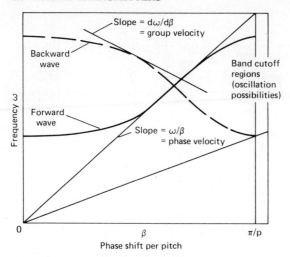

FIGURE 2–14 An ω-β diagram for backward-wave and forward-wave CFA slow-wave structures.

oped; it exhibits some desirable characteristics. Unfortunately, tubes using backward-wave structures are voltage-tunable amplifiers; i.e., the operating voltage for constant power output depends upon the frequencies being amplified. The development of suitable forward-wave circuits made possible a constant-voltage amplifier, which is desirable when operating from a dc supply.

Reentrant operation is employed in CFAs to increase the efficiency, often with considerable effect. However, RF feedback, like any feedback, opens up the possibility of oscillation. Electron bunching occurs, as shown in Figure 2–15, and debunching of the electron stream is some-

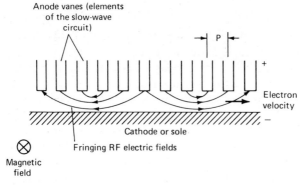

FIGURE 2–15 Details of field structure in the interaction region of a CFA. [36]

times employed to eliminate the possibility of oscillation while retaining the enhanced efficiency of the reentrant configuration. A schematic representation of a reentrant CFA, illustrating the debunching of the electron stream, is given in Figure 2–16.

Recent developments in CFA design have involved the injection of the input signal into the cathode region, an approach which provides

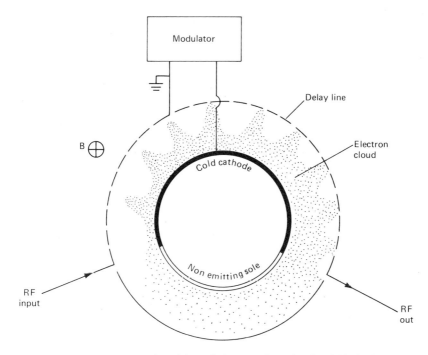

FIGURE 2–16 Debunching of electrons in a circular CFA. [20]

substantially increased gain. Gains on the order of 30 to 40 dB have been demonstrated by using this approach, but devices of this design are still in the development stage at this time [25].

The crossed-field amplifier is not a linear amplifier, but acts more as a phase- or input-locked oscillator. Its power is determined principally by the amount of power supplied to the tube from the external power supply, and therefore the bandwidth of the tube as such has no meaning. However, there is a range of frequency over which the tube will operate stably for a specific set of terminal conditions and a specific value of RF drive power. For a given level of input drive power, there is a range of power output over which the tube can operate. The upper limit is normally fixed by one of three factors: either a limit on available cathode current, the onset of a competing oscillation, or a limitation in the gain of the main amplifying mode. In most cases, the onset of the upper-mode boundary is the practical limit on the operation of the tube, as shown in Figures 2–17 and 2–18. The performance of a continuous-wave crossed-field amplifier, showing the upper- and lower-mode regions

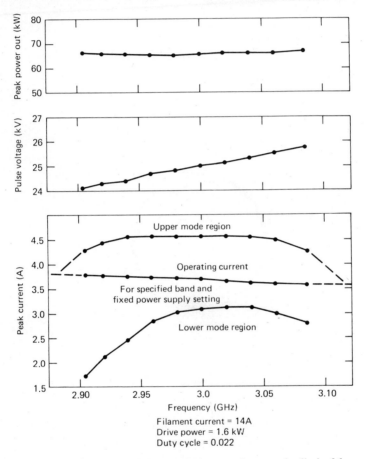

FIGURE 2–17 Range of normal CFA operation may be limited by upper-mode boundary. [37]

for the tube, is illustrated in Figure 2–17; operation of the tube must normally fall within these regions.

Figure 2–19 shows a plot of the terminal characteristics of a backward-wave crossed-field amplifier, indicating the sensitivity of operating voltage with frequency; it is desirable to operate such devices from a source

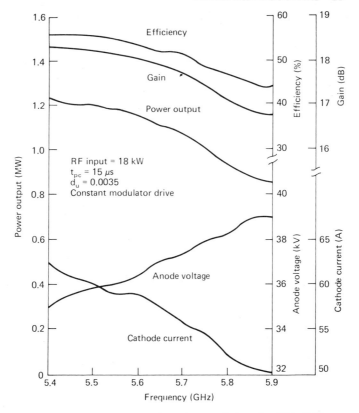

FIGURE 2–18 Operating characteristics of a CFA. [36]

that more closely approximates a constant-current source. Figure 2–20 shows the characteristics for a forward-wave CFA; operation from a constant-voltage source is desirable for such a device. Details of interaction for a backward-wave tube are given in Figure 2–21, which illustrates desirability of operating with a modulator approximating a constant-current source if it is desired to minimize changes in output power as the frequency is changed.

There is considerable similarity between the terminal properties of a crossed-field amplifier and those of a magnetron; in particular, there is a very definite biased-diode characteristic associated with a CFA. It should be noted that such operation is normally achieved only when adequate levels of RF drive are applied at the input to the crossed-field amplifier, and that the application of voltage with inadequate drive may result in tube operation in undesirable modes, with a resulting substantial variation in the terminal V-I characteristics.

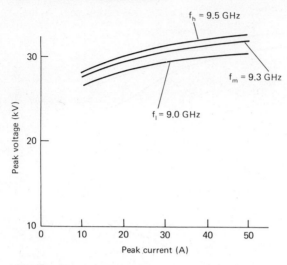

FIGURE 2–19 Cathode *V-I* characteristics of a back-ward-wave CFA. [36]

One important property of the CFA is the ability of high-power tubes to operate with cold cathodes. This cold-cathode operation is slightly enhanced by the reentrant structure. However, Amplitrons have experienced difficulty starting with short pulses, requiring either excessive RF drive or a heater for satisfactory operation. Cold-cathode operation

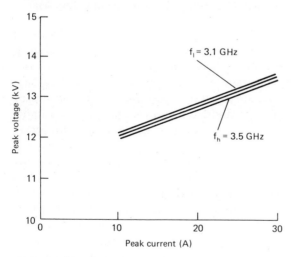

FIGURE 2–20 Cathode *V-I* characteristics of a for-ward-wave CFA. [36]

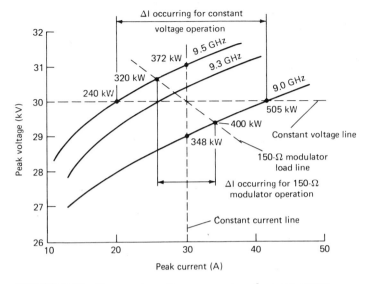

FIGURE 2-21 **Changes in voltage, current, and power output for a backward-wave CFA as frequency is varied. Interaction is plotted for a constant-current modulator, for a constant-voltage modulator, and for a modulator with an internal impedance of 150 Ω. Note the reduction in power variation achieved with the 150-Ω and constant-current modulators. [36]**

of lower-power CFAs is generally not feasible because of the possibility of poisoning the cathode in case of an accidental overvoltage application to the cathode.

Another important property of the CFA is its ability to be operated from a dc power supply. In this mode of operation, forward-wave amplifiers having large constant-voltage bandwidths and completely cold secondary emitting cathodes are utilized. A constant dc voltage is applied to the tube, which remains essentially an open circuit until RF energy entering the tube causes the secondary emission process to begin. The amplification process continues until the RF drive pulse is removed. At the termination of the RF drive pulse, the accumulated space charge can support noiselike oscillation in reentrant tubes. An additional control electrode is included to remove this space charge and terminate the RF output, as shown in Figure 2-22. The accumulated space charge gives no trouble in nonreentrant CFAs; these tubes can be made entirely self-pulsing.

An example of a system incorporating such a self-pulsing cold-cathode tube is the AN/MPS-36 radar, which utilizes a Varian SFD-257 cold-cathode tube with an electrode incorporated to sweep out excess elec-

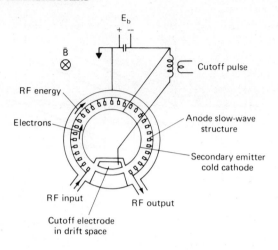

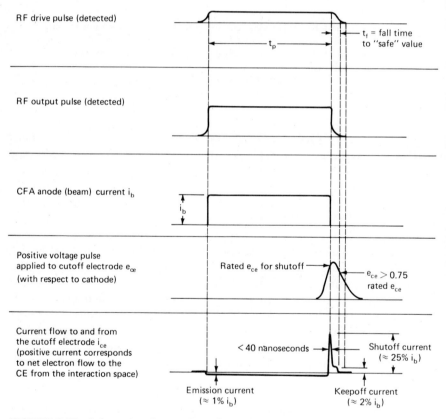

FIGURE 2–22 Schematic of operation of cutoff electrode in a self-pulsing forward-wave CFA, and timing of pulses associated with operation of such a CFA. [38]

trons [38]. The entire amplifier consists of a cathode-pulsed TWT, a cathode-pulsed CFA, and the final self-pulsing crossed-field amplifier. A plot of power output as a function of frequency and a plot of efficiency are shown in Figure 2–23. It should be noted that the resulting configuration is quite rugged and relatively straightforward, but that operation of self-pulsing cold-cathode tubes is normally limited to high-power, relatively long–pulse-length applications (the MPS-36 operates with 0.25- to 5-μs pulses). The normal time relationships for such operation are shown in Figure 2–22.

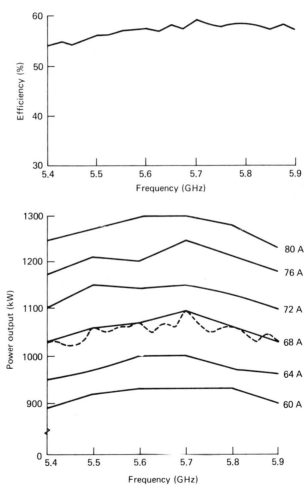

FIGURE 2–23 **Efficiency and power output for the SFD-257 self-pulsing CFA used in the MPS-36. [38]**

As discussed in the Chapter 1, the phase characteristics of the crossed-field amplifier are quite important in its application to radar systems. The fact that the CFA is an electrically short device, and does in fact phase-lock its oscillation to the input, gives rise to the supposition that its phase stability might be of a high order, and that the CFA might be particularly suitable for multitube applications in which phase coherence among the tubes is an important parameter. The phase characteristics that are of the most importance are phase sensitivity to changes in the input voltage or current, phase sensitivity to changes in RF drive power, phase linearity with frequency, and behavior under multiple-signal-input drive conditions. Figure 2–24 shows the phase sensitivity to input-power changes and to cathode-voltage changes. Figure 2–25 shows the sensitivities of phase to change in current and to frequency. Fitted data for a forward-wave crossed-field amplifier showing the phase change in degrees as a function of changes in RF drive and as a function of changes in anode voltage are shown in Figure 2–26. Phase sensitivity to changes in dc conditions for forward-wave and backward-wave devices are quite similar.

The linearity of phase with frequency is determined almost entirely by the external circuit reflections and by the gain of the tube. The electrical length of forward-wave types is typically larger than that of backward-wave types, but sufficient care in manufacturing can usually result in deviations of less than 5° from linearity for either type of tube.

Since the CFA is not a linear amplifier, it cannot accept multiple signals simultaneously and reproduce these without distortion or suppression. Figure 2–27 shows the effects of driving a forward CFA with two signals. The second signal reduces the available power for the first signal, but the overall total power output and the tube efficiency remain approximately the same.

It has been supposed that tubes that operate with a constant DC potential applied may act as noise generators. However, such has not appeared to be the case, and the tube appears to be a largely passive object with noise levels approaching that of thermally generated noise. Values of noise power spectral density as low as −115 dBm/MHz have been measured, with typical values approximately −106 dBm/MHz. There have been a number of intrapulse noise measurements on CFAs made in recent years, some of which are summarized in Table 2–3 on page 53. Representative values obtained for both AM and phase modulation (PM) noise are from −60 to −30 dBm/MHz, where values have been referenced to an equivalent CW value to remove the effects of the duty cycle on measured data.

It has been observed that certain classes of CFAs generate less broadband noise than others. In particular, it has been noted that certain

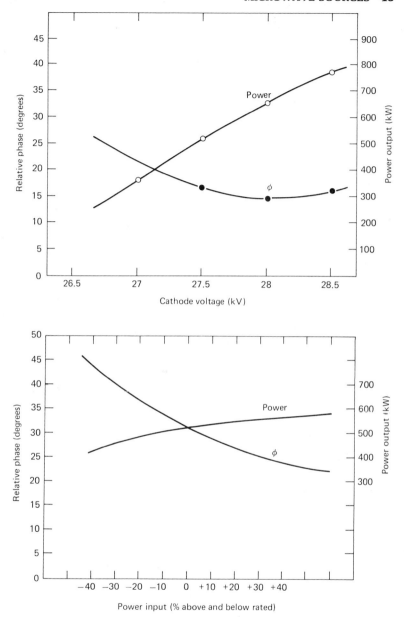

FIGURE 2–24   CFA phase sensitivities (phase of output signal to input signal) to changes in cathode voltage and power output. [20]

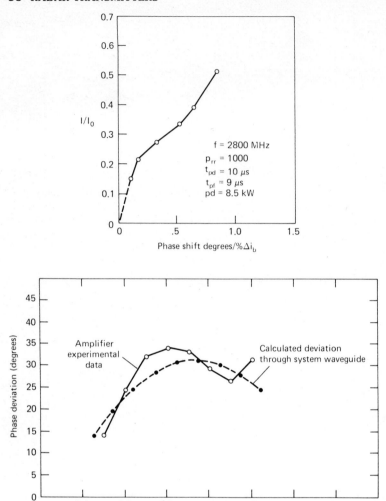

FIGURE 2–25 CFA phase sensitivities to changes in current [37] and frequency [20].

forward-wave devices generate approximately 20 dB less noise power spectral density than similar backward-wave devices. It is not known whether this is a general characteristic of CFAs or whether it is merely an isolated instance.

CFAs evidence a few anomalous effects that are perhaps worthy of note. The first of these is the tendency of CFAs, like any high-power, high-voltage device, to occasionally develop arcs between the cathode

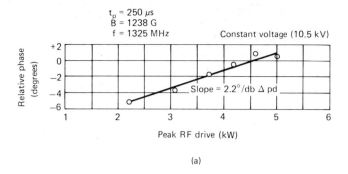

(a)

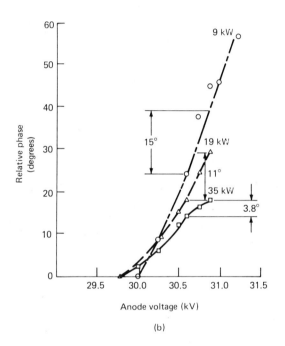

(b)

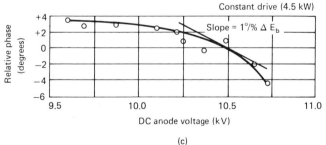

(c)

FIGURE 2–26 Numerical fits for phase sensitivities of a CFA (*a*) to changes in RF drive with voltage held constant [37], (*b*) to changes in voltage for three RF drive levels [20], and (*c*) to changes in anode voltage with RF drive held constant [37].

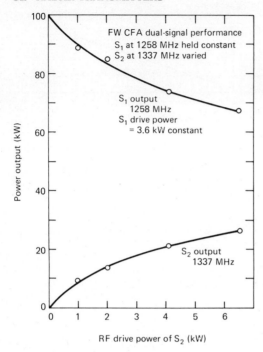

FIGURE 2–27 Effects on output power of a CFA caused by driving a forward-wave (FW) CFA with two signals, holding one fixed and varying the other. [37]

and the body of the tube. Provisions must be made to limit the energy dissipated in the device under such conditions, and to promptly restore proper system operation once the arc has been quenched.

Another anomaly of the CFA is that considerable RF energy may be propagated out through the stem of the tube. This RF energy can adversely affect the operation of other parts of the system, and care should be taken to confine any such RF leakage. There is the possibility that this cathode leakage will introduce resonances into the system that may in turn produce sideband modulations on the primary RF energy; under the worst possible conditions, this energy may introduce arcing or waveguide breakdown into the system. Sufficient care with cathode connections will usually alleviate such problems [37].

Another potential difficulty results from the possibility that high-Q resonant modes in the waveguide output system will occur at frequencies where the waveguide is propagating but where the tube's slow-wave structure is cut off. Such a mode would be attenuated through the slow-wave structure but would display an RF field pattern to the electron stream that could couple appreciable energy into these frequencies. The presence of the high Q in the waveguide circuit might provide sufficient field strength to break down the waveguide and result in arcing. Thus,

TABLE 2-3   CFA INTRASPECTRUM PM NOISE MEASUREMENTS [37]

Radar band	Peak power (kW)	S_b/N_b* (dB)	BW† (Hz)	S_o/N_o‡ (dB/MHz)	Pulse width (μs)	PRF (kHz)	Duty cycle (dB)	S/N§ (dB/MHz)
L band	100	71.8	10	21.8	11	1.3	18.38	40.2
L band	100	67.0	50	24.0	11	1.3	18.38	42.2
L band	100	74.4	150	37.2	30	1.0	15.22	52.4
L band	100	73.0	50	29.0	10	1.0	20.0	49.0
C band	500	69.0	200	32.0	1	5.0	23.0	55.0
C band	660	78.0	3	21.7	20	0.160	25.0	46.7
C band	600	78.9	3	22.6	20	0.150	25.2	47.8
S band	750	83.0	50	39.0	10	4.0	14.0	53.0
S band	750	88.0	50	44.0	10	4.0	14.0	58.0
S band	60	71.0	10	21.0	5.5	1.25	21.6	42.6
S band	60	76.0	10	26.0	5.5	1.25	21.0	47.6
S oand	60	70.0	10	19.0	5.5	1.5	20.8	40.0
S band	60	77.0	10	26.9	5.5	1.5	20.8	47.0
S band	666	79.0	3	22.0	29.5	0.189	22.5	44.5
S band	60	76.7	10	25.7	10	0.585	23.3	49.0
S band	60	60.9	50	16.0	33.4	0.585	16.6	32.6

* Measured noise power relative to spectral line power.
† Filter bandwidth for measurement.
‡ Measurements normalized for 1-MHz bandwidth.
§ Equivalent CW signal-to-noise power-density ratio.

the output waveguide system should be carefully examined for any high-Q resonances before a crossed-field amplifier is operated in such a system [37].

It should be noted that some of these anomalous behaviors are a function of the specific tube configuration, or of the tube operating point. Thus, testing a different tube, or the same tube operated at a different power level or frequency, may not uncover these difficulties. A carefully designed test program should be carried out in order to determine if such difficulties exist.

Several types of commercially available CFAs are listed in Table 2–4. Several trends are evident from the data and from previous discussions: the reentrant types are more efficient than the nonreentrant types, the gain of the linear tubes can be increased by increasing device length, and CFAs with no RF feedback are less prone to spurious oscillation than tubes with RF feedback. Several other parameters, such as phase and amplitude stability, are important in comparing these tube types with tubes for similar applications; the particular choice of tube format also affects the modulator design, constant-voltage pulsers being desired for forward-wave amplifiers and constant-current pulsers for backward-wave devices.

In summary, the crossed-field amplifier is a coherent amplifier characterized by relatively broad bandwidth and high efficiency but low gain. It possesses a high degree of phase stability and, in some applications, may be largely self-pulsing. Advantages which are particularly important in mobile systems are its relatively small size and weight and its low operating voltages. The tube evidences excellent reproducibility, and lives in excess of 5000 hours (h) have been experienced in numerous operating systems. To date, thousands of CFAs have been delivered and operated in the field, most of these being high-power, cathode-pulsed tubes installed in radar systems operating between 100 kW and 5 MW of peak power output with average powers in excess of 1 kW [37].

2–2 LINEAR-BEAM TUBES

In contrast to the crossed-field devices, there exists an additional class of tubes, called the *linear-beam* tubes. Some members of the class of linear-beam tubes are the klystron, the traveling-wave tube (TWT), the Twystron®, and the extended-interaction klystron.

Klystrons [40]

The high-power pulsed klystron is an amplifier that is characterized by high gain, high peak power, and good efficiency, but it has

TABLE 2-4 SOME COMMERCIALLY AVAILABLE HIGH-POWER PULSED CFAs

Tube type	Center frequency (GHz)	Peak P_o (MW)	Frequency range (GHz)	Maximum duty cycle	Peak		Gain (dB)
					Voltage (kV)	Current (A)	
1AM10	1.288	1.8	1.225–1.350	0.02	46	50	9.2
QKS1452	2.998	3.0	2.994–3.002	0.0015	47	100	
SFD222	5.65	1.0	5.4–5.9	0.001	35	60	18
SFD237	5.65	1.0	5.4–5.96	0.01	35	60	13
QKS506	9.05	1.0	8.7–9.4	......	40	45	7
SFD236	16.5	0.1	16–17	0.001	14	23	17

relatively narrow bandwidths and requires relatively high voltages. The large physical size of most klystrons and their associated modulators and X-ray shielding has limited the application of klystrons in many radar systems. High-power klystrons also find applications in high-energy linear accelerators; the klystrons originally developed for the Stanford Linear Accelerator were the first truly high-power microwave amplifiers and formed the basis for a number of large, ground-based coherent radar systems.

A cutaway schematic representation of a high-power cavity klystron is shown in Figure 2–28, which illustrates the separation of the various principal parts of the device. This separation permits each area to be optimized individually and contributes to the relatively high levels of performance that have been achieved with klystron amplifiers.

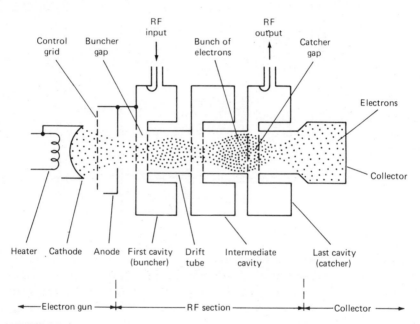

FIGURE 2–28 Schematic cutaway view of a klystron amplifier.

A characteristic of the klystron amplifier is that there is no interaction between the various portions of the RF circuitry, except that which is provided by the electron beam, which propagates from the cathode to the collector. The design of the cavities for the klystron is well established and usually assumes the form of an annular cavity. However, the injection of electrons into this interaction structure, and the focusing of the electron beam as it passes through the cavities, are of central importance in klystron operation.

The electron beam is generated by an electron gun, and for a tube that is cathode-pulsed, the electron gun assumes a particularly simple form; an outline view of such a gun is shown in Figure 2–29. However,

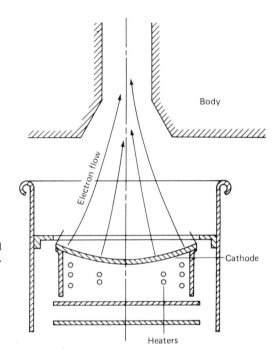

FIGURE 2–29 Cathode and electron gun of a cathode-pulsed klystron. [4]

for many applications, the inclusion of an appropriate control electrode in the electron gun permits a considerable simplification of the modulator requirements for the system. Three principal types of electron-gun control electrodes are illustrated in Figure 2–30: the modulating anode, the control-focus electrode, and the shadow grid. A primary figure of merit for these various control electrodes is the cutoff amplification factor μ_c, defined as the negative ratio of control-electrode voltage to anode voltage at the point where the emission is safely cut off. Another figure of merit is the total amplification factor μ of the gun, which is the ratio of the control-electrode voltage swing to the beam voltage. It is desirable that each of these amplification factors be high, yet it is desirable to maintain a well-focused beam when the tube is turned on, in order to reduce heating from electrons impinging on the tube body.

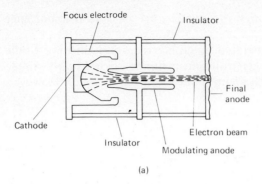

(a)

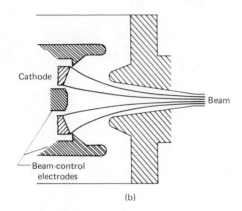

(b)

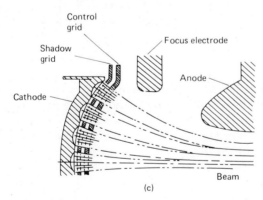

(c)

FIGURE 2–30 **Three principal types of gridded electron guns.** (*a*) **Modulating anode.** (*b*) **Control-focus electrode.** (*c*) **Shadow grid.** [40]

Table 2–5 compares the characteristics of several types of these control elements, and it can be seen that the intercepting or shadow-gridded types have the largest values of μ. The characteristics of a shadow-gridded electron gun are summarized in Figure 2–31. For extremely high-power applications, the shadow-gridded tubes are unsatisfactory

TABLE 2–5   CHARACTERISTICS OF CONTROL ELECTRODES

Type	μ	μ_c	Capacity (pF)	Interception	Low-voltage focusing
Modulating anode	1–3	. . . .	50	0	Good
Control-focus electrode	2–10	2–10	100	0	Poor
Intercepting grid	50	100	50	15%	Fair
Shadow grid	30	300	50	0.1%	Fair

because of the spreading of the electron beam and the resultant heating of the tube body. For such applications, modulating-anode structures are normally selected, in spite of the extremely large voltage swings required for their operation.

Focusing of the electron beam is particularly critical once the electrons

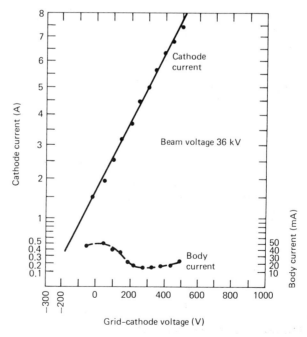

FIGURE 2–31   Transfer characteristic of a shadow-gridded gun. [40]

leave the gun area, and with a length-to-diameter ratio of the beam on the order of 100 to 1, small variations in electron spreading can produce appreciable electron interception and tube heating. In high-power, CW applications, near perfect beam transmission is often required, sometimes on the order of 99%. However, for lower–duty-cycle, pulsed applications, less critical values may be utilized, figures of 60 to 70% being more representative. Focusing of the electron beam is most normally accomplished by a magnetic field generated uniformly along the axis by a solenoid wound coil surrounding the klystron. While the coil produces an extremely uniform field, its size and the bulk of the associated power supplies may be objectionable. To reduce size and weight, periodic–permanent-magnet (PPM) focusing and electro-static focusing have been applied to klystrons, but have not yet found wide acceptance.

The klystron appears to follow the familiar space-charge-limited diode law; that is, $I = kV^{3/2}$ (where k is the *perveance*, a constant for a particular tube), and the power is given by $kV^{5/3}$. For cathode-pulsed tubes, the load may often be approximated as a linear resistance, paralleled by the cathode capacity of the tube. More detailed consideration must involve the tube nonlinearities, but the differences thus produced are normally small.

The klystron is typically a narrow-band amplifier, but by stagger tuning of the various cavities involved, the bandwidth may be increased at the expense of tube gain. An example of the bandpass that can result, and the tuning for the various cavities, is shown in Figure 2–32. The characteristics of several high-power klystrons are summarized in Table 2–6.

Klystrons are typically rather low-noise amplifiers. A representative

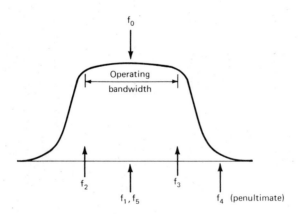

FIGURE 2–32   Stagger tuning of five klystron cavities to achieve increased bandwidth.

TABLE 2–6   SOME COMMERCIALLY AVAILABLE HIGH-POWER KLYSTRONS

Tube type	Center frequency	Peak P_o (MW)	Frequency range	Maximum duty cycle	Peak Voltage (kV)	Peak Current (A)	Gain (dB)
VA-1513	0.4–0.45 GHz	20	15 MHz BW	Approx. 0.015	230	280	40
TV2023	1.3 GHz	40	1.2–1.4 GHz	0.001	300	230	53
F2049	2.856 GHz	30	2.856 GHz	0.008	290	295	50
VKS-8262	2.9 MHz	5.5	5 MHz BW	0.001	125	88	50
SAC42	5.65 GHz	3.3	5.4–5.9 GHz	0.002	135	112	23.5
SAX191	9015	1.25	8.83–9.2 GHz	0.0048	85	50	50

background-noise level for phase modulation noise is 125 dB/kHz below the carrier, and the AM noise is typically 10 dB lower than these values, as shown in Figure 2–33(*a*). Figure 2-33(*b*) shows the typical klystron output-noise power as a function of gain measured in a 1-kHz bandwidth, 50 kHz from the carrier frequency.

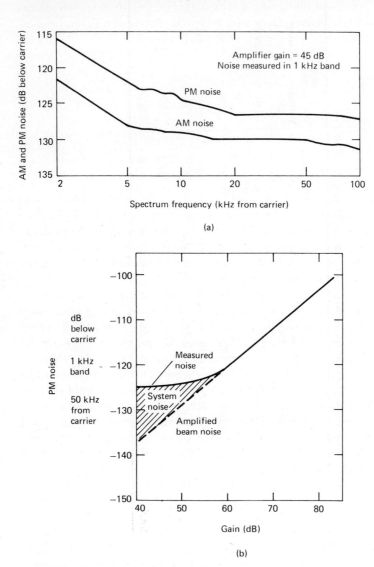

(a)

(b)

FIGURE 2–33 Noise characteristics of a klystron: (*a*) amplitude modulation and phase modulation noise as a function of separation from carrier frequency, and (*b*) variations in phase noise with tube gain. [40]

There are other potential sources of noise, including the possibility of ion oscillation, which can produce spurious sidebands as great as 50 dB below the carrier. The only cure for this is care in the fabrication and evacuation of the tube by the manufacturer. Other spurious responses can result from power-supply ripple voltages or ringing on the various electrodes of the klystron. The amplitude modulation sensitivity due to a change in beam voltage may be readily derived by differentiating the expression for power output of the klystron,

$$\frac{dP}{dV} = \frac{5}{2}\frac{P}{V} \tag{2-1}$$

and for phase modulation

$$\frac{d\theta}{dV} = \frac{\theta_o}{2V_o} \tag{2-2}$$

In Equations 2–1 and 2–2, θ_o is the phase length of the klystron and is typically on the order of 6 to 10 radians (rad) for each of the drift spaces between the klystron cavities. It should be noted that if ac voltage is used on the heaters of the klystron, there typically results an AM sideband approximately 50 dB below the carrier; operation with dc heaters alleviates this particular difficulty.

As with any high-power tube, considerable care in the application and operation of the klystron is necessary if good performance and long life are to be achieved. In particular, protection against defocusing the beam or excessive beam voltage must be provided, normally by monitoring beam current and body current in the tube. In addition, the focusing magnetic field should be monitored and high-voltage-interlocked with the presence of this magnetic field. Similarly, coolant flow is normally interlocked with the beam voltage to prevent tube melting.

A frequent mode of failure for a high-power klystron is a fractured output window, normally caused by arcing in the waveguide structure. In order to prevent such occurrences, reflected RF power at the tube output is normally monitored and the interior of the waveguide continuously checked for the presence of light. Excessive reflected power or light inside the waveguide should initiate an immediate shutdown of the klystron.

There is always a possibility that internal arcs will develop within the tube, and in that event, the beam voltage must be removed rapidly. In order to accomplish this, a so-called *crowbar circuit* may be incorporated, which is a fast-acting switch connected across the power supply in order to discharge stored power-supply energy without damaging the klystron. Provision should normally be made for reinitiating the operation of the klystron once the arc has had sufficient time to extinguish.

Traveling-Wave Tubes [26,40]

The high-power traveling-wave tube (TWT) is a microwave amplifier characterized by high gain, large bandwidth, relatively low efficiency, and high operating voltages. In addition to the RF input and output connections, most TWTs have a body electrode, a collector, a cathode or electron gun, an interaction region, and some means of focusing the electrons into a linear beam.

A cutaway schematic representation of a TWT is given in Figure 2–34. The heart of the TWT is the so-called delay-line structure, which

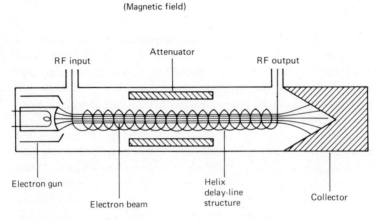

FIGURE 2–34 Longitudinal-section view of a TWT.

is shown schematically as a helix, and in fact, helices are extensively utilized at low power levels. However, at higher power levels, simple helices are not often used; instead either the ring-and-bar-type configuration, the two-tape contrawound helix, or the coupled-cavity TWT, all shown in Figure 2–35, is utilized. Approximately 90% of all high-power TWTs employ the coupled-cavity approach, because of its excellent electrical characteristics (its impedance, bandwidth and mode structure), its mechanical simplicity, its shape, which is well-suited for PPM focusing, its ruggedness, and the versatility of its scaling with frequency, power, and bandwidth.

The focusing of the electron beam is critical to proper TWT performance, as was the case with the klystron, and several common methods

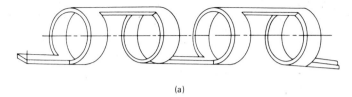

(a)

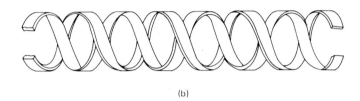

(b)

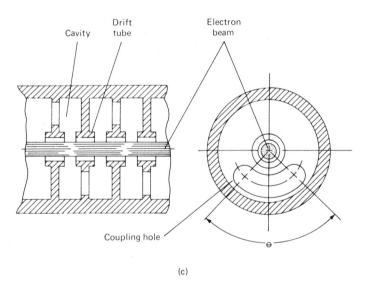

(c)

FIGURE 2–35 TWT interaction circuits: (a) ring-bar, (b) contra-wound-helix, and (c) coupled-cavity approaches. [26]

of focusing are illustrated in Figure 2–36. The two that are most commonly used in high-power tubes are the PPM methods and solenoidal focusing. In solenoidal focusing, the coils are typically foil-wound as an integral part of the tube, to hold mechanically induced variations in the magnetic field to considerably less than 1%. The PPM approach does not provide the degree of focusing that a solenoid-focused TWT achieves, but its smaller size and weight and the absence of additional power supplies and power consumption make it quite attractive for a number of applications.

One of the principal drawbacks of the TWT is its relatively low efficiency. There are two primary ways that this problem has been attacked,

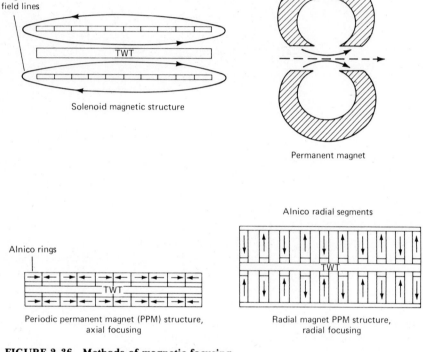

FIGURE 2-36 **Methods of magnetic focusing.**

the first of which involves depressing the collector, i.e., operating with the collector at a potential below that of the body. The second approach is so-called *velocity resynchronization*, which is achieved by taking the last portion of the periodic structure and *jumping* or increasing its potential by a relatively small amount. A cross section of such a TWT arrangement is shown in Figure 2-37; it illustrates one of the significant problems with velocity resynchronization: insulating that portion of the structure without introducing additional RF reflections and mismatches. Increases in efficiency to levels of 50 to 60% have been achieved by depressing the collector and by using resynchronization.

A list of some commercially available high-power TWTs is given in Table 2–7. Most of these tubes are representative of the maximum power output readily available in each frequency band, except for the QKW1132A, which is included as a tube typical of one that might be utilized to drive a higher-power amplifier. A plot of the variation in

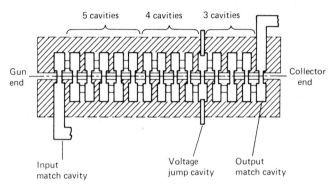

FIGURE 2–37 **Schematic of jumped-collector TWT for velocity resynchronization.** [26]

output power for a high-power TWT tube, the Hughes 750H, is shown in Figure 2–38, along with the depressed-collector efficiency. Depressing the collector increases the efficiency at the expense of equipment complexity. The same tube operated with the collector at ground potential would exhibit an efficiency of 10 to 20% over the same band of frequencies. A plot of the ranges of peak and average powers for TWTs in field use is shown in Figure 2–39, but all of these designs are subject to improvement with additional developmental effort.

TWTs may be cathode-modulated or may utilize the same types of control grid as are incorporated in the klystrons. There is a tendency, particularly in the gridded tubes, for arcs to develop in the TWT structure. Once an arc is established it draws sufficient energy from the power supply to damage the internal structure of the TWT, and perhaps the associated grid modulator. The mechanism of such an arc is believed to be as follows: an arc forms between the anode and the grid-support structure, carrying the grid positive with respect to the cathode, eventually forming an arc between the grid wires and the cathode surface, and damaging the grid wires. Spark gaps may sometimes be utilized to limit the grid-to-cathode voltage to values that will not initiate the grid-to-cathode arcs.

TABLE 2-7 SOME COMMERCIALLY AVAILABLE HIGH-POWER TWT'S

Tube type	Center frequency (GHz)	Peak P_o		Frequency range	Maximum duty cycle	Peak		Gain (db)
						Voltage (kV)	Current (A)	
QKW1490	1.3	700	kW	1250–1350 MHz				
VTS-5754A1	3.0	125	kW	2.9–3.1 GHz	0.006	42	14	47
TPOM4131	2.85	750	kW	2.7–3 GHz	0.007	45	35	20
560H	3.2	250	kW	3.1–3.3 GHz	0.02	53	21	50
VA146	5.65	4.5	MW	5.4–5.9 GHz	0.002	130	94	35
752H	8.9	150	kW	8.4–9.4 GHz	0.01	50	15	16
8716H	9.1	120	kW	9.0–9.2 GHz	0.0025	43	13.5	50
QKW-1132A	9.25	1.5	kW	8.5–10 GHz	0.01	11	1.5	34–40
750H	9.5	25	kW	9.0–10.0 GHz	0.01	24	5.5	47
893H	16.25	100	kW	16.0–16.5 GHz	0.005	62	7.8	50

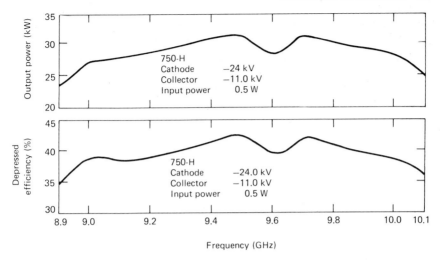

FIGURE 2–38 Peak power output and depressed-collector efficiency as a function of frequency for a Hughes 750H TWT. (*Hughes*)

As with the klystron, defocusing of the beam, loss of coolant, excessive beam current, and excessive voltage call for removal of the high potential from the tube, necessitating the use of crowbar circuits in many instances. As with the case of the klystron, provisions should be made for reapplication of appropriate voltages once the arc has been extinguished, since occasional arcing in most high-power tubes is not necessarily indicative of tube problems, but is a feature which is normally encountered.

The TWT is a space-charge-limited diode, as is the klystron, and shows variations in power output and in phase with variations in beam voltage similar to those shown by klystron. Sensitivities of a representative TWT to changes in various electrode voltages are summarized in Table 2–8. It should be noted that the insertion phase of a TWT is somewhat more sensitive to variations in supply voltage than is the insertion phase of a klystron, because of the longer effective electrical length of the TWT. The noise figure and noise power spectral density near the carrier frequency of the TWT are not dissimilar to those of the klystron.

Twystron Amplifiers

The need to design a hybrid device that consists of a klystron driving section and a TWT output section in order to achieve increased bandwidth with a high level of efficiency has resulted in the Twystron amplifier. This combination achieves large bandwidth, as schematically

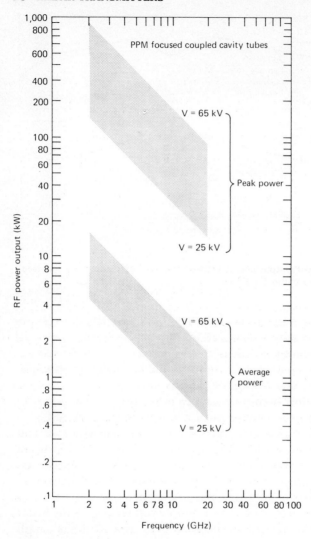

FIGURE 2-39 Ranges of peak and average powers for pulsed TWTs in field use. [26]

shown in Figure 2–40. A set of representative characteristics for some Twystron amplifiers is given in Table 2–9. Operation and sensitivities are not dissimilar to those for high-power TWTs and klystrons, but in general, the gain and phase are not as uniform as can be achieved for some coupled-cavity TWTs. Phase excursions of ±25° from linearity over a 10% bandwidth are representative, but smaller values have been achieved.

TABLE 2–8 TYPICAL SENSITIVITIES FOR A 10-kW,
5% BANDWIDTH, 60-dB-GAIN TWT [40]

Voltage parameter	AM	FM
Cathode to body	(0.5 db)/1%	30°/1%
Cathode to anode or grid*	(0.1 db)/1%	5°/1%
	(0.15 dB)/1%	7°/1%
Cathode to collector	(0.02 dB)/1%	0.5°/1%
Heater (dynamic)	(0.00005 dB)/1%	0.001°/1%
Solenoid	(0.00001 dB)/1%	0.0005°/1%
Drive power		2.2°/(1 dB)

* This assumes either anode or grid is used to control beam current.

Extended-Interaction Klystrons

Extended-interaction klystrons, which couple between the resonant cavities, as shown in Figure 2–41, have been developed in order to improve the power-handling capability of the klystron. The advantages are perhaps illustrated by an extended-interaction klystron that achieved over 1 MW average power at X-band frequencies.

However, an increasing application of the extended-interaction klystron oscillator (EIO) is being found at millimeter wavelengths, where the extended-interaction oscillator has proven to be one of the more reliable sources of RF energy in the several-kilowatt range at frequencies up to several hundred gigahertz. A cross-sectional schematic view of an EIO is shown in Figure 2–42. The separation of the cathode region from the interaction region permits low cathode-current densities, even at millimeter wavelengths, thus providing a highly reliable tube. A representative set of pulsed-EIO characteristics is summarized in Table 2-10.

Recent development efforts have resulted in an extended-interaction amplifier (EIA) operating in the 95-GHz region. This EIA is mechanically tunable over a 1-GHz range and has an instantaneous 3-dB bandwidth of 200 MHz. The tube has achieved 2.3 kW peak RF power with 33 dB gain. The device uses a samarium-cobalt magnet and occupies a volume of less than 90 cubic inches (in³). The tube is cathode-pulsed and, like many cathode-pulsed linear amplifiers, exhibits a period of self-oscillation during turn-on and turnoff; close attention to modulator rise and fall times may minimize the effects of these undesired oscillations.

In order to simplify modulator requirements, development of control-gridded millimeter-wave EIOs and EIAs is under way, but no operating tubes have been demonstrated.

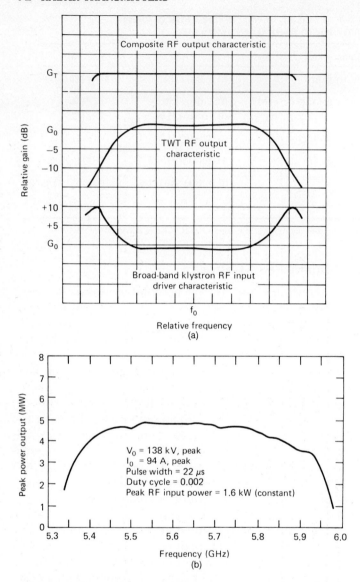

FIGURE 2–40 Frequency characteristics of a Twystron amplifier [18, 40], showing (a) principle of obtaining more uniform frequency response by using different input and output circuits and (b) the frequency response actually obtained [40].

TABLE 2-9 SOME TWYSTRON CHARACTERISTICS [42]

Center frequency (GHz)	Peak power (MW)	Average power (kW)	Gain (dB)	1.5-dB bandwidth (MHz)	Efficiency (%)	Duty cycle	Pulse width (μs)	Beam voltage (kV)	Beam current (A)
2.7–2.9	2.5	5.0	37	200	35	0.002	6	117	80
2.715–2.915	3.0	8.5	42	200	40	0.0025	10	126	82
2.75–2.95	5.0	12	40	200	40	0.0025	10	125	92
2.9–3.1	2.5	5	37	200	35	0.002	7	117	80
3.015–3.215	3.0	8.5	42	200	40	0.0025	10	126	82
5.4–5.9	2.5	20	36	500	33	0.004	20	135	93
5.4–5.9	3.2	10	36	500	33	0.002	12.5	135	95

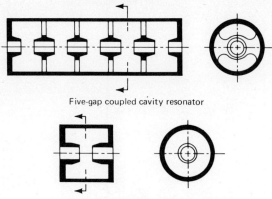

Five-gap coupled cavity resonator

Single-gap klystron cavity

FIGURE 2–41 **Cavity configuration of extended-inter-action klystron cavities and a conventional klystron cavity.** [40]

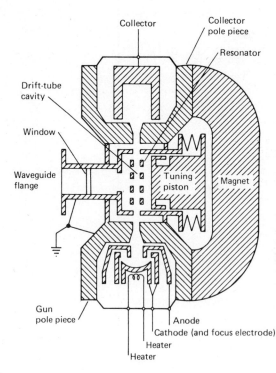

Collector

Collector pole piece

Resonator

Drift-tube cavity

Window

Waveguide flange

Tuning piston

Magnet

Gun pole piece

Anode

Cathode (and focus electrode)

Heater

Heater

FIGURE 2–42 **Cross-sectional view of a millimeter-wave ex-tended-interaction oscillator, showing the removal of the ca-thode from the interaction region.** (*Varian Associates*)

TABLE 2-10 REPRESENTATIVE CHARACTERISTICS
OF AN EIO OPERATING NEAR 95 GHz

Center frequency	95 GHz
Tuning range	94–95 GHz
Peak power	1 kW
Beam voltage	21 kV
Peak beam current	650 mA
Anode voltage	8 kV
Peak anode current	10 mA
Duty cycle	0.005
Electronic tuning range (anode)	150 MHz
Cathode modulation sensitivity	0.15 MHz/V
Anode capacitance	30 pF
Cathode capacitance	15 pF

2-3 SOLID-STATE TRANSMITTERS

Recently, in order to obtain increased reliability and reduced cost, a number of solid-state transmitting sources have been developed; unfortunately, such devices are capable only of relatively low peak powers, and so their usefulness is limited to applications where they may be combined, or where only small amounts of transmitted power are required. Typical of the capabilities of transistor amplifiers are single-package units capable of generating 600 W at a frequency of approximately 1 GHz [33]. The output of a number of such devices can be combined, as for example in the case of the PAVE PAWS radar system, which uses 3584 individual transmitter modules in a phased-array configuration, each one capable of generating 440 W peak over a frequency range of 420 to 450 MHz [12]. Another example of combining is a system that provides 25 kW peak in a single-output waveguide, using 40 modules, each one with a peak-power capability of 650 W, and operating over the frequency range 1250 to 1350 MHz [19]. At higher frequencies, gallium arsenide (GaAs) FET amplifiers are often used, typical capabilities being 5 W peak over a 4- to 8-GHz band [29], or 15 W at a frequency of 6 GHz [41], decreasing to 10 W at a frequency of 8 GHz [13]. As is the case with other transistor amplifiers, power combining may be used in order to increase the total effective power; successful power-combining techniques have been utilized through the K_u band [5,28,35].

For higher-frequency operation, IMPATT diodes may be used as amplifiers or oscillators; again, the outputs of several amplifiers may be combined to increase the total output power [34]. Care must be employed in using IMPATT diodes, since they do appear rather noisy and have a high degree of sensitivity to both current and voltage changes [2,7,17,24]. At the present time, 5 to 10 Watts is available at 95 GHz [3], and laboratory development models have evidenced 3 Watts at 140 GHz [27], with devices at 225 GHz under development [16]. Because of the relatively low peak powers associated with most solid-state transmitting devices, conventional circuit-design techniques may be used for the modulators, and the special techniques that are required for higher-power devices will not be necessary. Because of the distinctly different, and somewhat simpler, requirements for modulators in solid-state transmitters, these will not be discussed further in this text, which will be confined rather to high-power thermionic tubes and the modulator techniques required in order to provide the tens to hundreds of kilowatts of peak power needed to operate such devices.

2–4 OTHER DEVICES

Other types of RF power sources are sometimes encountered in radar systems. At lower frequencies, vacuum-tube transmitters are sometimes employed, but at frequencies above 3 GHz these are rarely encountered. Semiconductor devices are continually making inroads at lower frequencies and lower power levels, but at the extremely high power levels, thermionic tubes are still unchallenged. There are a number of devices that show promise but have never been fully developed; these include the Ubitron, beam plasma amplifiers, and relativistic beam devices. In recent years, a new class of microwave and millimeter-wave oscillators and amplifiers has been developed. These devices, called *gyrotrons,* or electron-cyclotron masers [1,8,10,11,14,15,45], show promise of providing peak powers at millimeter-wave frequencies that are considerably higher than those obtainable from using previous techniques.

Gyrotron devices typically utilize a relativistic electron beam and convert constant electron energies to microwave energies in an intense electromagnetic field. Initial results typically involved operation at megavolt levels, and the use of superconducting magnets was necessary to obtain the extremely high magnetic fields required; however, it is possible to build devices having much more modest voltage and magnetic-field requirements, although they operate at somewhat lower power levels.

Figure 2–43 is a presentation of the achievable and predicted gyrotron power levels over a range of frequencies, while Tables 2–11 and 2–12 present additional details on a number of Soviet devices. It should be mentioned that relativistic devices are capable of substantially higher peak powers, but because of the large accelerating voltages, the large

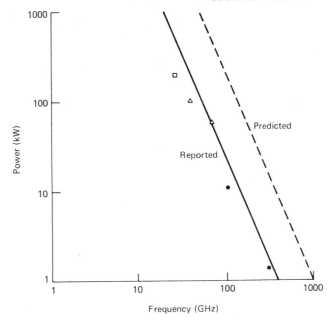

FIGURE 2–43 **Gyrotron state-of-the-art power capabilities.**

currents, the extremely high magnetic fields, and the large size and weight associated with such devices, it appears unlikely that they are suitable for many applications. Thus, the data presented in Figure 2–43 and Table 2–12 appear to be representative of present and projected gyrotron capability.

Up to this point, discussions have centered about the utilization of gyrotrons as oscillators; however, it is possible to configure gyrotrons

TABLE 2–11 PEAK POWER LEVELS FROM CYCLOTRON MASERS DRIVEN BY INTENSE RELATIVISTIC ELECTRON BEAMS [11]

Wavelength (cm)	Peak microwave power (MW)	Accelerating voltage (MV)	Diode current (kA)
4	900	3.3	80
2	350	2.6	40
0.8	8	0.6	15
0.4	2	0.6	15

TABLE 2-12 REPORTED GYROTRON OPERATING CONDITIONS AND OUTPUT PARAMETERS [11]

Model no.	Mode of oscillation	Wavelength (mm)	CW or pulsed	Harmonic number	β-field (kG)	Beam volts (kV)	Beam amps	Output power (kW)	Measured efficiency (%)	Theoretical efficiency (%)
1	TE_{021}	2.78	CW	1	40.5	27	1.4	12	31	36
2	TE_{031}	1.91	CW	2	28.9	18	1.4	2.4	9.5	15
2	TE_{231}	1.95	pulsed	2	28.5	26	1.8	7	15	20
3	TE_{231}	0.92	CW	2	60.6	27	0.9	1.5	6.2	5

as amplifiers as well, by providing appropriate input and output couplings in order to initially bunch the electron beams and to extract energy from the resulting beam. Simplified schematic drawings of a number of such arrangements are presented in Figure 2–44. To date, most activities have concentrated about the implementation of a gyroklystron as an amplifier in the lower portion of the millimeter-wave spectrum.

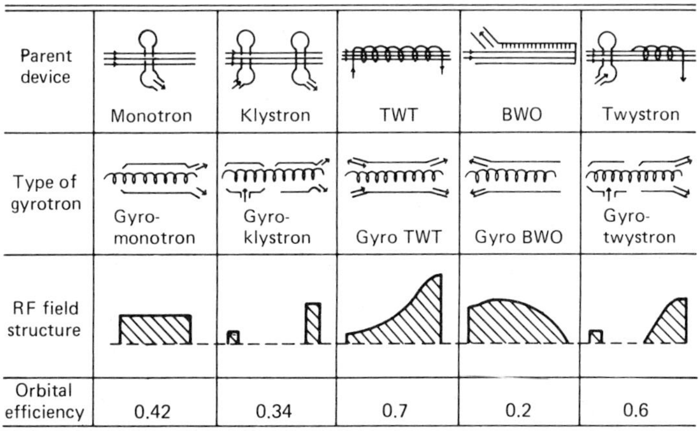

Parent device	Monotron	Klystron	TWT	BWO	Twystron
Type of gyrotron	Gyro-monotron	Gyro-klystron	Gyro TWT	Gyro BWO	Gyro-twystron
RF field structure					
Orbital efficiency	0.42	0.34	0.7	0.2	0.6

FIGURE 2–44   Types of gyrotron amplifier configurations. [8]

The desire for long-range, high-resolution radar systems has stimulated interest in the direct generation of extremely short, very high-power pulses. The dielectric strength of air increases with decreasing pulse lengths to the point where gigawatt and terawatt peak-power pulses become possible for pulse lengths less than approximately 10 nanoseconds (ns). Techniques for generating such pulses vary from hertzian generators (spark gaps) to relativistic beams, and a number of researchers are actively engaged in this field [43].

2–5   COMPARISON OF DEVICES

As is now evident, one has a considerable variety of microwave RF-transmitter devices to choose from when selecting a radar transmitter. For a pulsed, noncoherent source, the magnetron is almost always the suitable choice. Again if a pulsed, noncoherent, frequency-agile source, with capabilities within the tuning rates and frequency ranges of magnetrons, is desired, either a reciprocation- or a rotary-tuned magnetron can be chosen. For a narrow-bandwidth coherent system, the klystron might well be the preferred approach, but if a wider-band coherent system is desired, the traveling-wave tube, the Twystron, and the

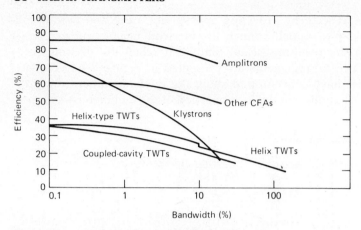

FIGURE 2–45 Efficiency vs. bandwidth for various tubes, illustrating the tradeoff of efficiency for bandwidth. [39]

crossed-field amplifier are all suitable candidates. At higher frequencies an EIO or a gyrotron might also be a possibility.

A comparison of the efficiencies available from a number of different sources is presented in Figure 2–45. Bandwidth capabilities of microwave tubes in the S- to X-band ranges as a function of power level are contained in Figure 2–46, and it is particularly interesting to note the increase in bandwidth at the higher peak powers for klystrons and Twystrons. Table 2–13 contrasts characteristics of a number of available tubes.

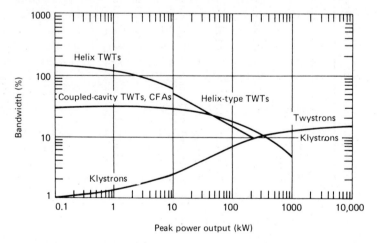

FIGURE 2–46 Bandwidth vs. power output for various tubes. Note particularly the increase in bandwidth for Twystrons and klystrons at the higher power levels. [39]

TABLE 2–13 RADAR TRANSMITTER TUBE COMPARISONS

Tube type	P_o	Efficiency	Instantaneous BW	Frequency range	Gain
Magnetron	High	High	N/A	VHF–>100 GHz	
CFA	High	High	Large	VHF–K_μ band	Low
TWT	Moderate	Low	Large	VHF and up	High
Klystron (magnetic focus)	High	High	Small	VHF–K_μ band	High
Klystron (electrostatic focus)	Moderate	......	Large	L–X band	High
Twystron	High	Moderate	Intermediate	L–C band	
EIO	Moderate	Low	......	mm wave	
Vacuum tubes	Moderate	......	......	VHF	

The decision to incorporate a specific microwave device into a radar system, as opposed to other tubes or solid-state devices, may be influenced by projected sales and availability of the devices considered. Over the past few years, sales of microwave tubes have declined substantially, although their total dollar volume has increased, as shown in Figure

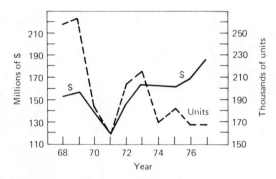

FIGURE 2–47 Sales of microwave tubes since the late 1960s by units and by dollars. [9]

2–47. It is interesting to compare the sales among the various types of microwave tubes, shown in Table 2–14 together with expectations of sales for the 1976 to 1985 time frame [9].

The replacement of low-power tubes by solid-state devices is expected to accelerate as time progresses, and those tubes that are highly vulnerable to solid-state, to inroads to new technology, and to being replaced by other tube types are identified in Table 2–15. In spite of the fact that a portion of the microwave tube market is steadily being eroded, there are a substantial number of applications for microwave tubes for which no immediate replacements are visible on the horizon, and for such high-power, high-gain, higher-frequency devices there will be available sockets in quantity in radar systems for the immediate future.

In this section, we have attempted to provide a broad background describing the general properties of available high-power microwave tubes. However, selection of a tube is only a part of the transmitter specification process, since suitable voltages and currents must be applied to the tube terminals in order to permit it to operate in a satisfactory fashion. The device that provides these required terminal characteristics, called the *pulser*, or *modulator*, is discussed in Chapter 3.

TABLE 2-14   PROJECTED MICROWAVE TUBE SALES THROUGH 1985 [9]

| | Unit sales 1976–1985, thousands of units | | | | Sales 1976–1985, millions of 1977 dollars | | | |
| | Actual | | Projected | | Actual | | Projected (1977 $) | |
	1976	1977	1981	1985	1976	1977	1981	1985
Reflex klystron	68.2	67.5	37	7	12.5	13.2	7.4	1.3
Klystron oscillator	1.7	1.2	0.8	0.4	1.9	2.2	1.5	0.8
Klystron amplifier	6.4	7.5	7.3	7	26.7	32.1	31	30
Magnetron	54.3	54.3	58	49	27.7	35.5	37.8	36.1
TWT, CW	24.2	24.7	22.8	20.8	55.1	55	57.5	57.4
TWT, pulse	4	3.9	3.7	4.4	28	32.7	38.9	38.9
BWO (M and O types)	6.9	6.8	6.5	5.9	8.8	7.1	6.8	6.1
CFA	1.6	1.7	1.8	2.0	8	7.7	8.3	9.3
Total	167.3	167.7	138	96.5	168.7	185.5	189.2	179.9

TABLE 2-15 MICROWAVE TUBES WHOSE STATUS IS UNCERTAIN [9]

Tube type	1977 units (168K)	1977 $(186M)
HIGHLY VULNERABLE TO SOLID STATE		
Reflex klystron Low-noise TWT CW TWT <1 W Pulsed TWT <1 kW Low-power OBWO	80.6K (48%)	$38M (20%)
INROADS BY NEW TECHNOLOGY		
TWT 1–10 W CW Fixed-pulsed magnetron <40 kW	13.2K (8%)	11.3M (6%)
REPLACED BY OTHER TUBE TYPES		
Fixed-pulsed magnetron <500 kW Fixed-pulsed magnetron 1–40 kW Klystron oscillator OBWO, high-power MBWO Pulsed klystron <100 kW (military)	4.3K (2.5%)	6.3M (3%)

REFERENCES

1. Ahn, Saeyoung, "Design Study of Gyrotron TWA: Initial Consideration on Low Magnetic Field," in *Proc. 1978 Intern. Electron Devices Conf.*, pp. 394–395.

2. Bellemare, Y., and W. Chudobiak, "Thermal and Current Tuning Effects in GaAs High Power IMPATT Diodes," *Proc. IEEE*, vol. 67, no. 12, December 1979, pp. 1667–1669.

3. Chang, K., et al., "High Power 94 GHz Pulsed IMPATT Oscillators," in *1979 IEEE MTT-S Intern. Microwave Symp. Dig.*, IEEE cat. no. 79CH1439–9MTT, pp. 71–72.

4. Chodorow, M., E. L. Ginzton, I. R. Neilsen, and S. Sonkin, "Design and Performance of a High-Power Pulsed Klystron," *Proc. IRE*, vol. 41, no. 11, November 1953, p. 1587.

5. Cohn, M., B. Geller, and J. Schellenberg, "A 10 Watt Broadband FET Combiner/Amplifier," in *1979 IEEE MTT-S Intern. Microwave Symp. Dig.*, IEEE cat. no. 79CH1439–9MTT, pp. 292–297.

6. Collins, G. B., *Microwave Magnetrons*, Rad. Lab. series, vol. 6, McGraw-Hill, New York, 1948.

7. Fank, F. B., J. D. Crowley, and J. J. Berenz, "InP Material and Device Development for MM-Waves," *Microwave Journal*, vol. 22, no. 6, June 1979, pp. 86–91.

8. Flyagin, V. A., A. V. Gaponor, M. I. Petelin, and V. K. Yulpatov, "The Gyrotron," *IEEE Trans. Microwave Theory and Techniques*, vol. MTT-25, no. 6, June 1977, pp. 514–521.

9. Garoff, K., "US Microwave Tube Industry Through the Mid-1980's," *Microwave Journal,* vol. 22, no. 2, February 1979, p. 22.

10. Granatstein, V. L., P. Sprangle, R. K. Parker, and M. Herndon, "An Electron Synchrotron Maser Based on an Intense Relativistic Electron Beam," *Journal of Applied Physics,* vol. 46, no. 5, May 1975, pp. 2021–2028.

11. Hirshfield, J. L., and V. L. Granatstein, "The Electron Cyclotron Mass: An Historical Survey," *IEEE Trans. Microwave Theory and Techniques,* vol. MTT-25, no. 6, June 1977, pp. 522–527.

12. Hoft, D. J., "Solid State Transmit/Receive Module for the PAVE PAWS Phased Array Radar," *Microwave Journal,* vol. 21, no. 10, October 1979, p. 33.

13. Honjo, K., "15-Watt Internally Matched GaAs FET's and 20 Watt Amplifier Operating at 6 GHz," in *1979 IEEE MTT-S Intern. Microwave Symp. Dig.,* IEEE cat. no. 79CH1439–9MTT, pp. 289–291.

14. Jory, H., et al., "Gyrotron Developments," *Microwave Journal,* vol. 21, no. 8, August 1978, pp. 30–32.

15. Jory, H. R., et al., "Gyrotrons for High Power Millimeter Wave Generation," in *Proc. 1977 Intern. Electron Devices Conf.,* pp. 234–237.

16. Kuno, H. J., and T. T. Fong, "Hughes IMPATT Device Work above 100 GHz," in *Millimeter and Submillimeter Wave Propagation and Circuits, AGARD Conf. Proc.* no. 245, September 1978, pp. 14–1 and 14–2.

17. Kuno, H. J., and T. T. Fong, "Solid-State MM-Wave Sources and Combiners," *Microwave Journal,* vol. 22, no. 6, June 1979, p. 47.

18. LaRue, A. D., "The TWYSTRON Hybrid TWT," Varian Associates, Palo Alto, Calif., Dec. 23, 1963, p. 2.

19. Lee, K, J., "A 25 kW Solid State Transmitter for L-Band Radars," in *1979 IEEE MTT-S Intern. Microwave Symp. Dig.,* IEEE cat. no. 79CH1439–9MTT, pp. 298–302.

20. Litton Electron Tube Division, "Litton Distributed Emission CFA's," vol. 2, no. 516 5CCA871, San Carlos, Calif., 1971.

21. Litton Electron Tube Division, "Litton Gyro-Tuned Coaxial Magnetrons," no. 515 5CCA671, San Carlos, Calif., 1971.

22. Litton Electron Tube Division, "Litton Hi-Fi Tuned Coaxial Magnetrons," no. 522 5CJA374, Williamsport, Pa., 1974.

23. Martin, J. R., "The Frequency Agile Magnetron Story," Varian Associates, no. 3757, Beverly, Mass., 1977.

24. Masse, D., et al., "High Power GaAs Millimeter Wave IMPATT Diodes," *Microwave Journal,* vol. 22, no. 6, June 1979, pp. 103–105.

25. McMaster, G., and K. Dudley, "Final Report for Cathode-Driven, High Gain, Crossed Field Amplifier," Final Report on Contract no. N00039–72-C-0166, Raytheon Corp., AD B004553, Waltham, Mass., Apr. 15, 1975.

26. Mendel, J. T., "Helix and Coupled-Cavity Traveling-Wave Tubes," *Proc. IEEE,* vol. 61, no. 3, March 1973, pp. 280–298.

27. Ngan, Y. C., and E. M. Nakaji, "High Power Pulsed IMPATT Oscillator Near 140

GHz," in *1979 IEEE MTT-S Intern. Microwave Symp. Dig.*, IEEE cat. no. 79CH1439–9MTT, pp. 73–74.

28. Niclas, K., "Planar Power Combining for Medium Power GaAs FET Amplifiers in X/Ku Bands," *Microwave Journal*, vol. 22, no. 6, June 1979, p. 79.

29. Ohta, K., et al., "A Five Watt 4–8 GHz GaAs FET Amplifier," *Microwave Journal*, vol. 22, no. 11, November 1979, pp. 66–67.

30. Okress, E. C., *Crossed-Field Microwave Devices*, vols. I and II, Academic Press, New York, 1961.

31. Okress, E. C., *Microwave Power Engineering*, vols. I and II, Academic Press, New York, 1968.

32. Pickering, A. H., "Electronic Tuning of Magnetrons," *Microwave Journal*, vol. 22, no. 7, July 1979, p. 73.

33. "Pulsed Power Transistor: 1 hp at 1 GHz," *Microwave Journal*, vol. 22, no. 6, June 1979, p. 34.

34. Quine, J., J. McMullen, and D. Khandelwal, "Ku-Band Impatt Amplifiers and Power Combiners," in *1978 IEEE Intern. Microwave Symp. Dig.*, IEEE cat. no. 78CH1355–7MTT, pp. 346–348.

35. Rucker, C., "Multichip Power Combining: A Summary with New Results," in *1979 IEEE MTT-S Intern. Microwave Symp. Dig.*, IEEE cat. no. 79CH1439–9MTT, pp. 303–305.

36. SFD Laboratories, "Introduction to Crossed-Field Amplifiers," Union, N.J., April 1967.

37. Skowron, J. F., "The Continuous-Cathode (Emitting-Sole) Crossed-Field Amplifier," *Proc. IEEE*, vol. 61, no. 3, March 1973, pp. 330–356.

38. Smith, W., and A. Wilczek, "CFA Tube Enables New-Generation Coherent Radar," *Microwave Journal*, vol. 16, no. 8, August 1973, p. 39.

39. Staprans, A., "High-Power Microwave Tubes," in *Tech. Dig. Intern. Electron Devices Mg.*, IEEE cat. no. 76CH1151-OED, Dec. 6–8, 1976, pp. 245–248.

40. Staprans, A., E. W. McCune, and J. A. Ruetz, "High-Power Linear-Beam Tubes," *Proc. IEEE*, vol. 61, no. 3, March 1973, pp. 299–330.

41. Tserng, H., "Design and Performance of Microwave Power GaAs FET Amplifiers," *Microwave Journal*, vol. 22, no. 2, June 1979, p. 94.

42. Varian Associates, "Twystron Amplifier Catalog," no. 3725, Palo Alto, Calif., 1979.

43. Van Etten, P., "The Present Technology of Impulse Radars," in *Proc. Radar-77 Intern. Conf.*, IEE Conference Publication no. 155, 1977, pp. 535–539.

44. Weil, T. A., in M. I. Skolnik, ed., *Radar Handbook*, McGraw-Hill, New York, 1970, chap. 7, pp. 7–11.

45. Zapevalov, V. Ye., G. S. Korablev, and Sh. Ye. Tsimring, "An Experimental Investigation of a Gyrotron Operating at the Second Harmonic of the Cyclotron Frequency with an Optimized Distribution of High-Frequency Field," *Radio Engineering and Electronic Physics*, vol. 22, no. 8, August 1977, pp. 86–94.

3
MODULATORS

The purpose of the modulator, or pulser, is to provide a voltage or current waveform that will permit the selected microwave source to operate in a proper manner [8,21]. There are a number of important considerations in the selection and design of a modulator for a particular transmitter tube, including:

- Pulse length
- PRF
- Operating voltage and current
- Tube protection (from arcs)
- Spurious modes
- Pulse flatness (amplitude and phase)
- Cost
- Size and weight
- Efficiency
- Reliability and maintainability

There are several basic types of modulators, and numerous offshoots of each type. All of the modulators have one characteristic in common: they contain some means for storing energy and a switch to control the discharge of energy into the load, as is shown in Figure 3–1(a). The energy-storage element may store energy in a magnetic field or in an electric field. The energy in the energy-storage element must be replenished from the power supply, and an isolating element to prevent interaction is often included. A block diagram of such a complete system is shown in Figure 3–1(*b*).

There are two principal types of modulators: *line-type* and *hard-tube*. In the line-type modulator all the energy stored in the energy-storage device is dissipated in the load during each pulse, while the hard-tube

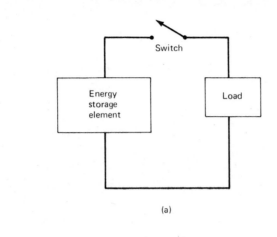

(a)

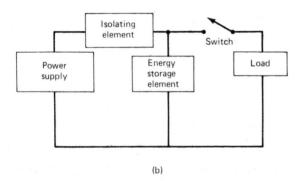

(b)

FIGURE 3–1   Basic modulator configurations, illustrating discharge of stored energy into the load.

modulator dissipates only some fraction of the stored energy during each pulse. These modulator types will now be discussed in greater detail.

3–1   HARD-TUBE MODULATORS

The hard-tube modulator is essentially a class C pulsed amplifier. A simplified diagram of a hard-tube modulator is shown in Figure

3–2. A positive pulse on the grid turns on the tube, and the capacitor couples the resulting step in plate voltage to the load. The hard-tube modulator is usually larger and more complex than other types of modulators, but it is also more versatile, not being as strongly influenced by load characteristics, and its output pulse length may be easily changed.

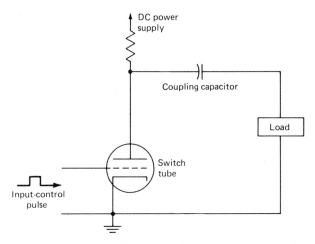

FIGURE 3–2 Simplified hard-tube modulator schematic diagram.

Hard-Tube Modulator Configurations

There are a number of variations on the basic hard-tube modulator, several of which are shown in Figure 3–3. Figure 3–3(*a*) is the conventional capacitor-coupled hard-tube modulator already outlined earlier; Figure 3–3(*b*) is the transformer-coupled hard-tube modulator; while Figure 3–3(*c*) is the capacitor- and transformer-coupled hard-tube modulator; and Figure 3–3(*d*) is the series-discharge, parallel-charge hard-tube modulator with capacitive coupling. The conventional capacitively coupled hard-tube modulator is by far the most common configuration encountered, and one which we will consider in some detail [5]. A number of different loads may be attached to such a modulator, including a resistive load (which is usually a good approximation of a klystron or TWT); a biased-diode load, such as a magnetron, with resistive charging; or a biased-diode load with an inductive recharging path.

A special form of hard-tube modulator is sometimes used with tubes containing a modulating anode, such as TWTs and klystrons. This is the *floating-deck* modulator; it is illustrated schematically in Figure 3–4. When the microwave tube is off, tube 1 is turned on and tube 2 is

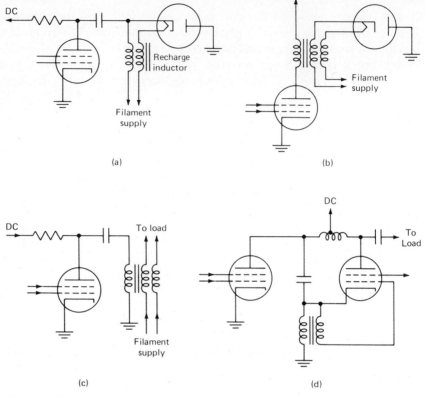

FIGURE 3–3 Some commonly encountered types of hard-tube modulator configurations; (*a*) capacitor-coupled; (*b*) transformer-coupled; (*c*) capacitor- and transformer-coupled; (*d*) parallel charge, series discharge.

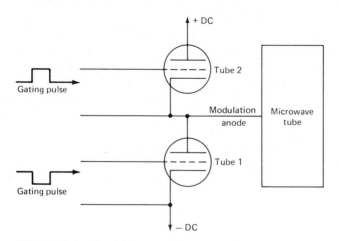

FIGURE 3–4 Simplified representation of a floating-deck modulator.

nonconducting. In order to turn on the microwave tube, tube 1 is turned off and tube 2 turned on. At the end of the pulse, tube 2 turns off and tube 1 turns on. The gating pulses to each tube may be capacitively coupled, transformer-coupled, optically coupled, or coupled by means of RF energy. Floating-deck modulators are typically utilized with large klystrons, and swings of 200 kV are not uncommon for this application. There are a number of different means of implementing such floating-deck modulators; several of the more common implementations are summarized in Figure 3–5. Also, floating-deck modulators are sometimes

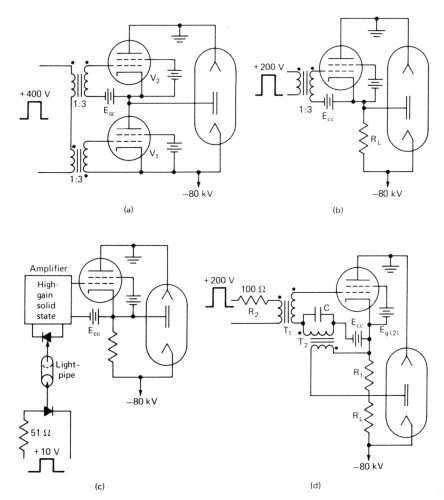

(a)

(b)

(c)

(d)

FIGURE 3–5 Various floating-deck modulator configurations [6]: (a) dual-tube, high-L coupling transformers; (b) single-tube, high-L coupling transformers; (c) light–pipe interface; (d) "blocking-oscillator" regenerative modulator.

used to cathode-pulse tubes directly when a very wide range of pulse widths with rapid rise and fall times must be accommodated.

Types of Hard-Tube Modulator Switches [5,19]

The switches that are typically utilized for hard-tube modulators may be triodes, tetrodes, or pentodes; however, mainly triode and tetrode tube configurations have been utilized for such applications.

Triodes

A triode vacuum tube consists of a cathode, which emits electrons, a grid, which controls the flow of electrons, and a plate, or anode, which receives the electrons. The total current flow in a triode tube is determined by the electrostatic field in the region of the cathode, which is in turn controlled by both the grid potential and the anode potential. The total cathode current of an ideal triode may be approximated as

$$I_k = k \left(E_c + \frac{E_b}{\mu} \right)^{3/2}$$

where I_k = cathode current
   k = perveance
   E_c = grid-cathode voltage
   E_b = plate-to-cathode voltage
   μ = amplification factor

One of the more important parameters associated with a triode is its voltage amplification factor μ. The μ of a triode can be approximated as follows:

$$\mu = \frac{\Delta E_b}{\Delta E_c} \qquad \text{with plate current held constant}$$

where ΔE_b = change in plate voltage
   ΔE_c = change in grid voltage

Tetrodes

A tetrode is a tube containing four elements: the cathode, the control grid, the screen grid, and the plate or anode. Tetrodes are often utilized in high-power modulators as switch tubes because relatively small control voltage swings are required in order to control large amounts of power in the tube. This is due to the presence of the additional or screen grid between the control grid and the anode; the screen grid serves as an accelerating element and also screens the control grid from the effects of the anode. As in any vacuum tube, the field near the cathode controls the current through the tube; the current is given by

$$I_k = k\left(E_{c1} + \frac{E_{c2}}{\mu_s} + \frac{E_b}{\mu_p}\right)^{3/2}$$

where E_{c1} = control-grid voltage
  E_{c2} = screen-grid voltage
  μ_s = screen amplification factor
  μ_p = plate amplification factor

The effect of the additional grid is to largely decouple the effect of changes in plate voltage from the cathode current; thus, a tetrode tends to operate as a constant-current device for a given value of control-grid voltage, regardless of the particular plate voltage applied. It should also be noticed that variations in screen-grid voltage can affect the current through the tube; therefore, the screen grid must either be driven from a well-regulated source, or bypassed sufficiently with a low-inductance capacitor so as to minimize screen-grid voltage variations during the time the tube is turned on.

Under certain conditions not uncommon in high-power tubes, the screen grid can actually become an emitter, and current will appear to flow out of the screen. It is essential that the tube designer provide a sufficiently low-impedance path for any such reverse electron flow in order to prevent a resultant increase in screen-grid voltage and possible damage to the tube. Thus, the screen-grid voltage supply must be well regulated, must be thoroughly bypassed, and must represent a low impedance to any reverse current that might flow out of the screen grid.

It is also possible for electrons to be emitted from the grid, particularly for tubes operated under conditions of high average power. For that reason, one should be prepared to accommodate reverse currents from the control grid when designing the control-grid driving circuit. Often tube elements are gold-plated in order to reduce secondary emission, and it should be kept in mind that the amount of secondary emission from both the control grid and the screen grid may increase during the life of the tube, particularly when the tube operates with oxide cathodes.

Operation of Vacuum Tubes in Hard-Tube Modulators [5]

Important in determining the suitability of a given tube for a particular application are the maximum values of plate voltage, grid voltage, grid dissipation, and plate dissipation. However, since it is difficult to give an analytical representation that connects grid voltage and current and plate voltage and current over a wide range of operating parameters, graphical representations are often utilized. In order to determine the interaction of the tube with the load, *static-characteristic* curves are normally utilized representing (1) plate current as a function of plate voltage with constant grid-drive curves as parameters, or (2) grid voltage as a function of plate voltage with constant plate and grid current curves as parameters.

In addition to designing for the interaction of the tube with the load, it is necessary to control the plate current during the interpulse period in order to control the overall anode dissipation of the tube. For this reason, a curve of plate voltage as a function of negative grid bias for cutoff conditions is normally given, as shown in Figure 3–6. This curve is particularly important, since even a relatively small current flow during the interpulse period may contribute substantially to overall anode dissipation, and because the negative bias voltage must be added to the positive grid-drive voltage in order to determine the total required grid

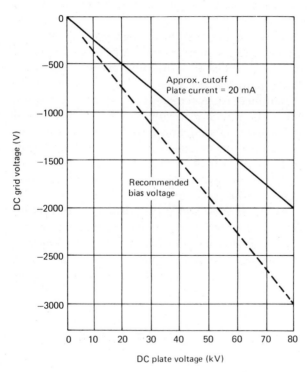

FIGURE 3–6   Grid bias versus plate voltage for cutoff condition for the ML-7560 triode tube. [5]

voltage swing. The required cutoff-bias voltage will vary with the plate voltage of a triode and with both the plate and the screen voltages of a tetrode. All high-voltage tubes may exhibit some field emission from the grid, and it should be noted that this field emission is independent of grid bias. Plate current flowing during the interpulse period may give rise to appreciable X-radiation, necessitating adequate shielding for personnel protection.

The constant–grid-drive voltage curves for a typical triode, the ML-7560 tube, are shown in Figure 3–7, which gives plate current and grid current as functions of plate voltage. Operation in the region at the left of the constant–grid-drive characteristic curves, on the so-called *diode line*, represents *saturated* operation of the tube.

The use of so-called *shielded grid tubes* can result in an appreciable reduction in grid current, as shown in the characteristic curves of Figure

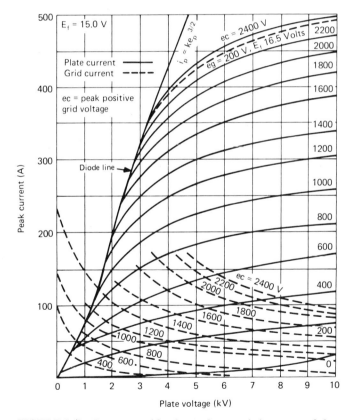

FIGURE 3–7 Constant–grid-voltage characteristic curves of the ML-7560 triode. [5]

3–8 for a shielded-grid triode. There are a number of advantages that favor the use of shielded-grid tubes at higher power levels, including the following: (1) grid-control current is reduced; (2) the shield-grid current is zero; (3) an arc to the shield grid will not transfer to the cathode; (4) grid dissipation is relatively low; (5) the structure is rugged;

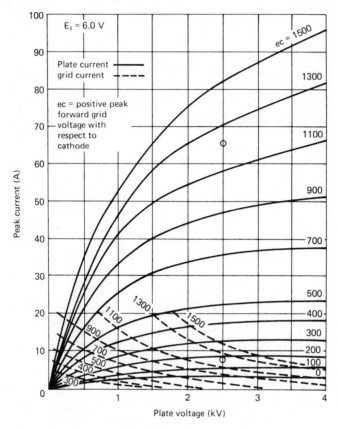

FIGURE 3–8   Constant–grid-voltage curves for the ML-6544 shielded-grid triode. [5]

(6) no screen-grid power supply is required; (7) the amplification factor is high; and (8) negative–grid-bias requirements are relatively low.

At low and moderate power levels, tetrode-type vacuum tubes are more often utilized as switches. Figure 3–9 shows a set of tube characteristics for the 4PR1000A tetrode; a screen voltage of 1500 V was used for the constant–grid-voltage and constant-current characteristics. Note that the required grid bias for cutoff is a function of both the screen and plate voltages. The screen grid shields the cathode from the plate potential, with the result that cutoff bias is determined primarily by the screen-grid voltage. The total grid voltage required to obtain rated cathode emission is less in a tetrode than in a triode, and relatively little control-grid current is drawn. The grid current in a tetrode is not appreciably affected by plate voltage variations, but if the plate voltage is reduced sufficiently, this may no longer be the case. Of course, in a tetrode, appreciable screen-grid current is usually drawn when the control grid is driven positive, and both a low-impedance power supply and sufficient capacitive decoupling are required in order to achieve stable operation over a wide range of conditions.

Occasionally, pentodes or specially designed tetrodes are utilized in high-power modulators, usually for those applications where their approximately constant-current capabilities are a particular advantage [1]. In such applications, the relatively high tube drop required in order to achieve constant-current operation often necessitates an undesirable amount of switch-tube power dissipation and considerably increased dc supply voltages.

Whether a triode, tetrode, or pentode is selected for the switch tube during the design process, it is first necessary to specify the required pulse voltage and pulse current for the load. If a pulse transformer is utilized, then the peak pulse power can be used to select the tube and the turns ratio adjusted to match the tube ratings. If it is desired to capacitively couple the pulse-modulator tube directly to the load, then a modulator tube must be selected such that the maximum dc plate voltage is approximately 10% greater than the required pulse voltage delivered to the load, and the tube must be capable of switching the full output pulse current. ·

Once a tube has been selected, the next step is to determine the cutoff bias required during the interpulse period in order to limit plate dissipation to a reasonable value. This value then determines the cutoff condition for the tube. One next picks a positive grid drive from the grid voltage versus plate voltage characteristic curves so that the tube can deliver the required plate current to the load; this is the switch ON condition, and it involves a compromise between low plate voltage and grid-drive power requirements. One should check carefully at this point to ensure that neither the control- nor screen-grid dissipation has been exceeded. For triodes, the operating point will normally be where the grid current is from 10 to 30% of the peak plate current. In tetrodes, the operating points should be picked so that the screen-grid current is not excessive and so that screen-grid dissipation remains within safe limits.

The choice of operating point is particularly critical in considering

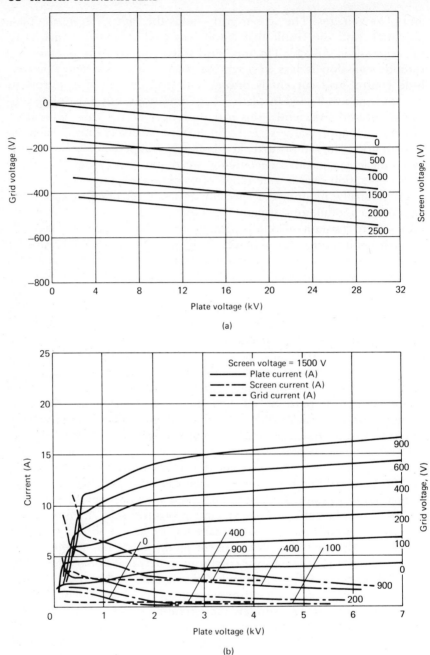

FIGURE 3–9 **Tube characteristics for the 4PR1000A tetrode switch tube:** (*a*, *top*) **typical plate cutoff characteristics for less than 50 μa plate current;** (*b*, *bottom*) **typical constant–grid-voltage characteristics;** (*c*, *top right*) **typical constant-current characteristics.** (*Eimac*)

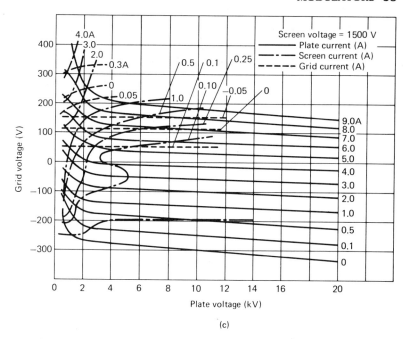

(c)

the effects of changes in high voltage and grid drive on the pulse delivered to the load. These dependences may be treated by using conventional load-line analysis, using a simplified set of static tube characteristics. Such a set of simplified static characteristics and load lines is shown in Figure 3–10 for saturated operation below the knee of the plate-current curve, and for an unsaturated operation above the knee of the plate-current curve. The two sets of load lines shown in each of the diagrams of Figure 3–10 are the straight load line, which connects E_{bb} and OP 1, valid for resistive loads, and the bent load line, connecting E_{bb}, E_d, and OP 1, which is valid for a biased-diode load such as a magnetron.

If adequate positive grid-drive voltage is available to keep the operating point for the tube OP 1 saturated [below the knee of the characteristic curve, as is shown in Figure 3–10(a)], irregularities in the top of the grid-driving pulse will not be observed in the output pulse. However, since such operation results in high grid currents in a triode and high screen-grid currents in a tetrode, care must be taken to keep the grid dissipation within appropriate limits. The disadvantage of operating the tube saturated is that any changes in E_{bb} are transmitted directly to the load, thus necessitating a well-regulated high-voltage supply.

If the tube is operated in an unsaturated region, as shown in Figure 3–10(b), and the grid-drive voltage changes over the range from C to

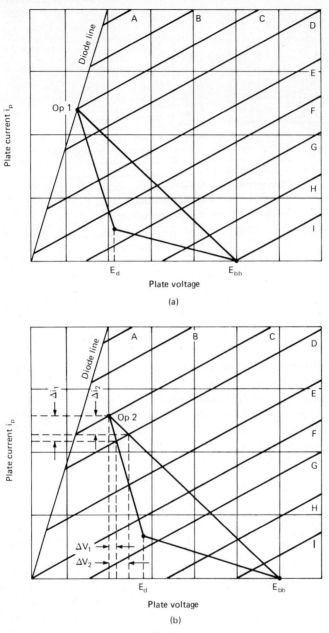

FIGURE 3–10 Idealized tube characteristics and load lines for hard-tube modulator operation with resistive and biased-diode loads showing (*a*) saturated (below knee of curve) and (*b*) unsaturated (above knee of curve) operation. [5]

D, then the operating point changes by an amount that depends upon the nature of the load (whether biased-diode or resistive). Changes in load current are greater for the low-dynamic-resistance biased-diode load ($\Delta i_1 > \Delta i_2$), while the change in the output voltage is less than would be the case for a purely resistive load ($\Delta V_1 < \Delta V_2$). Thus, when the switch tube is operated in an unsaturated condition, irregularities in the grid-voltage drive pulse are transferred to the load.

Expressions for plate current as a function of various tube parameters may be differentiated in order to obtain the sensitivities of plate current to changes in other circuit parameters. An important utilization of these relationships is to determine the changes in load current associated with changes in plate voltage. For the triode operating above the knee of the circuit and a magnetron load, the appropriate relationship is

$$\frac{di_p}{i_p} = \frac{1}{1 + (\mu_p e_g - E_d)/E_{bb}} \frac{dE_{bb}}{E_{bb}}$$

and for a tetrode,

$$\frac{di_p}{i_p} = \frac{1}{\dfrac{\mu_p(e_g + E_{sg}/\mu_{sg} - E_d/\mu_p)}{E_{bb}} + 1} \frac{dE_{bb}}{E_{bb}}$$

where i_p = instantaneous value of plate current
e_g = instantaneous value of grid voltage
μ_p = plate voltage-amplification factor
μ_{sg} = screen-grid voltage-amplification factor
E_d = magnetron diode voltage
E_{sg} = screen-grid voltage
E_{bb} = plate supply voltage

For the triode or tetrode operating below the knee of the curve, the appropriate equation becomes

$$\frac{di_p}{i_p} = \frac{1}{1 - E_d/E_{bb}} \frac{dE_{bb}}{E_{bb}}$$

To compare hard-tube modulator regulation for saturated and unsaturated switch tube operation, consider a magnetron load that requires at 11 kV and 10 A. Assume E_d will be 9.7 kV. For a 4PR60 switch tube operating below the knee of the curve, the plate voltage E_{bb} will be approximately 11.7 kV, the screen-grid voltage 1250 V, and the grid voltage 0; then

$$\frac{di_p}{i_p} \approx 5.85 \frac{dE_{bb}}{E_{bb}}$$

For operation above the knee of the curve, E_{bb} will be approximately 13 kV, μ_{sg} approximately equal to 4, and μ_p approximately equal to 70. E_g will equal -35 V, and

$$\frac{di_p}{i_p} \approx 0.57 \frac{dE_{bb}}{E_{bb}}$$

Thus, regulation in plate current due to variations in supply voltage is improved by a factor considerably greater than 1 when operating in an unsaturated condition. Of course, for operation in an unsaturated mode it is necessary to carefully regulate both the control-grid and screen-grid voltages. A similar comparison with a pure-resistance load ($E_d = 0$) would result in a ratio of approximately 2.5, rather than the ratio of slightly greater than 10 achieved above with a biased-diode load.

The use of grid-drive saturation to give flat-top pulses is normally confined to low- to medium-power applications, since it often produces excessive screen-grid dissipation in tetrodes and excessive control-grid dissipation in triodes. However, if a shielded-grid triode is utilized, grid-drive saturation is usually satisfactory even in higher-power tubes, because the grid is capable of handling the required dissipation. In a tetrode, the flow of pulse current to the screen grid and the plate–screen-grid capacitances necessitate the use of a large bypass capacitor between the screen grid and the cathode. If fast-rising pulses are utilized, the self-inductance of the capacitor must be small enough to present a low impedance at the maximum useful frequency component of the pulse. The sensitivity of output voltage to screen-grid voltage in a tetrode usually necessitates the regulation of this power-supply voltage; it is sometimes possible to compensate for changes in plate voltage by adjusting the screen-grid voltage, which may be simpler than regulation of the plate power-supply voltage.

In the event of arcing, it is necessary to limit arc dissipation within the tube to a few joules or less, and at low to medium power levels sufficient series resistance may suffice for this purpose; however, at power levels above 10 kW, it is essential to use fast-acting crowbar circuits to divert stored energy from the tube to a safe discharge path. This crowbar circuit must act in less than approximately 10 μs, to divert energy from an arcing tube to a shunt circuit and to prevent damage to the switch tube. This energy diverter must, in general, be some form of gaseous-discharge device such as a thyratron or a spark gap, so that it will have a low internal impedance. It is also necessary to utilize fast-acting circuit breakers, since once the crowbar fires, energy will be fed in from the lines until the primary power is removed. It should be emphasized that the design of the crowbar circuitry must be such that the discharge through the crowbar is critically damped. If a resonant, underdamped condition exists, damage to the tube may be encountered even if a crowbar circuit is utilized, because the oscillatory discharge may cause the crowbar to deionize before the stored energy is dissipated.

In order to protect the switch tube from transients produced when the load arcs, the control grid may be clamped back to the bias whenever an arcing condition is sensed. Of course, the plate current should not be cut off too abruptly; otherwise large transient plate voltages associated with the interruption of current through an inductor may be generated. A thyratron in the switch-tube grid circuit, as shown in Figure 3–11,

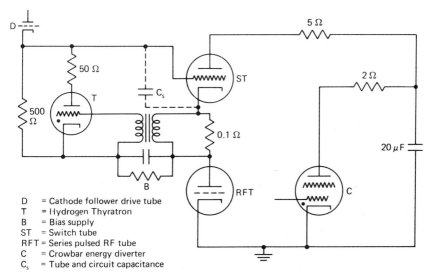

D   = Cathode follower drive tube
T   = Hydrogen Thyratron
B   = Bias supply
ST   = Switch tube
RFT = Series pulsed RF tube
C   = Crowbar energy diverter
C_s = Tube and circuit capacitance

FIGURE 3–11 Circuit with thyratron in switch-tube grid circuit to ensure tube cutoff in the event of an arc in the load. [5]

with a proper time constant can be of considerable value in protecting high-power switch tubes. In fact, with this circuit it is sometimes possible to shut off the switch tube without using the crowbar to short the plate power supply when the load device arcs.

Output Waveforms

The loads analyzed up to this point were either purely resistive or of a biased-diode nature; of course, any realistic application involves the consideration of the effects of various reactive elements associated with or connected to the load. Various stray capacitances and inductances and additional reactive elements affect peak currents and voltages in the switch tube and the load and also strongly influence the achievable rise times, fall times, and flatness of pulse. The analysis of the output-pulse shape is simplified by subdividing the pulse into regions, as shown in Figure 3–12.

A particularly simple case is that of a resistive load with some associated stray capacitance, giving rise to the equivalent circuit shown in

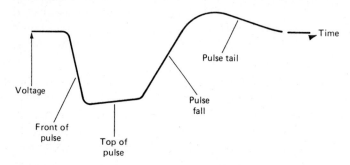

FIGURE 3–12   **Hard-tube modulator output pulse, showing principal parts of the pulse.**

Figure 3–13. In Figure 3–13, the vacuum switch tube is represented as an equivalent plate resistance R_p and an ideal switch, while the load is represented by a load resistance R_l in parallel with some stray capacitance C_s. For calculation of the rise time, assume that the value of C_c, the coupling capacitor, is much larger than C_s, and that R_p is much

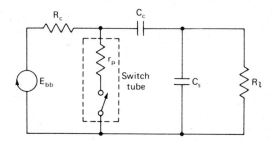

FIGURE 3–13   **Simplified equivalent circuit for a hard-tube modulator.**

less than the value of the recharging resistor R_c. For this configuration, the equivalent charging time constant is

$$C_s \frac{r_p R_l}{r_p + R_l}$$

which gives a rise time (from 10% to 90% of full amplitude) of

$$t_r = 2.2 C_s \frac{r_p R_l}{r_p + R_l}$$

The top of the pulse can be analyzed by assuming that the voltage droop is relatively small, enough that C_s can be essentially disregarded, and the appropriate time constant is then given by

$$C_c(R_l + r_p)$$

and the corresponding current droop is given by

$$\text{Droop} \approx \frac{\tau}{C_c(R_l + r_p)}$$

where τ is the pulse duration.

Once the switch opens, the fall time may be calculated by noting again that the value of C_c is much greater than C_s, so that the time constant for discharge is dominated by the time constant determined by R_l and R_c in parallel and C_s. Thus the fall time (from 90% to 10% of full charge) is given by

$$t_f = 2.2 C_s \frac{R_l R_c}{R_l + R_c}$$

Note that in general the fall time is substantially longer than the rise time for such a resistive load.

Next, consider a biased diode with a resistor R_s in parallel with the load in order to permit the recharge of the coupling capacitor. An equivalent circuit for the modulator is given in Figure 3–14(a). If one assumes that during the rise time R_c has a value much greater than R_p and that the biased-diode switch does not close until almost the full output voltage is reached, then an equivalent circuit for the rise time is as given by Figure 3–14(b). The time constant for the rise time is dominated by the stray capacitance and an equivalent resistance given by the parallel combination of R_s, R', and r_p. In general, r_p is by far the smallest of these resistances, so that the 10% to 90% rise time is given by

$$t_r = 2.2 C_s r_p$$

The analysis of the top of the pulse is critically dependent upon particular circuit parameters. However, if the change in output load current is small, then this change in current is

$$\text{Current droop} = \frac{\Delta I}{I_o} \approx \frac{\tau}{C_c r_d}$$

For the fall of the pulse, the stray capacity and the parallel combination of R_s, R_c, and r' dominate, since the switch is open. Thus, the fall time is

$$t_f = 2.2 C_s (R_s \| r' \| R_c)$$

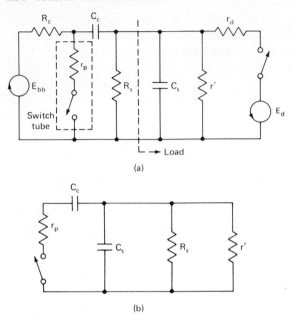

(a)

(b)

FIGURE 3–14 Equivalent circuit for (a) hard-tube modulator with biased-diode load and resistive recharging and (b) rise time calculation.

The third commonly encountered configuration utilizes a biased-diode load with an inductive recharge path. An equivalent circuit for such a configuration is given by Figure 3–15(a). The equivalent circuit for the rise time is given by Figure 3–15(b); since it is usually good design practice to choose L_s so that its initial current is small, its contribution during the rise time may be ignored. Thus the rise time is

$$t_r = 2.2\, C_s \frac{r_p r'}{r_p + r'}$$

During the top of the pulse, again assume that the droop is small enough that the equivalent circuit is that given by Figure 3–15(c). Then the current drawn from the capacitor may be approximated by a constant I_0 and the change in output current may be approximated by

$$I_0 = \tau \frac{I_0 + I_m/2}{r_d C_c}$$

The performance of the equivalent circuit valid for the tail of the pulse given by Figure 3–16 is a relatively complex function of a number of parameters. If an air-core inductor is used so that linear circuit analysis

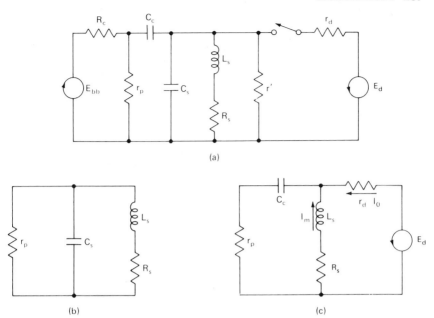

(a)

(b)   (c)

FIGURE 3–15 (*a*) **Equivalent circuit for hard-tube modulator with biased-diode load and inductive recharging path. Simplified circuits are given in (*b*) valid for the rise time and in (*c*) valid for the top of pulse.**

may be employed, then the tail-of-pulse performance is primarily a function of circuit damping and the ratio of current in the inductor to the load current at the end of the pulse. Figure 3–17 shows underdamped (oscillating), critically damped, and overdamped responses for increasing values of Δ, which is the ratio I_m/I_0, illustrating the decreased fall time but increased value of backswing associated with increased values of Δ. In general, the underdamped condition should be avoided to prevent any spurious outputs if the cathode voltage should go negative, and large values of backswing voltage should be avoided to reduce any chance of tube arcing. It is desirable to have the voltage fall to zero quickly

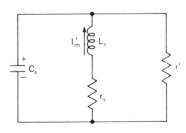

FIGURE 3–16 Equivalent circuit for the hard-tube modulator of Figure 3–15 which is useful for calculation of the fall of the pulse.

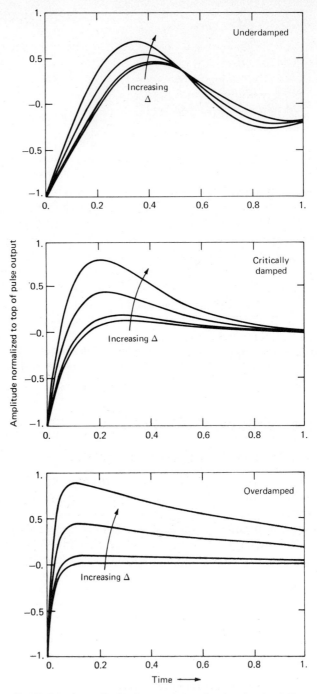

FIGURE 3–17 Tail-of-pulse responses for the circuit of Figure 3–16 for underdamped, critically damped, and overdamped conditions, illustrating effects of increasing Δ, the ratio of inductor current to load current at the end of the pulse top. Plots are for a negative pulse, and are normalized to the pulse voltage at the end of the pulse.

but to have little backswing and not to become negative again (to prevent spurious oscillations). One approach to achieve this is to provide enough damping that the voltage never recrosses the baseline; this corresponds to the critically damped condition

$$\frac{R_s}{L_s} = \frac{2}{\sqrt{C_s L_s}}$$

In practice, achieving this desirable condition often requires an excessively long fall time. Thus, some small amount of negative overshoot is typically allowed. The amount of negative overshoot is dependent on the specific circuit parameters and the initial current flowing in the inductor. Smaller values of L_s, and higher values of inductor current at the end of the pulse, result in faster fall times but larger values of overshoot, as shown in Figure 3–17.

It may be that requirements for fast fall time and minimum negative overshoot with no recrossing of the axis cannot be met simultaneously. In this case, it is often necessary to incorporate a clipping diode in order to limit the backswing on the output voltage. In some cases, it may be desirable to incorporate additional coupling elements to improve output pulse shape [16,17]. In cases where extremely rapid fall time is required, a "tail biter," which is an active switch connected directly across the load, may be used to rapidly discharge the stray capacity.

3–2 LINE-TYPE MODULATORS

The Pulse-Forming Network (PFN)

The line-type modulator derives its name from the similarity of the behavior of its energy storage element to that of an open-circuited transmission line [8,11]. If a length of transmission line having one-way propagation $\tau/2$ is connected as in Figure 3–18, charged to voltage V, and then discharged through its characteristic impendance Z_0, a pulse length of τ and amplitude $V/2$ is generated across the load. For practical

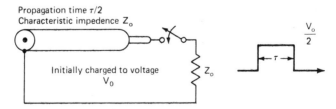

FIGURE 3–18 Generation of a rectangular pulse by discharge of a charged open-circuited transmission line into its characteristic impedance.

pulse lengths and voltages, the required bulk of cable often becomes excessive, and in practice a network of lumped inductors and capacitors is often used. Such a network is shown in Figure 3–19 and is called a *pulse-forming network* (PFN). The PFN resembles the lumped-circuit approximation of the actual transmission line, but there are some significant

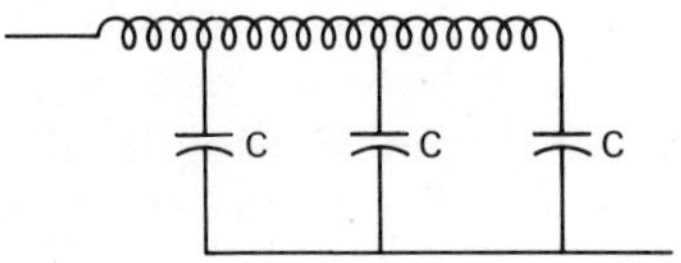

Important relationships are:

$$Z_0 = \sqrt{\frac{L_n}{C_n}} \qquad\qquad L_n = \frac{\tau Z_0}{2}$$

$$\tau = \sqrt{L_n C_n} \qquad\qquad \frac{l}{d} = \frac{4}{3}$$

$$C_n = \frac{\tau}{2 Z_0} \qquad\qquad \frac{L_c}{L} = 1.1 \text{ to } 1.2$$

where C_n = total network capacitance L = inductance per section L_n/n
       L_n = total network inductance L_c = inductance of section on closed end
       τ = pulse width at 50% points C = capacitance per section C_n/n
       Z_0 = characteristic impedance l = length of coil in one section
       n = number of sections d = coil diameter

FIGURE 3–19 Guillemin E-type pulse-forming network circuit arrangement and key design parameters.

differences. The PFN shown in Figure 3–19 is sometimes called the Guillemin E-type network. It consists of equal-valued capacitors and a continuously wound, tapped coil whose physical dimensions are chosen so as to provide the proper mutual coupling at each mesh. The total capacitance and inductance are given by

$$C_n = \frac{\tau}{2 Z_0}$$

$$L_n = \frac{\tau Z_0}{2}$$

where C_n = total network capacitance
$\quad L_n$ = total network inductance
$\quad \tau$ = pulse width at 50% points
$\quad Z_0$ = characteristic impedance

The number of sections is chosen to provide the desired rise time.

Operation of a Line-Type Modulator

The load for a line-type modulator often requires extremely high voltages. In order to reduce the voltages on the PFN, a step-up transformer is often inserted between the PFN and the load. Bifilar secondary windings on the step-up transformer often provide a convenient means to provide heater current for the transmitting device.

A device must be used to isolate the switch from the power source. A resistor could be utilized, but it would limit the maximum efficiency to 50%. An inductor is often utilized because of the increased efficiency obtained, and because it is then possible to charge the PFN to approximately twice the dc supply voltage. A charging diode is often utilized to prevent discharge of the PFN once it is charged. A more typical schematic diagram of a line-type pulser is shown in Figure 3–20; it in-

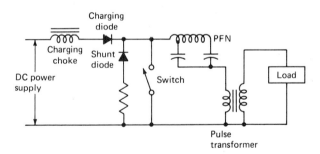

FIGURE 3–20 Simplified schematic representation of a typical line-type modulator. PFN = pulse-forming network.

cludes a shunt diode and resistor to damp out any reflected voltage due to load mismatch.

Analysis of the operation of a line-type modulator can be perhaps best understood by breaking the operation into subintervals: a recharge interval, during which time the energy stored in the PFN is replenished, and the discharge interval, during which time the energy stored in the PFN is discharged into the load, normally through the pulse transformer.

Recharge Interval

Since the energy-storage element is completely discharged on each pulse, some means of efficiently replenishing this energy must be provided. It is conceptually possible to incorporate charging through a resistor from a dc power supply, but efficiency with such an arrangement is limited to no more than 50%. A more customary means of replenishing the PFN charge is by so-called *inductive charging.*

Analysis of the charging circuit of a line-type modulator may be accomplished by assuming that the equivalent series inductance of the energy-storage element is relatively small so that the equivalent circuit shown in Figure 3–21 suffices for analysis. If one assumes that C_n is initially

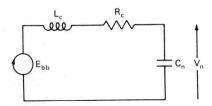

FIGURE 3–21 Equivalent circuit for inductive charging of PFN.

discharged and the current in L_c has not yet begun to appreciably increase at the beginning of the recharge interval, then an expression for the voltage is given by

$$V_n(t) = E_{bb} + e^{-at}[-E_{bb}(\cos \omega t + \frac{a}{\omega} \sin \omega t)$$

where $\quad a = \dfrac{R_c}{2L_c}$

$$\omega_0 = \frac{1}{\sqrt{L_n C_n}}$$

$$\omega = \sqrt{\omega_0^2 - a^2} = \sqrt{\frac{1}{L_n C_n} - \frac{R_c^2}{4 L_c^2}}$$

The natural oscillations are thus damped sinusoids; however, note that the first peak is only slightly less than twice the supply voltage and that the resonant frequency is given by

$$\frac{1}{2\pi \sqrt{L_c C_n}}$$

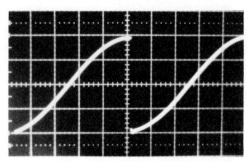

FIGURE 3–22 PFN voltage charging waveform for resonant charging condition, when the switch closes at the peak of the charging waveform.

If one picks the pulse-repetition frequency equal to twice the resonant frequency, then

$$\mathrm{PRF} = \frac{1}{\pi \sqrt{L_c C_n}}$$

and the peak voltage on the network is approximately twice the dc supply voltage. In order to achieve maximum voltage output for minimum dc power-supply voltages, it would be desirable to close the switch at the peak of the charging voltage, as shown in Figure 3–22; this is called *resonant charging*. However, this would then require complete control of the interpulse period. More flexibility may be achieved if a series, or *charging diode* is incorporated in series with the charging inductor, giving rise to a *subresonant charging* voltage waveform of the form shown in Figure 3–23. For this condition, the peak voltage is normally between 1.9 and 2.0 E_{bb}, for an inductor Q greater than 10.

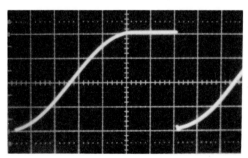

FIGURE 3–23 PFN voltage charging waveform for subresonant charging, with a charging diode used to prevent discharge of the PFN until the switch is closed.

The average current is given by

$$I_{c(av)} = PRF\, C_n V_{n(peak)}$$

and the ratio of rms to average current for resonant charging by

$$\frac{I_{c\,(rms)}}{I_{c\,(av)}} = 1.11$$

and the ratio of peak to average current by

$$\frac{I_{c\,(max)}}{I_{c\,(av)}} = 1.57$$

If subresonant charging is used, then these values must be adjusted appropriately.

The charging efficiency of such a line-type modulator is given by

$$\eta_c = 1 - \frac{\pi}{4Q}$$

where $Q = \dfrac{\text{energy stored per cycle}}{\text{energy lost per cycle}}$

This charging efficiency is the ratio of the energies extracted from the power supply to the energy transferred to the pulse-forming network.

In the event the load arcs, a negative initial voltage may be reflected to C_n. In this case, the peak charging voltage may exceed twice the dc supply voltage, and may be limited by the Q of the charging choke. Such high voltages are undesirable and may result in damage to the modulator, the load, or both. For this reason, a shunt, or clipping, diode, is often connected across the switch to remove any residual voltage present on C_n.

Discharge Interval

In analysis of the discharge interval, we assume that the capacitors in the pulse-forming network have been charged to their peak voltage, and that the switch is closed. If the PFN then has the basic characteristics of a transmission line, if the pulse transformer is ideal, and if the load is purely resistive and matched to the transmission line, then a rectangular output pulse will be obtained.

In the event that the load does not match the characteristic impedance of the transmission line, the pulse generated will no longer be rectangular, but will have steps, as shown in Figure 3–24. The middle waveform in Figure 3–24 for the condition where the termination is larger than the characteristic impedance of the line, showing a series of same-polarity steps, while the bottom waveform shows the condition where the load impedance is less than the characteristic impedance of the line. It is customary to mismatch the load slightly in order to promote formation of a slight negative voltage on the switching device in order to enhance recovery of the switch.

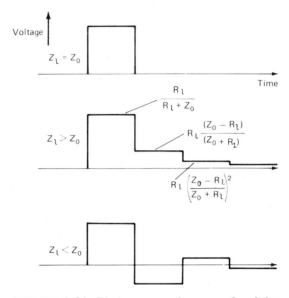

FIGURE 3–24 Discharge waveforms produced by charged transmission lines for various terminating impedances.

Unfortunately, (1) the load is rarely a pure resistance, biased-diode loads such as magnetrons of CFAs being more common; (2) the pulse transformer is not ideal, but has some magnetizing inductance, leakage inductance, and stray capacitance; and (3) the pulse-forming network is not an ideal transmission line, but is a lumped constant network having certain specific properties.

As indicated earlier, the choice of pulse width and impedance level determines the properties of the pulse-forming network. The pulse width is usually set by system requirements, but the impedance level of the PFN can be varied over a fairly wide range by the choice of the output-transformer turns ratio. A choice of too high an impedance level results in high voltages on the pulse-forming network, while utilization of extremely low impedance levels results in high currents, high switch-tube drops, and losses in the pulse transformer primary, which make it difficult to achieve efficient operation. When hydrogen thyratron switches are used, pulse-forming-network impedance levels of 25 and 50 Ω have proved to be a reasonable compromise between high currents and high voltages, and a variety of hydrogen thyratrons have been designed so that their power-handling capability is maximized at the 50- or 25-Ω impedance level. However, if silicon controlled rectifiers (SCRs) are being utilized as the switch for the line-type modulator, a lower-impedance PFN may be indicated, because of the limited peak forward voltage–handling capability of most SCRs. It is normal practice to slightly mismatch the PFN to the load in order to reflect a small negative voltage onto the switch to promote rapid turnoff.

An important characteristic of the modulator is its regulation for changes in line voltage and with the load. Transmission-line theory indicates that a relatively simple equivalent circuit will permit a meaningful calculation of regulation during the principal output pulse; such an equivalent circuit for the line-type modulator is given in Figure 3–25. In

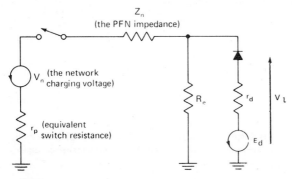

FIGURE 3–25 Equivalent circuit of line-type modulator used to analyze regulation.

this equivalent, the switch ON voltage drop is represented by resistance r_p and the transformer loss by an equivalent parallel resistance R_e. Analysis of this circuit is given in Glascoe and Lebacqz [8], where the expression for the load voltage is given by

$$V = \frac{V_n r_d + E_d Z_n \beta}{Z_n \beta + r_d \alpha}$$

where $\alpha = 1 + \dfrac{Z_n + r_p}{R_e}$

$$\beta = 1 + \frac{r_p}{Z_n}$$

and voltage regulation for changes in network voltage is obtained by taking the derivative

$$\frac{dV_l}{dV_n} = \frac{r_d}{Z_n\beta + r_d\alpha}$$

which can be rearranged to give the change in load voltage for a change in PFN charging voltage as

$$\frac{\Delta V_l}{V_l} = \frac{1}{1 + (E_d Z_n/V_n r_d)\beta} \frac{\Delta V_n}{V_n}$$

If the modulator is operated under conditions which result in maximum power transfer to the load, i.e., if

$$\frac{V_s}{V_n} = \frac{1 - r_d\alpha/Z_n\beta}{2\alpha}$$

the equation for voltage regulation becomes

$$\frac{\Delta V_l}{V_l} = \frac{2}{1 + Z_n\beta/r_d\alpha} \frac{\Delta V_n}{V_n}$$

In a similar manner, an expression for current regulation for changes in network voltage is given by

$$\frac{\Delta I_l}{I_l} = \frac{1}{1 - (E_d/V_n)\alpha} \frac{\Delta V_n}{V_n}$$

In the event that no dc regulation or charging regulation is used, this change in network voltage will be equal to the change in line voltage; however, if suitable circuits are incorporated to improve the regulation of the network voltage, this regulation must be included in the calculations to obtain the overall change in voltage and current with changes in line voltage.

It is interesting to evaluate some changes for representative choices of parameters. If

$$Z_n/r_d = 10$$

$$\alpha = \beta = 1$$

then

$$\frac{\Delta I_l}{I_l} = 1.82 \frac{\Delta V_n}{V_n}$$

Thus, for a biased-diode load such as a magnetron, the changes in load current may be substantially worse than the changes in input voltage.

The output pulse produced at the load of a line-type modulator deviates from the ideal rectangular pulse because of a number of factors. A photograph of the output pulse associated with a line-type modulator driving a magnetron load is given in Figure 3–26, which illustrates the principal regions to be considered in analyzing the output pulse: the

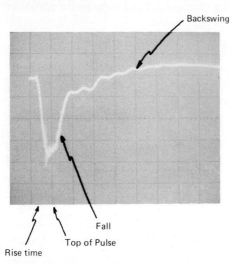

FIGURE 3–26 Line-type modulator output pulse showing principal portions of the pulse.

rise time, the top of the pulse, the fall time, and pulse backswing. It is usually desired that the rise time be sufficiently short for reasonable pulse shape, but not so short as to introduce moding or starting problems in the load. The top of the pulse should be reasonably flat and free from oscillations that would introduce frequency modulation through pushing, and the fall of the pulse should remove the voltage from the magnetron fairly rapidly and should not have excessive backswing, which could break down the tube. The tube voltage should not significantly recross the zero line, since even small negative voltages applied to the cathode may produce low-level RF noise outputs.

Detailed calculations of the pulse shape of a line-type modulator can be quite involved, but for many cases of interest, the particular choice of circuit constraints in a well-designed modulator may permit a considerable simplification. The analysis of the circuit is simplified, as was the case for the hard tube modulator, by breaking the circuit down into three time intervals: the rise of the pulse, the flat top, and the fall of the pulse.

While, in general, the analysis of the rise-time behavior involves the solution of a moderately complex network, for a number of situations one may consider that the pulse-forming network and the pulse transformer are two independent components such that the rise time of the overall combination is given by the square root of the sum of the squares of their rise times.

$$t_r = \sqrt{t_{r(\text{PFN})}^2 + t_{r(\text{xfmr})}^2} \qquad (3\text{--}1)$$

Behavior of the top of the pulse is simplified by the fact that most well-designed modulators produce approximately flat-top pulses, and the dominant circuit element that influences any droop on the top of the pulse is the magnetizing current of the transformer; it can be shown that for a biased-diode load, the change in load current is approximately equal to the magnetizing current. It is generally considered good design practice to design for approximately 10% of the load current to constitute magnetizing current at the end of the pulse; it is usually the case that this amount of current droop can be compensated for by adjustment of the pulse-forming network in order to obtain a reasonably flat top on the pulse.

Analysis of the tailing edge of the pulse is complicated by the nonlinear behavior of the pulse transformer and by the opening of the switch in the primary circuit during the recovery interval; since the details of this analysis are intimately bound with the design of the pulse transformer, detailed consideration of this behavior will be deferred until Chapter 4, on pulse transformers.

The Variable Pulse-Width Line-Type Modulator

The line-type modulator has been widely used because of its relatively small size and weight and good efficiency. However, some serious disadvantages of a line-type modulator are, first, that the interpulse period may not easily be varied over a wide range and, second, that the pulse width may not easily be varied. While the variation in interpulse period is largely fixed by the values of the recharging components, it is possible to arrive at a number of schemes for varying the pulse width in a line-type modulator.

Figure 3–27 illustrates a number of circuit configurations that can result in the ability to vary the output-pulse width of a line-type modulator [14,21]. Each of these schemes essentially involves first a discharge initiation of the line in a manner analogous to normal line-type modulator operation, followed by a second switching action that tends to terminate the output pulse before the line normally completely discharges

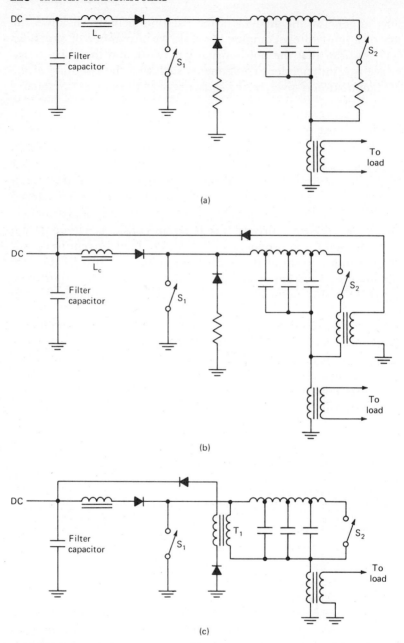

(a)

(b)

(c)

FIGURE 3–27 Three circuit configurations for obtaining variable output-pulse width from a line-type modulator by varying the relative closing times of switches S_1 and S_2. Arrangements (b) and (c) provide for return of a portion of the unused stored energy to the power supply.

itself into the load; the leftover charge may be either dissipated in an auxiliary resistor, as in Figure 3–27(*a*), or returned to the power supply, as shown in Figure 3–27(*b*).

Figure 3–27(*c*) is a schematic diagram of another successful variable–pulse-width line-modulator concept. Charging of the pulse-forming network and initiation of network discharge by closing S_1 is conventional with this arrangement. However, when it is desired to terminate the pulse, switch S_2 is closed, with the result that the output pulse terminates and the voltage reverses across the PFN; this voltage reversal is coupled to the power supply through transformer T_1 and the diodes, so that a portion of the unused stored energy is returned to the power supply. One of the keys to a successful circuit of this type is the careful design of transformer T_1 in order to minimize losses due to fringing at the air gaps of the core; in some cases, the use of several distributed air gaps has been resorted to in an attempt to increase efficiency.

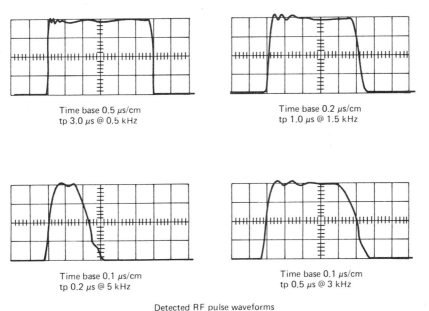

Time base 0.5 μs/cm
tp 3.0 μs @ 0.5 kHz

Time base 0.2 μs/cm
tp 1.0 μs @ 1.5 kHz

Time base 0.1 μs/cm
tp 0.2 μs @ 5 kHz

Time base 0.1 μs/cm
tp 0.5 μs @ 3 kHz

Detected RF pulse waveforms

FIGURE 3–28 Detected RF pulse waveforms generated by a magnetron pulsed with a variable-width line-type modulator with energy return. (*Raytheon*)

Figure 3–28 shows the types of waveforms that can be obtained by using this approach, showing detected RF for a range of pulse widths from tenths of a microsecond to several microseconds.

Magnetron-Moding Control in Line-Type Modulators

One of the problems involved with the operation of a microwave magnetron is the tendency for the tube to oscillate in other than the desired mode. This type of operation is highly undesirable for a number of reasons. It has been observed that the rate of rise of voltage applied to the tube at the time when the tube initially begins to conduct is a primary factor in determining the tendency of a particular tube-modulator combination to operate stably and in the desired mode [7]. As will be shown in Chapter 4, the rate of rise of voltage may be controlled to a certain extent by the use of proper design techniques and by achieving specific values of distributed capacitance and leakage inductance in the transformer itself. However, attempts to reduce the rate of rise of voltage by increasing capacity often have the result that undesirably large amounts of energy are stored in the transformer, with a resultant loss in efficiency and an undesirable heating of the modulator components. Another approach that can be used to control the rate of rise of voltage is the connection of an RC network, at either the primary or the secondary side of the pulse transformer. If it is used at the primary side, the RC network is often called a *despiking* network. Such despiking networks are often used to eliminate a large spike of current occurring at the beginning of the pulse, often associated with improper transformer design. An RC network on the output side of the transformer can conveniently be used to control the rate of rise of voltage on the tube, and in fact the resistors are often made selectable to tailor the modulator to a particular tube. Unfortunately, each of these approaches results in a withdrawal of energy from the modulator, which reduces overall modulator efficiency, and such approaches may also make it difficult to achieve a reasonably rectangular pulse shape.

One approach to achieving stable magnetron operation is to use a so-called *pedestal technique* [18]. A pedestal technique involves initially applying a waveform of slowly rising voltage to the tube, bringing the cathode potential to approximately 90% of its normal operating voltage, followed by rapidly increasing the voltage to its full value, as shown in Figure 3–29. Using such techniques, conventional magnetrons have been made to oscillate stably with pulse widths as short as 10 ns.

Another approach, which may be considerably simpler, is the so-called corner-cutter circuit, or pulse-bender arrangement, shown in Figure 3–30 [2,12]. This approach places a large load on the output of the line-type modulator at approximately 75% of the normal operating voltage, slowing the rate of rise of voltage to the tube substantially, and permitting stable operation with reasonably fast rise times, a highly rectangular RF pulse, and rapid fall time.

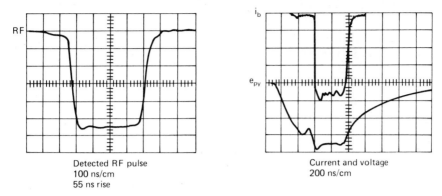

Detected RF pulse
100 ns/cm
55 ns rise

Current and voltage
200 ns/cm

FIGURE 3-29 **Detected RF pulse, and voltage and current waveforms of a pedestal-pulsed C-band magnetron.** (*Raytheon*)

Operation of the corner-cutter circuit involves the charging of capacitors C_1, C_2, and C_3 to a voltage determined by the zener voltage stack, typically approximately 75% of normal operating voltage. Thus, for voltages less than this voltage, the diodes disconnect the output, and the voltage rises normally. However, once the voltage becomes more negative than the zener voltage, a load consisting of capacitors C_1, C_2, and

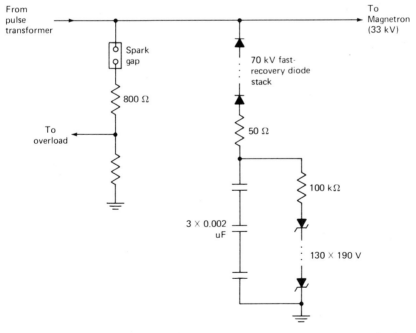

FIGURE 3-30 **Schematic diagram of a zener diode "corner-cutter" or "pulse-bender" circuit.**

C_3, R_1, and the forward impedance of the diodes is connected across the modulator, substantially reducing the rate of rise of voltage applied to the tube. Once the tube has reached its full operating voltage, the capacitors are charged to this voltage and little current flows through the diodes, so that efficient tube operation results. Between pulses, the capacitor voltage is stabilized at the zener voltage in anticipation of the next pulse. A set of waveforms illustrating operation of the corner cutter circuit is given in Figure 3–31. In the event that variation of the interpulse period is not required, it may be possible to eliminate the zener diode stack and operate with the resistors, the diodes, and the capacitors alone.

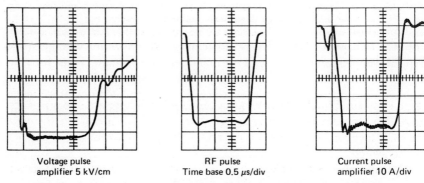

| Voltage pulse amplifier 5 kV/cm | RF pulse Time base 0.5 µs/div | Current pulse amplifier 10 A/div |

FIGURE 3–31   Voltage, current, and RF waveforms associated with a magnetron pulsed by a line-type modulator with the corner-cutter circuit shown in Figure 3–30. (*Raytheon*)

3–3 SCR-MAGNETIC MODULATORS

In recent years, there have been developed a particular class of line-type modulators called *SCR-magnetic* modulators [3,4,13,15]. These systems utilize saturating magnetic cores as switches in order to provide improved reliability over the hydrogen thyratron switch or in order to accommodate higher peak currents or more rapid rate of rise of current than can be accommodated by solid-state controlled rectifiers.

A simplified schematic diagram of one type of magnetic modulator is shown in Figure 3–32. Operation of the system is critically dependent upon the saturable reactors that are involved. These saturable reactors are typically coils wound on gapless toroids, and are designed to have a high unsaturated inductance and a very low saturated inductance, and to make a rapid transition from the unsaturated condition to the satu-

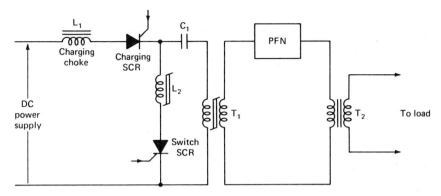

FIGURE 3–32 **Magnetic-SCR line-type modulator using SCR switch and saturating magnetic devices. Bias windings have been omitted for clarity, but L_2, T_1, and T_2 are all magnetically biased. T_2 need not be biased, but if it is not, a resistor-diode combination must be connected across the primary to provide a low-impedance path for charging of the PFN.**

rated condition. Such a device can act as a switch. There are two purposes for which such devices may be useful: to decrease the rate of rise through the SCR (see Section 7–3), and to reduce the peak-current requirements of the switch.

The operation of a magnetic-SCR modulator may be broken down into a number of separate subintervals: the charging interval for C_1, the transfer of charge from C_1 to the PFN, and the discharge of the PFN into the load.

The operating cycle begins with C_1 and the PFN initially discharged, and both the charging and switch SCRs in the OFF condition. Operation is initiated by triggering the charging SCR, which resonantly charges C_1 through L_1 to twice the dc power-supply voltage, as was the case for the line-type modulator. The charging period is given by $\pi \sqrt{L_1 C_1}$. Once the voltage on C_1 has reached its maximum value, the current through the charging SCR attempts to reverse, turning off the SCR and holding the voltage at C_1 at.its maximum value.

The next step in the operation of the modulator is initiated by turning on the switching SCR. Once the switching SCR has been triggered, the full voltage across C_1 is developed across L_2. During this interval, only a small amount of current flows through L_2, permitting the switch SCR to turn on completely; after an interval of time sufficient for the SCR to completely turn on, inductor L_2 saturates, becoming a relatively low impedance, placing much of the voltage across C_1 across the primary T_1 and resonantly transferring charge from C_1 to the PFN through T_1 and through the saturated primary winding of T_2. In order for this transfer to be efficient, T_2 must represent a low impedance for charging of the PFN, and for that reason it is often biased to saturation. If this is not done, a diode may be connected across the T_2 primary.

Figure 3–33 is an equivalent circuit valid for this charge-transfer pe-

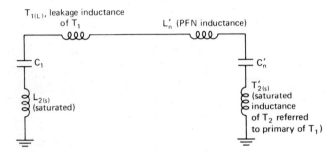

FIGURE 3–33 **Equivalent circuit of magnetic modulator during charge transfer from C_1 to C_n.**

riod, a resonant transfer of energy from C_1 to the network capacity C_n taking place through an inductance consisting of the saturated inductance of L_2, the leakage inductance of T_1, the saturated inductance of T_2, and the network inductance L_n. In Figure 3–33 L'_n, C'_n, and $T_{2(s)}$ are all values which are referred to the primary winding of T_1; that is, if L_n is the PFN inductance, C_n the network capacitance, $T_{2(s)}$ the saturated inductance of T_2, and n_1 the turns ratio of T_1,

$$L'_n = \frac{L_n}{n_1^2}$$
$$C'_n = n_1^2 C_n$$

and

$$T'_{2(s)} = \frac{T_{2(s)}}{n_1^2}$$

The transfer of charge from C_1 to the PFN takes place in a time given by

$$\pi \sqrt{(T_{1(l)} + L_{2(s)} + T'_{2(s)} + L'_n) \frac{C_1 C'_n}{C_1 + C'_n}} \tag{3-2}$$

Any attempt to discharge the pulse-forming network back through T_1 is defeated by back-biasing action of both the switch SCR and the saturated inductor L_2.

At this point in time, the pulse-forming network is fully charged, and the full voltage appears across the secondary of transformer T_1. Once the required volt-time integral has been applied to T_1, T_1 saturates, discharging the PFN into the load through transformer T_2. An equivalent circuit for the discharge of the pulse-forming network is given in Figure 3–34. However, if more detailed calculations of output-pulse shape are required, the methods of Kadochnikov [9,10] may be used.

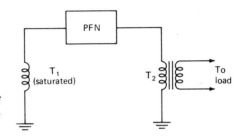

FIGURE 3–34 Equivalent circuit of magnetic modulator during discharge of PFN into load.

There are a number of design considerations that impact the choice of component values in such a modulator. The values of C_1 and the charging inductors are chosen so that resonant charging is accomplished within a relatively short interval, yet the charging current through the charging SCR and transformer T_1 should remain relatively low. L_2 in the unsaturated condition should represent a high impedance, and in the saturated condition an inductance that dominates the resonant transfer of charge from C_1 to the pulse-forming network. This saturated inductance should be small, in order to rapidly charge the pulse-forming network, but too rapid a charge of the pulse-forming network results in excessive peak currents flowing through the switching SCR. Transformer T_1 should be designed to have a low value of saturated reactance, and a volt-time integral product sufficient to permit complete charging of the pulse-forming network with some "guard" interval to accommodate variations in the temperature and voltages. Design equations for L_2 and T_1 are presented in Section 7–5. The design of transformer T_2 is more conventional in nature and follows the guidelines in Chapter 4, but magnetic biasing of the transformer core may permit larger flux excursions. A set of waveforms is given in Figure 3–35, which shows magnetic modulator operation. Figure 3–35(a) shows the PFN voltage, illustrating the resonant charge transfer to C_n, the guard interval (the

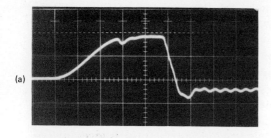

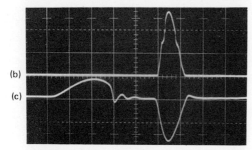

FIGURE 3–35 Magnetic modulator waveforms showing (a) PFN voltage, (b) current in a TWT load, and (c) output voltage.

constant-voltage interval), and the switching period where the voltage rapidly reduces to zero when the saturable inductor saturates. This discharge then produces the output-voltage pulse shown in 3–35(c). Note that in this modulator a diode-resistor pair was used across the transformer primary and so a portion of the PFN charging process was reflected in the output voltage.

Figure 3–32 is a much simplified diagram, and additional circuits are necessary in order to provide for proper functioning of the circuit. In order to ensure correct saturation, both L_2 and T_1 require an auxiliary bias supply for resetting; T_2 may require a bias winding also. In order to realize a truly constant peak charging voltage on C_1 (to reduce time jitter), some form of charging regulator, such as those discussed in Chapter 6, must be incorporated in place of the simple charging choke. The biased-diode nature of the load usually results in the reflection of some small voltage at the anode of the switch SCR. This voltage must be monitored, since arcing in the load, transformer, or pulse-forming network can result in excessive voltages reflected back at this point. Of course, dc power-supply overload circuits and appropriate protective circuits for the load (such as magnetron or TWT) must be provided if reliable operation is to be achieved.

The transfer of energy from C_1 to C_n and the discharge of energy stored in C_n into the load is accompanied by an increase in voltage level and a decrease in discharge or transfer time at each stage of the process. Typically, in a single stage, ratios of charging times to discharging times on the order of $10:1$ can be achieved. Additional sections may be added in order to provide the additional compression required for shorter pulse lengths, but care must be used to ensure complete transfer of charge between stages in such circuits [3].

3–4 DC POWER SUPPLIES

A common feature of these modulators is a dc power supply. Conventional design practice may be utilized for such systems, but a few special precautions are necessary. For the lower-voltage supplies such as are used with line-type and magnetic modulators, three-phase rectifiers and choke input filters are typically utilized. A simplified schematic diagram of such a system is shown in Figure 3–36, showing provisions for measuring overload current drawn from the supply directly, as well as conventional protection in the primary power lines. It must be emphasized that the power supply should be capable of sustaining

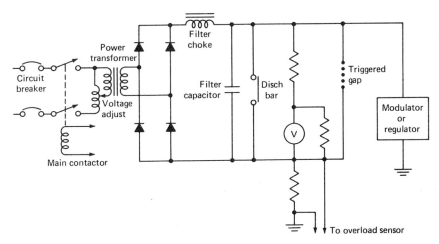

FIGURE 3–36 Representative modulator dc power supply, showing some overload circuits and sensing points.

occasional virtual short-circuit operation and of rapidly restoring normal operation once the short circuit has been removed. In order to provide adequate protection, the overload circuits must be rapid-acting.

Higher-voltage dc supplies such as are encountered with hard-tube systems will often involve the use of conventional voltage doublers in order to reduce output-voltage requirements on the power-supply transformers. With hard-tube modulators, particularly at higher power levels, crowbar circuits are often incorporated across the power-supply output in order to protect the relatively expensive tube, and the power supply must be specially designed in order to withstand the severe stresses imposed by such operation.

Finally, there are cases where the use of a high-frequency inverter is desirable in order to provide a high ripple frequency and to achieve small size and weight, or for operation from available low-voltage dc supplies.

For cases where the filtering provided by choke input filters is not adequate, series vacuum-tube regulators may be incorporated, as shown in Figure 3–37, in order to provide adequate power-supply regulation and ripple reduction. Where filtering is adequate for ripple reduction but additional regulation against line or load variations is desired, it may be adequate to sense a parameter such as tube current or peak

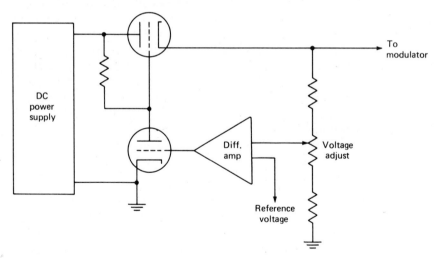

FIGURE 3–37 Series regulator that may be used for a high-stability, low-ripple modulator power supply.

charging voltage and to use a motor-driven autotransformer to vary the input voltage so as to keep this parameter constant.

In any of these high-voltage circuits, adequate provisions for operator safety must be incorporated, including interlocks, shorting switches, and bleeder resistors on all high-voltage capacitors.

3–5 OVERLOADS AND PROTECTIVE CIRCUITS

Throughout the book, the subject of safeties and overloads for various faults is discussed. In this section, a number of these will be brought together, both to have them readily available in one location, and also to indicate the extreme importance of a properly designed overload-protection and performance-monitoring system if a successful and reliable transmitter design is to be achieved. Because of the high voltages and substantial amounts of power associated with a high-power microwave transmitter, a certain number of malfunctions (such as occasional arcs) will normally be encountered, and the modulator and tube must be designed to accommodate these without damage to either the tube or the modulator. In addition, in the event of catastrophic failure either of a modulator component or of the RF tube itself, the overloads and monitoring circuits should be such that damage is confined to that particular unit and other portions of the system are not permanently affected. Finally, transmitter performance should be monitored to give an early indication of problems that might be encountered. In a high-power microwave radar transmitter, the protection requirements can be associated either with the microwave tube itself, or with the modulator utilized to drive the tube; in addition, there are often requirements for overall performance monitoring in order to verify proper operation of the entire transmitter.

Microwave Tube Protection

The requirements for protection of the microwave tube are particularly important, since the microwave tube is often a relatively expensive part of the system—one that requires considerable time to replace—and many of the high-power tubes occasionally evidence occasional arcs or abnormal operation which if not properly monitored and accommodated could permanently damage the device.

The particular type of protection required is dependent upon the type of microwave tube being utilized. For magnetrons, the peak and average current through the tube are particularly sensitive indications of tube operation and should be monitored; operation outside normally acceptable bounds should immediately terminate operation of the modulator. In the event that the magnetron fails to oscillate, if a line-type modulator is utilized, the cathode voltage will rise to unacceptably high levels; in order to avoid this, a spark gap that breaks down at a voltage slightly in excess of the normal operating voltage is often connected to the magnetron cathode. Cooling of high-power magnetrons is quite important; temperature should be monitored at the point specified by the manufacturer, and the presence of appropriate cooling media, either air, liquid, or both, should be monitored and lack of adequate cooling or overtemperature should result in the removal of voltage from the tube. Since the output load has a significant effect on the operation of a magnetron, its status should be monitored by means of a voltage—standing-wave ratio (VSWR) monitor or reflected-power monitor, and excessive reflected power should terminate operation. Waveguide arcs can be extremely damaging if they propagate through the waveguide system to the output window of the tube; optical arc detectors that sense the presence of light within the waveguide system have been developed and are often recommended for monitoring the output waveguide system.

A crossed-field amplifier has protection requirements essentially identical to those of a magnetron, with some additions necessitated by the fact that the CFA is an amplifier rather than an oscillator. In particular, provisions must normally be made to ensure that high voltages are not applied to the CFA if adequate RF drive is not present at the tube input, and the frequency of the RF signal at the input must be such that the CFA is in a region of normal operation. The alignment of RF drive pulses is perhaps one of the more difficult requirements for CFA operation to achieve reliably, particularly for short-pulse operation. While magnetron coolant and temperature monitoring requirements also apply to CFAs, because of their higher average power such monitoring may be much more critical to reliable CFA operation than is the case for many magnetrons.

In the linear-beam tubes, such as the TWT and the klystron, the requirements for tube monitoring are perhaps more severe than is the case for the crossed-field devices. In particular, the monitoring of various features that indicate the defocusing of the electron beam and the corresponding intercept of current by the physical tube structure are particularly important. In many tubes, collector current, beam current, focus-coil or solenoid current, and temperature and coolant flow must be monitored, and modulator operation must be disabled if abnormal values are sensed. The rapid protection of the tube in the event of catastrophic beam defocusing is particularly important, since tube meltdown can occur in a relatively short period of time. Particularly for gridded tubes, the presence of arcs within the tube body must be accommodated. In order to protect the grid-driver circuitry, it is often desirable to include a spark gap from the grid to the cathode in order to prevent excessive grid voltages in the event of a tube arc; in addition, if the tube arcs, the high voltage must be removed from the tube for a sufficient time for the arc to dissipate; this often necessitates the incorporation of a crowbar circuit directly across the tube, and the power supply must be such that it will withstand repeated firings of this crowbar circuit without damage. Also, as was the case in the crossed-field devices, reflected power should often be monitored, to indicate any abnormal VSWR of the load and to prevent the possible self-oscillation of the linear-beam tube.

Modulator Monitoring and Safeties

Monitoring of various test points in the modulator itself is important to ensure proper transmitter operation, since in many cases abnormal operation of the microwave tube is reflected in unusual modulator operation, and also to protect against failures in the modulator components. All modulator designs should have adequate interlocking and safeties to prevent inadvertent operator contact with the potentially lethal high voltages that are often present within the modulator. Complete enclosure of all high-voltage areas, shorting bars with which to discharge all high-voltage capacitors if the enclosure is open, bleeder resistors to discharge capacitors, and interlocks to disable the modulator if access can be achieved by the operator are all important features that are normally an integral part of the modulator design. The specific additional safeties that may be required in a modulator are to a certain extent dependent upon the type that is being protected. Differing requirements exist for line-type, SCR-magnetic, and hard-tube modulators.

In a line-type modulator, if the magnetron fails to oscillate for any reason, the output voltage on the magnetron can double its normal value. Since this might lead to a breakdown of the output transformer or damage to the microwave tube, often a spark gap with a breakdown voltage slightly in excess of the normal operating voltage is connected across the magnetron.

In the event of a mismatch of the load, a portion of the stored energy will be reflected back into the modulator, producing a negative voltage at the switch. In order to remove this voltage, and to prevent the resultant abnormal operation of the modulator, it is customary to connect an inverse diode (also called a *shunt* or a *clipping* diode) and a resistor in series with it across the switch so as to clip off any negative voltage that appears; current through this resistor is often monitored and excessive inverse voltage thus sensed and used to disable the operation of the modulator. This is particularly critical, since a negative voltage at this point at the beginning of the charging cycle results in a corresponding increase in the peak charging voltage, which can in turn further increase the negative voltage at the beginning of the next charging cycle, producing ever-increasing peak charging voltages on the PFN that can permanently damage the modulator.

Power-supply current should be continuously monitored, and excessive power-supply current should disable modulator operation; this is particularly important, since occasionally the switch may go into a condition of continuous conduction, which could rapidly damage either the switch, the power supply, or the charging choke. In addition, breakdown occurring within the modulator will often cause excessive power-supply current to be drawn; normally, the energy stored in the power supply will have to be carefully considered to determine whether disconnection from the power-supply line is sufficient, or whether a more rapidly acting overload device such as a crowbar is necessary. Finally, the temperature of various oil-filled, high-voltage components and the pressure of the oil within these units can be monitored and often provides an early indication of device failure.

For an SCR-magnetic modulator, in addition to providing a spark gap on the magnetron and monitoring temperature at certain critical points, it is normal to monitor inverse voltage on the SCR, peak power-supply current, and magnetron average current. Excessive values of peak power-supply current or magnetron average current will typically be used to interrupt the charging of the modulator by disabling triggers to the charge SCR and turning off the main power-supply contactor. A small amount of inverse voltage on the SCRs at the termination of the pulse is often desirable to aid in SCR recovery; however, excessive voltage at this point indicates abnormal operation of either the modulator or the load and should promptly initiate interruption of the modulator operation.

In a hard-tube modulator, protection is usually centered about the high-voltage switch tube and the load, since arcs can occur in either the switch tube or the output load, particularly for voltages above the 30- to 40-kV region. For these voltages, incorporation of a crowbar circuit across the high-voltage power supply is a virtual necessity for reliable operation. When utilizing such a crowbar, one needs to carefully ensure that an oscillatory discharge will not be encountered if the crowbar is fired, since such a condition could result in crowbar deionization and potential damage to the circuit. Initiation of the crowbar firing can often be accomplished by the sensing of peak currents through either the switch tube or the load, and excessive current should promptly initiate crowbar firing. In some cases, adequate protection can be achieved for the switch tube by connecting the grid voltage to a large negative voltage in the event of a malfunction, as was discussed in Section 3–2. Again, as with any high-power tube, coolant interlocks and temperature monitoring should be an integral part of the protection for the modulator tube.

Transmitter-Performance Monitoring

Perhaps the most important overall performance monitor associated with a radar transmitter is the power output of the device, either peak or average, which can be monitored at the device output. In addition, reflected power or VSWR is normally monitored both as an indication of normal system operation and as protection for the high-power RF tubes. It may be desirable also to monitor a number of additional circuits or functions, but most of these are satisfied by the requirements for tube or modulator protection already outlined. The advent in recent years of microprocessor technology provides a means not only for monitoring a number of these various tube, output, and modulator parameters, but also for providing a permanent record of overall transmitter performance and for monitoring trends or combinations of monitored variables that are indicative of incipient failure, permitting their rectification during normally scheduled maintenance operations, with a resultant increase in system availability.

3–6 LOAD EFFECTS ON MODULATOR DESIGN

The modulator must provide proper operating voltages to the load, but in many instances the characteristics of the particular load will influence the design of the modulator. Tubes requiring extremely high voltages may require special techniques, such as Blumlein or Marx generators, and if short HV pulses are utilized, rise-time enhancement networks may be required. Oscillation and excessive backswing must be avoided after the pulse to prevent the generation of spurious signals. If the tube arcs or shorts regularly, protection must be provided to allow the arcs to extinguish. Also, in line-type modulators, arcing loads may cause excessive voltages to appear on the modulator if the shunt-

TABLE 3-1 STABILITY FACTORS [20]

Type	FM or PM sensitivity	Ratio of dynamic to static impedance	Current or voltage change to 1% change in HVPS voltage	
			Line-type modulator	Hard-tube modulator
Magnetron	$\dfrac{\Delta F}{F} = 0.001 + 0.003\,\dfrac{\Delta I}{I}$	0.05–0.1	$\Delta I = 2\%$	$\Delta I = 10\text{-}20\%$
Magnetron (stabilized)	$\dfrac{\Delta F}{F} = 0.0002 + 0.0005\,\dfrac{\Delta I}{I}$	0.05–0.1	$\Delta I = 2\%$	$\Delta I = 10\text{-}20\%$
Backward-wave CFA	$\Delta\phi = 0.4\text{-}1°$ for 1% $\Delta I/I$	0.05–0.1	$\Delta I = 2\%$	$\Delta I = 5\text{-}10\%$
Forward-wave CFA	$\Delta\phi = 1\text{-}3°$ for 1% $\Delta I/I$	0.1 –0.2	$\Delta I = 2\%$	$\Delta I = 5\text{-}10\%$
Klystron	$\dfrac{\Delta\phi}{\phi} = \dfrac{1}{2}\dfrac{\Delta E}{E}\quad \phi \approx 5\lambda$	0.67	$\Delta E = 0.8\%$	$\Delta E = 1\%$
TWT	$\dfrac{\Delta\phi}{\phi} \approx \dfrac{1}{3}\dfrac{\Delta E}{E}\quad \phi \approx 15\lambda$ $\Delta\phi = 20°$ for 1% $\dfrac{\Delta E}{E}$	0.67	$\Delta E = 0.8\%$	$\Delta E = 1\%$
Triode or tetrode	$\Delta\phi = 0\text{-}0.5°$ for 1% $\Delta I/I$	1.0	$\Delta I = 1\%$	$\Delta I = 1\%$

TABLE 3-2 MODULATOR COMPARISON

Type	Switch	Flexibility		Pulse length			Working voltages	Application	Size and cost
		Duty	Pulse width	Long	Short	Flatness			
Line-type	Thyratron	Limited by charging circuit	No	Large PFN	Good	Ripples	High	Most common	Small size
	SCR						Medium		Smallest size higher cost
Hard-tube	Capacitor-coupled	Limited	Yes	Large capacitor	Good	Good	High	Fairly common	Large
	Transformer-coupled	Limited	Yes	Capacitor and xfmr gets large	Good	Fair	High	Not often used	Large
	Modulation-anode (floating-deck)	No limit	Yes	Good	OK	Excellent	High	Usually high-power	Quite large
	Grid	No limit	Yes	Good	Good	Excellent	Low	Widely used at low power	Small and inexpensive
SCR-magnetic	SCR and magnetic cores	Limited by charging circuit and magnetic cores	Normally fixed	Large PFN	Losses may be high	Ripples	Low in initial stages	Becoming more common	Small; initial design costs high

diode circuitry is poorly designed. Crowbar circuits may be necessary in order to fully protect the microwave source and modulator.

Of particular importance are the stability factors achievable by using the various tube-modulator combinations. Some of these data are summarized in Table 3–1 [20].

From this brief discussion, we can appreciate the interaction of tube characteristics with modulator design. An optimum selection of a microwave transmitter should include the modulator requirements as a prime consideration, and optimum modulator design is only achieved when the modulator designer has a thorough knowledge of the characteristics and peculiarities of the modulator load. In summary, the characteristics of a number of important modulator types are compared in Table 3–2.

3–7 COMPARISONS OF COST

Comparisons of cost associated with various modulator types are often of major interest to the radar designer, and are one parameter associated with a radar transmitter that is difficult to accurately define. This difficulty is complicated by the variation in overhead rates, employee efficiency, and materials cost from manufacturer to manufacturer, and from design concept to design concept. Cost also varies with the level of performance required and with the environmental requirements.

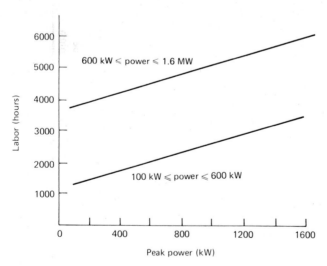

FIGURE 3–38 Engineering labor hours for transmitter design and integration for ground-based radar operating over the 0–55°C temperature range.

However, the estimation of labor hours for various phases of modulator design, fabrication, and checkout may be a useful piece of information for the engineer, and may serve as the basis for more detailed estimates to be generated later in the design process. Estimates of labor requirements for design, fabrication, and checkout, for ground-based radar transmitters designed to operate over the temperature range from 0 to 55°C are presented in Figures 3–38, 3–39, and 3–40. It should be

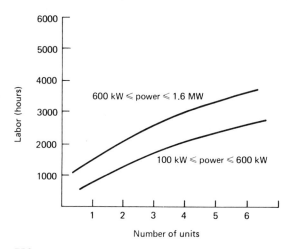

FIGURE 3–39 Labor-hours for transmitter assembly for ground-based radars operating over the 0–55°C temperature range.

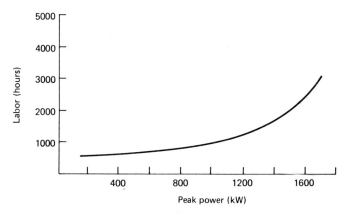

FIGURE 3–40 Labor-hours for transmitter subsystem testing for ground-based radars operating over the 0–55°C temperature range.

emphasized that these are general, representative guidelines only, and that stringent performance or environmental requirements will result in increases, while lenient requirements may result in substantial decreases. Of course, if similar designs can be adapted, there may be a substantial reduction in the design labor requirements.

REFERENCES

1. Alsmeyer, R., "A Constant Current Hard Tube Modulator," in *Conf. Rec. 1973 11th Modulator Symp.*, September 1973, pp. 75–78.

2. Ashworth, J., and R. Browne, Raytheon, personal communication, Nov. 12, 1979.

3. Busch, K. J., et al., "Magnetic Pulse Modulators," *Bell System Technical Journal*, vol. 34, no. 5, September 1955, pp. 943–993.

4. Coate, G. T., and L. T. Swain, Jr., *High-Power Semiconductor-Magnetic Pulse Generators*, MIT Press, Cambridge, Mass., 1966.

5. Doolittle, H. D., "Vacuum Power Tubes for Pulse Modulation," Machlett Laboratories, Stamford, Conn.

6. Doss, J. D., et al., "80 Kilovolt Blocking Oscillator Modulator," in *Proc. 10th Modulator Symp.*, May 1968, pp. 10–21.

7. Gillette, P. R., and K. Oshima, "Pulser Component Design for Proper Magnetron Operation," *IRE Trans. Component Parts*, March 1956, pp. 26–31.

8. Glasoe, G. N., and J. V. Lebacqz, *Pulse Generators*, MIT Rad. Lab. series, vol. 5, McGraw-Hill, New York, 1948. (Also available in Dover and Boston Technical Publishers editions.)

9. Kadochnikov, A. I., I. E., Korobeynikova, and M. A. Kheyfets, "Calculation of the Current Pulse in a Section of a Magnetic Pulse Generator," *Telecommunications and Radio Engineering*, pt. 2, vol. 29, no. 8, 1974, pp. 90–94.

10. Kheyfets, M. A., and A. I. Kadochnikov, "Switching Properties of Saturable Reactors in Magnetic Pulse Generator Sections," *Telecommunications and Radio Engineering*, pt. 1, vol. 32, no. 2, February 1978, pp. 81–84.

11. Limansky, I., "How to Design a Line-Type Modulator," *Electronic Design*, vol. 8, no. 4, Feb. 17, 1960, pp. 42–45.

12. Main, J. H., "A Self-Biased Solid-State Diode Despiker," in *Proc. 8th Symp. Hydrogen Thyratrons and Modulators*, May 1964, pp. 416–422.

13. Manteuffel, E. W., and R. E. Cooper, "D-C Charged Magnetic Modulator," *Proc. AIEE*, vol. 78, January 1960, pp. 843–850.

14. Martinovitch, V. N., "Generation of Output Pulses Having a Continuously Variable Pulse Width in a Line-Type Modulator," in *Proc. 6th Symp. Hydrogen Thyratrons and Modulators*, May 1960, pp. 106–110.

15. Melville, W. S., "The Use of Saturable Reactors as Discharge Devices for Pulse Generators," *Proc. IEE* (London), vol. 98, pt. III, 1951, pp. 185–207.

16. Nordenberg, H. M., *Electronic Transformers*, Reinhold, New York, 1964.

17. O'Meara, T. R., "Ladder Transformer Coupling Networks for Pulse Amplifiers and Hard-Tube Modulators," *Trans. IRE Gp. on Circuit Theory,* vol. 7, no. 3, September 1960, pp. 239–246.

18. Parker, T. J., "A Modulator Technique for Producing Short Pulses in High Powered Magnetrons," *IRE Nat. Conv. Rec.,* 1954, pp. 142–151.

19. Sutherland, R. I., *Care and Feeding of Power Grid Tubes,* Varian, Eimac Div., San Carlos, Calif., 1967, sec. 2.

20. Weil, T. A., "Transmitters," in M. I. Skolnik, ed., *Radar Handbook,* McGraw-Hill, New York, 1970, chap. 7.

21. Numerous modulator examples and discussions are contained in the proceedings of the modulator symposia sponsored by the U.S. Army Electronics Command and the Pulse Power Conference:

Title	AD number
Proc. 5th Symp. Hydrogen Thyratrons and Modulators, 1958	AD 650 899
Proc. 6th Symp. Hydrogen Thyratrons and Modulators, 1960	AD 254 102
Proc. 7th Symp. Hydrogen Thyratrons and Modulators, 1962	AD 296 002
Proc. 8th Symp. Hydrogen Thyratrons and Modulators, 1964	
Proc. 9th Modulator Symp., 1966	
Proc. 10th Modulator Symp., 1968	AD 676 854
Proc. 11th Modulator Symp., 1973, IEEE 73 CH 0773–2 ED	
Proc. 12th Modulator Symp., 1976, IEEE 76 CH 1045–4 ED	
Proc. 13th Pulse Power Modulator Symp., IEEE 78 CH 1371–4 ED	
Proc. Intern. Pulsed Power Conf., IEEE 76 CH 1197–8 REG 5	
Dig. Tech. Papers, 2d IEEE Intern. Pulsed Power Conf., IEEE 79 CH 1505–7	
Proc. 14th Pulse Power Modulator Symp., IEEE 80 CH 1573–5 ED	

4
PULSE-
TRANSFORMER
DESIGN AND
FABRICATION

Pulse transformers find wide use in a number of electronic circuits. In high-power transmitters they are often used to couple the output of a line-type modulator to the load, and to a lesser extent high-power transformers are utilized in hard-tube modulators. These high-power pulse transformers are typically step-up transformers, which provide a voltage and impedance transformation from their primary to the secondary.

The design of pulse transformers for high-power modulators may be approached in a number of different ways. However, all of the design procedures and approaches are designed to produce a transformer that satisfies a number of differing, and often contradictory, criteria [2,4–20,22–25]. These criteria include the following:

- Achieving specified rise time

- Providing adequate pulse flatness

- Providing desired fall time and tail-of-pulse response

- Establishing conditions for proper tube operation

- Providing voltage transformation

- Holding temperature within reasonable limits
- Providing for a path of filament current for the tube
- Withstanding the required operating voltages
- Small size, weight, and cost
- Withstanding the required voltage stresses

The simultaneous optimization of all these differing requirements may not be possible, and the skillful tradeoff among these parameters is an important part of the design process.

4–1 EQUIVALENT CIRCUIT AND ANALYSIS OF BEHAVIOR

Pulse transformers come in a wide variety of winding configurations, core materials, and turns ratios. A "complete" equivalent circuit that is generally applicable is shown in Figure 4–1 [8,11,23]. As can

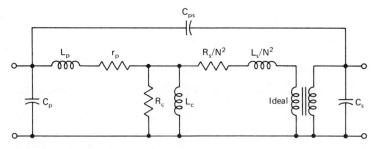

FIGURE 4–1 "Complete" equivalent circuit for a pulse transformer.

be seen, while the analysis of this circuit is not prohibitively complex, the specific pulse transformer performance is highly dependent upon a number of different ratios of the various equivalent circuit elements. In many cases, a substantial simplification is made possible by assuming that the turns ratio of the transformer is greater than 1:3. For such a condition, a considerably simplified equivalent circuit may be utilized, as shown in Figure 4–2 [6,7], where, for simplicity, all circuit elements have been transformed to the same side of the transformer, either the primary or the secondary.

Analysis of this equivalent transformer may be simplified by dividing the pulse into three distinct parts: the rise time, the top of the pulse, and the fall time, or tail of the pulse. For the analysis of rise time, the magnetizing current may usually be neglected; the result is the simplified equivalent circuit shown in Figure 4–3. It may normally be assumed that a step voltage is impressed on the primary of the pulse transformer that gives an output rise time related to the leakage inductance and the stray capacitance of the transformer, the distributed capacity of the

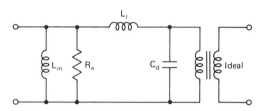

FIGURE 4–2   Simplified equivalent circuit for a step-up transformer.

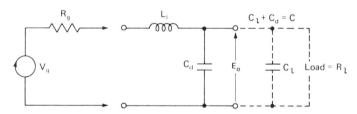

FIGURE 4–3   Simplified equivalent circuit for determining rise time of a pulse transformer.

load, and the nature of the load, i.e., whether it is a resistance load or a biased-diode load. Analysis of the circuit for the underdamped case shows that the output voltage is given by

$$E_o(t) = \frac{V_g R_l}{R_g + R_l}\left[1 - e^{-at}\left(\frac{a}{\omega}\sin \omega t + \cos \omega t\right)\right]$$

where $2a = \dfrac{R_g}{L_l} + \dfrac{1}{CR_l}$

$$b = \frac{1}{L_l C}\left(1 + \frac{R_g}{R_l}\right)$$

the damping coefficient k_1 is given by

$$k_1 = \frac{a}{\sqrt{b}}$$

and the frequency

$$\omega = \sqrt{b - a^2}$$

Figure 4–4 shows that a good compromise between fast rate of rise and minimum overshoot is obtained by a choice of the damping coeffi-

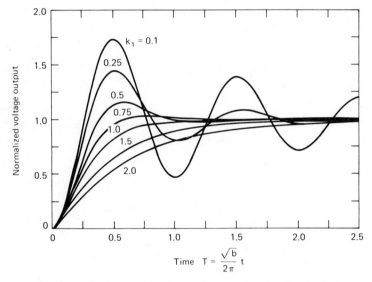

FIGURE 4–4 Output voltage of transformer given by circuit of Figure 4–3 for a range of values of damping coefficient k_1. See text for details of axis labeling.

cient k_1 between 0.5 and 0.75. When operating into a biased-diode load it is often desirable to choose

$$R_l = \sqrt{\frac{L_l}{C_d + C_l}} \tag{4-1}$$

so that current flowing in the leakage inductance just before the biased diode conducts is equal to the current through the load after it conducts. If the conditions of Equation 4–1 are met with a hard-tube modulator (where usually $R_g \ll R_l$ and $CR_g \ll L_l/R_l$), k_1 will equal 0.5; for the case of the line type modulator where $R_g = R_l$, k_1 will equal 0.71. Thus, the usual design procedure is to design for k_1 between 0.5 and 0.75. If k_1 is approximately equal to 0.5, then for a resistive load, the rise time will be given by

$$t_r = 1.78 \sqrt{L_l(C_d + C_l)}$$

If the load is a biased diode ($R_l \gg R_g$ during the rise time), the rise time for such a biased diode load is given by

$$t_r = 1.3 \sqrt{L_l(C_d + C_l)}$$

Analysis of the performance on the top of the pulse assumes that the voltage is approximately constant and the value of droop in tube current is related to the magnetizing current in the self-inductance of the transformer. For a biased-diode load, the decrease in device current during the pulse is approximately equal to the magnetizing current, i.e.,

$$I_m \approx \Delta I_d$$

where I_m = magnetizing current
ΔI_d = decrease in device current

while the droop in voltage for a linear resistance load is approximately

$$\frac{\Delta E}{E_o} = \frac{I_m}{2 I_o}$$

Analysis of performance for the tail of the pulse is somewhat more complex. For proper operation of the transmitter, it is desired that the voltage fall rapidly to zero, have no spurious oscillations, have a low value of backswing, and never assume the same polarity as the initial output voltage. Analysis of the tail-of-pulse performance is complicated by the fact that both the magnetron and the transformer magnetic core material exhibit distinctly nonlinear properties during this time. This behavior may result in a distinctly underdamped condition for the pulse transformer during recovery, possibly giving rise to oscillations on the voltage pulse that can produce RF pulses other than and in addition to the main transmitted pulse. Figure 4–5 shows a sketch of such a

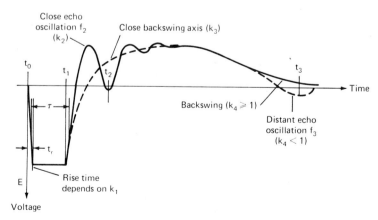

FIGURE 4–5 Line-type modulator output waveform showing oscillations and zero recrossings. [16]

voltage waveform, showing undesired oscillations both close to and distant from the main pulse.

The nonlinear behavior of the magnetron has been discussed earlier; the tube displays distinctly different properties depending upon the voltage applied to the tube. The *BH* curve for core materials used in the pulse transformer during the pulse, as shown in Figure 4–6, shows that

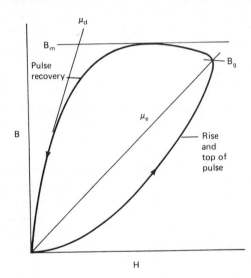

FIGURE 4–6 Pulse permeability of the output transformer core throughout the output pulse. [16]

permeability μ_e at the end of the pulse may be distinctly different from the permeability that occurs during the trailing edge of the pulse, designated μ_d.

Lee [16] has applied approximation techniques for analysis of this particular condition, and utilizes the equivalent circuit shown in Figure 4–7 for the analysis. In this equivalent circuit, C_n is the total pulse-

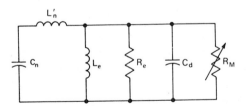

FIGURE 4–7 Equivalent circuit for line-type modulator used for analysis of tail-of-pulse response. [16]

forming network capacitance, L_n' is the sum of the leakage inductance and the PFN inductance, C_d is the stray capacitance of the transformer and load, R_m is the magnetron static resistance, and R_e is the equivalent resistance of the transformer. In addition, a factor J, the ratio of μ_e to μ_d, is also defined, along with an equivalent load resistance during the time interval close to the pulse, R_m. These parameters are then used to calculate three normalized constants, which can be used to check for the presence of close echoes (backswings across the axis close to the pulse), or distant false echoes or axis recrossings. These parameters are summarized in Table 4–1. The value of k_1 was chosen in an earlier

TABLE 4–1 KEY PARAMETERS IN TAIL-OF-PULSE ANALYSIS [16]

Part of pulse affected	Value of load resistance	Impedance ratio defined*	Condition for good pulse shape
Front edge	R_m	$k_1 = \dfrac{1}{2R_m}\sqrt{\dfrac{L_l}{C_d}}$	$k_1 = 0.5$ for minimum t_r with flat-top current pulse
Close echo	$R_i = \sqrt{R_m R_e}$	$k_2 = \dfrac{1}{2R_i}\sqrt{\dfrac{L_n'}{C_d'}}$	$k_2 \geq$ value in Fig. 4–8 for no close echo
Backswing axis close to pulse	$R_i = \sqrt{R_m R_e}$	$k_3 = \dfrac{1}{2R_i}\sqrt{\dfrac{L_e}{C_d'}}$	$k_3 > k_4$ by definition
Distant echo	R_e	$k_4 = \dfrac{1}{2R_e}\sqrt{\dfrac{L_e J}{C_d}}$	$k_4 \geq 1$ for no distant echo

* C_d is the parallel combination of C_d and C_n, all referred to the same side of the transformer.

portion of the design procedure in order to achieve acceptable front-edge performance. In order to check for the presence of close echoes, k_2 and k_3 are calculated. A value of k_3 and the ratio Δ of the magnetizing current to load current are entered into Figure 4–8, and the values of k_2 must be greater than the value obtained from Figure 4–8 for no close echo to exist. Finally, k_4 should be greater than or equal to 1 for no distant echoes to be present. Those interested in details of the derivation are referred to Lee [16] for a more complete discussion.

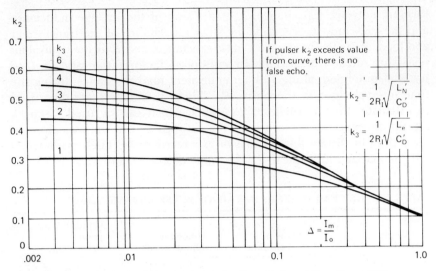

FIGURE 4–8   Graph for determining border line of close false echoes. [16]

4–2   WINDING CONFIGURATIONS

There are a number of possible transformer configurations, several of which are summarized in Figures 4–9 through 4–14, along with formulas for leakage inductance and stray capacitance for each configuration. It should be remembered that the leakage inductance and stray capacitance may be referred to either the low-voltage or the high-voltage side of the transformer. Values may be transformed to the other side of the transformer by dividing all inductances and multiplying all capacitances by the square of the transformer turns ratio. All values in Figures

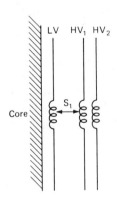

$$L_l = \frac{0.032 N_s^2 l_c}{l}\left(S_1 + \frac{\Sigma d}{3}\right)$$

$$C_d = \frac{0.225 k l_c l}{S_1}\left(\frac{1}{3} - \frac{2}{3n} + \frac{1}{3n^2}\right)$$

1. Traverse for all windings the same.
2. Layers HV₁ and HV₂ have same number of turns.

FIGURE   4–9   Single-layer-primary,   single-layer-secondary transformer winding. [6]

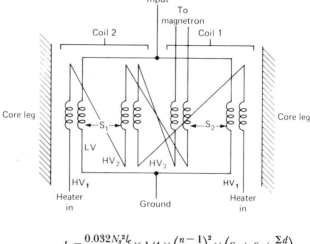

$$L_l = \frac{0.032 N_s^2 l_c}{t} \times 1/4 \times \left(\frac{n-1}{n}\right)^2 \times \left(S_1 + S_2 + \frac{\Sigma d}{3}\right)$$

$$C_d = 0.225 k l_c l \left(\frac{1/12 + 1/4 n^2}{S_2} + \frac{7/12 - 1/2 n + 1/4 n^2}{S_1}\right)$$

1. All traverse the same.
2. HV_1 and LV have same number of turns.
3. HV_2 and HV_3 have same number of turns.
4. HV_1 and LV are two wires wound side by side.

FIGURE 4–10   Lord-type transformer winding. [6]

$$L_l = \frac{0.032 N_s^2 l_c}{t} \left(\frac{n-1}{n}\right)^2 \left(S_1 + \frac{\Sigma d}{3}\right)$$

$$C_d = \frac{0.225 k l_c l}{S_1} \left(\frac{1}{3} - \frac{1}{3n} + \frac{1}{3n^2}\right)$$

1. All traverse the same.
2. HV_1, LV, HV_2 have same number of turns.
3. HV_3, HV_4 have same number of turns.

FIGURE   4–11   Interleaved-primary–single-secondary transformer. [6]

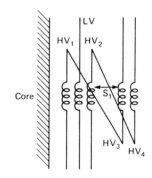

4–9 through 4–14 are referred to the high-voltage winding. The definitions of the symbols in Figures 4–9 through 4–14 are

C_d = distributed capacity of high-voltage winding (pF)
L_l = leakage inductances referred to the high–voltage winding (μH)

N_s = total number of high-voltage winding turns series-connected
l_c = average mean length of turn (in)
t = wire traverse (in)
n = ratio of high-voltage winding turns to low-voltage winding turns
S = insulation pad thickness (in)
k = relative dielectric constant of insulation
d = radial build of the copper of a winding layer, when the winding layer carries pulse current (in)

A representative cross section of a pulse transformer with single-layer primary and bifilar-wound single secondary is given in Figure 4–15, which shows the principal portions of the transformer and the appropri-

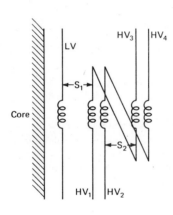

$$L_l = \frac{0.032 N_s^2 l_c}{t}\left(S_1 + \frac{S_2}{4} + \frac{\Sigma d}{3}\right)$$

$$C_d = 0.225 k l_c l\left(\frac{1/12 - 1/3n + 1/3n^2}{S_1} + \frac{1/4}{S_2}\right)$$

1. All traverse the same.
2. HV_1, HV_2, HV_3, and HV_4 have same number of turns.

FIGURE 4–12 Isolated–two-layer-secondary transformer. [6]

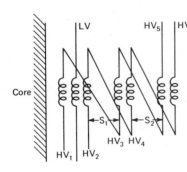

$$L_l = \frac{0.032 N_s^2 l_c}{t}\left(\frac{n-1}{n}\right)^2\left(S_1 + \frac{S_2}{4} + \frac{\Sigma d}{3}\right)$$

$$C_d = 0.225 k l_c l\left(\frac{1/12 + 1/4n^2}{S_1} + \frac{1/4 - 1/2n + 1/4n^2}{S_2}\right)$$

1. Traverse same for all windings.
2. HV_1, LV, and HV_2 have same number of turns.
3. HV_3, HV_4, HV_5, and HV_6 have same number of turns.

FIGURE 4–13 Interleaved-primary, double-layer-secondary transformer. [6]

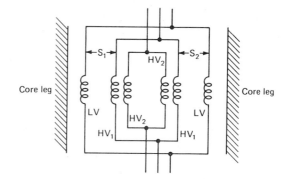

$$L_t = \frac{0.032 N_s^2 l_c}{t} \times \frac{1}{4}\left(S_1 + S_2 + \frac{\Sigma d}{3}\right)$$

$$C_d = 0.225 k l_c t\left(\frac{1/3 - 2/3n + 1/3n^2}{S_2} + \frac{1/3 - 2/3n + 1/3n^2}{S_2}\right)$$

1. All traverse the same.
2. $S_1 = S_2$.
3. HV_1 and HV_2 have same number of turns.

FIGURE 4–14   Paralleled primary and secondary transformer winding. [6]

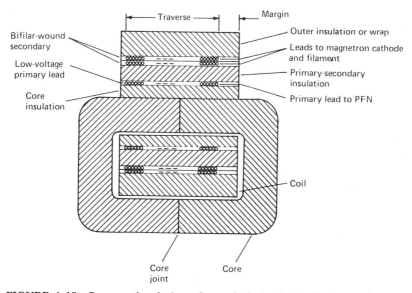

FIGURE 4–15   Cross-sectional view of a typical simple (single-layer primary, single-layer, bifilar-wound secondary) high-voltage pulse transformer, showing major features and nomenclature.

ate terminology. A large portion of the art of pulse-transformer design involves the choice of winding configuration, and dimensional ratios that result in desired values of L_l and C_d [5–7,9–11,14,15,17–20,24,25]. The detailed design of a high-power pulse transformer, however, involves a number of different parameters, including heat transfer, and physical winding configuration, all of which are treated in the following sections.

4–3 PROPERTIES OF MAGNETIC CORE MATERIALS

Almost all high-power pulse transformers are wound on cores of magnetic material. The most common configuration is the so-called C core, which is shown schematically in Figure 4–16. This core is made of grain-oriented silicon steel strips (Silectron), a thickness of 2 mils being a common value for use in high-power pulse transformers. Such material is available commercially under a number of different names, including Silectron, Hypersil, Magnesil, Microsil, and Supersil. A summary table of dimensions of a number of typical pulse-transformer C cores is included in Table 4–2.

The pulse permeability of the transformer core is a function of pulse length and flux change in the core. A summary of pulse permeability from Fenoglio et al. [6] is given in Figure 4–17, a manufacturer's typical data are given in Figure 4–18 [2], and the core loss per pulse is summarized in Figure 4–19.

There are cases when optimum permeability may be obtained only by shimming the air gap in the core or by applying a resetting magnetomotive force (mmf). This condition usually occurs only for those conditions for which the core is large or the required flux changes are large. The introduction of an air gap reduces the residual induction of the core, resulting in a larger ΔB for a given value of pulse magnetizing force H_m. If a resetting force is available, it may not be necessary to gap the core. By applying resetting mmf, it is possible to bias the core to achieve a large value of ΔB.

In order to obtain data such as are shown in Figures 4–17 and 4–18, the number of volts per turn is calculated for a given value of ΔB by the equation

$$V/N = \frac{6.45 AS\,\Delta B}{t \times 10^8}$$

where V = peak voltage at end of pulse (V)

N = number of turns

A = gross core area in^2 ($D \times E$)

S = stacking factor (0.89 for 2-mil Silectron)

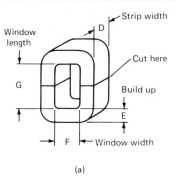

(a)

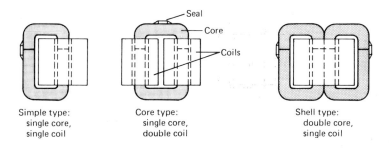

Simple type:	Core type:	Shell type:
single core,	single core,	double core,
single coil	double coil	single coil

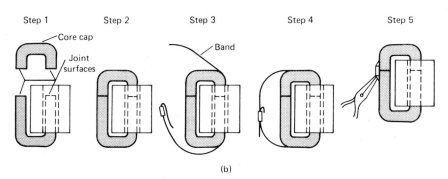

(b)

FIGURE 4–16 Cut C-core (*a*) nomenclature and (*b*) banding data. [2]

t = pulse length (s)

ΔB = induction change in gauss (G)

The pulse permeability is then calculated as

$$\mu_e = \frac{\Delta B \times l \times 2.54}{0.4\pi N I_m}$$

TABLE 4–2 REPRESENTATIVE SET OF 2-MIL C CORES [2]

Part no.	Strip width D	Build E	Window width F	Window length G	Core area $D \times E$	Core length $2F+2G+2.9E$
			Dimensions (in or in^2)			
L-6	$\frac{1}{2}$	$\frac{1}{4}$	$\frac{1}{4}$	$\frac{7}{8}$	0.125	2.98
L-8	$\frac{3}{8}$	$\frac{3}{8}$	$\frac{3}{8}$	$1\frac{3}{16}$	0.141	4.21
L-9	$\frac{1}{2}$	$\frac{3}{8}$	$\frac{3}{8}$	$1\frac{3}{16}$	0.188	4.21
L-13	$\frac{5}{8}$	$\frac{1}{4}$	$\frac{1}{2}$	$1\frac{1}{8}$	0.156	3.98
L-10	$\frac{5}{8}$	$\frac{3}{8}$	$\frac{3}{8}$	$1\frac{3}{16}$	0.234	4.22
L-12	$\frac{1}{2}$	$\frac{7}{16}$	$\frac{1}{2}$	$1\frac{1}{8}$	0.219	4.40
L-11	$\frac{3}{4}$	$\frac{3}{8}$	$\frac{3}{8}$	$1\frac{3}{16}$	0.281	5.62
L-78	$\frac{3}{4}$	$\frac{5}{16}$	$\frac{5}{16}$	$2\frac{1}{4}$	0.234	6.03
L-14	$\frac{1}{2}$	$\frac{1}{2}$	$\frac{1}{2}$	$1\frac{9}{16}$	0.250	5.58
L-18	$\frac{1}{2}$	$\frac{7}{16}$	$\frac{5}{8}$	$1\frac{9}{16}$	0.219	15.64
L-15	$\frac{5}{8}$	$\frac{1}{2}$	$\frac{1}{2}$	$1\frac{9}{16}$	0.313	5.58
L-16	$\frac{3}{4}$	$\frac{1}{2}$	$\frac{1}{2}$	$1\frac{9}{16}$	0.375	5.58
L-17	1	$\frac{1}{2}$	$\frac{1}{2}$	$1\frac{9}{16}$	0.500	5.58
L-19	1	$\frac{1}{2}$	$\frac{5}{8}$	$1\frac{9}{16}$	0.500	5.83
L-20	1	$\frac{5}{8}$	$\frac{5}{8}$	$1\frac{9}{16}$	0.625	6.19
L-24	1	$\frac{5}{8}$	$\frac{3}{4}$	$2\frac{5}{16}$	0.625	7.94
L-25	1	$\frac{7}{8}$	$\frac{15}{16}$	$2\frac{1}{2}$	0.875	9.41
L-248	$1\frac{1}{8}$	$\frac{3}{4}$	$1\frac{1}{8}$	$2\frac{7}{8}$	0.844	10.18
L-98	1	$\frac{5}{8}$	2	3	0.625	11.81
L-54	2	$\frac{3}{4}$	$\frac{3}{4}$	4	1.5	11.68
AL-1079	4	4	$8\frac{1}{2}$	16	16	60.60

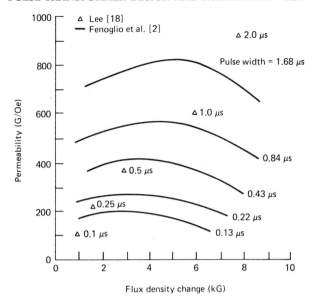

FIGURE 4–17 Pulse permeability vs. flux-density change for 2-mil Silectron.

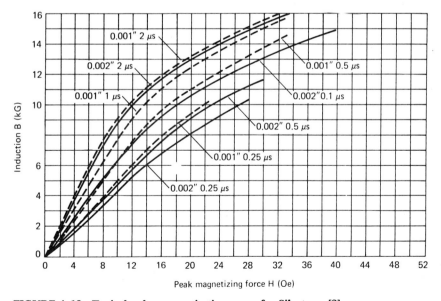

FIGURE 4–18 Typical pulse magnetization curve for Silectron. [2]

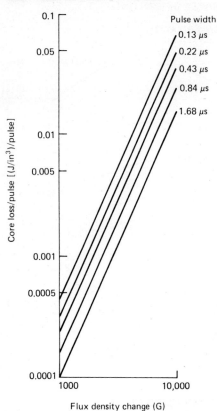

FIGURE 4–19 Pulsed core losses for 2-mil Silectron [6]. To obtain core loss in watts, multiply the number of joules per cubic inch per pulse by core volume (in³) by the number of pulses per second.

where μ_e = effective pulse permeability in gauss per oersted (G/Oe)
I_m = peak exciting current (A)
l = core length (in) $(2F + 2G + 2.9E)$

4–4 INSULATION

While dry types of solid insulation may be used below the 10- to 15-kV range, above that level vacuum-impregnated liquid-solid-composite insulation is used almost exclusively. The most common liquids are the transformer oils and the silicone fluids, and commonly used solids are kraft paper, Mylar, and Teflon. Properties of commonly used insulation are summarized in Table 4–3. In some cases, the insulation thickness and margins should be selected on the basis of physical strength rather than dielectric strength; Table 4–4 tabulates such thicknesses.

TABLE 4–3   PROPERTIES OF COMMONLY USED INSULATION MATERIALS

Material	Dielectric constant	Maximum working stress	
		Puncture	Creep (along surface)
Kraft paper in oil	4.5	50 V rms/mil low-frequency AC; 250–300 V/mil pulsed for less than 50 kV applied; 200–225 V/mil over 50 kV pulsed	20–30 V/mil pulsed less than 50 kV and low-frequency AC 10 V/mil over 50 kV pulsed
Mylar in oil	3.4	400 V/mil pulsed	30 V/mil pulsed
Teflon in oil	2.3	300–500 V/mil pulsed	30 V/mil pulsed

In no event should the insulation consist of less than two layers of insulating material. The core tube is normally selected for strength and layered with insulating material. Because of irregularities and sharp edges, core tubes are often stressed at one-half to one-third the normal insulation stress.

TABLE 4–4   MINIMUM LAYER INSULATIONS AND MARGINS FOR PHYSICAL STRENGTH

Wire size	Layer insulation (in)	Margins (in)
11–14	0.010	7/32
15–18	0.007	13/64
19–22	0.005	3/16
23–26	0.004	11/64
27–30	0.003	5/32
31–34	0.002	9/64

4–5   HEAT TRANSFER, COOLING, AND THERMAL DESIGN

There are several methods of calculating the hot-spot temperature in transformers [6,11]. Some rather exact methods are available, but these are somewhat involved. If one desires only an approximate answer,

some simplifying assumptions may often be made. In the following procedure, simplifying assumptions have been made, and the hot-spot temperatures calculated will be conservative. If more exact values are
desired, the methods given in the references are appropriate.

Calculation of Temperature Rise

The first step in calculating the temperature rise in a transformer
is to make a careful sketch of the problem and label all pertinent temperature rises, as shown in Figure 4–20. We now assume that the losses at
various places in the transformer have been calculated.

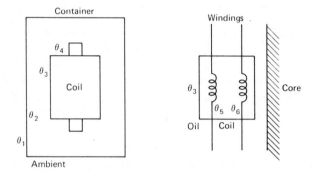

**FIGURE 4–20 Simplified schematic representation of
temperature drops in an enclosed transformer.**

1. The drop from case to ambient θ_1 is calculated as follows. Calculate the outside-envelope area of the can. This is determined
by multiplying the string distance around the can by the can
height and adding the product to the cover area. The base
area is not included unless it is known to be in direct contact
with a suitable cold surface. The total heat produced inside
the can is divided by the envelope area to find a heat-flux density. An equivalent temperature rise is then determined by a
combined radiation and convection curve such as the one in
Figure 4–21.

2. θ_2, the drop from case to oil, is calculated as follows. Calculate
the inside tank area that is contacted by the oil. Determine

the heat-flux density H_c for this area by dividing the total number of watts by this area. From a suitable curve such as Figure 4–22, determine θ_2.

3. θ_3, the drop from coil to oil, is calculated by using the same methods as were used to find θ_2. The area used is only the *vertical* surface of the coil.

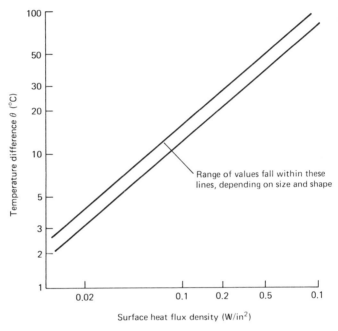

FIGURE 4–21   Total heat transfer by both convection and radiation at atmospheric pressure.

4. θ_4, the drop from core to oil, is computed by assuming the heat leaves the edges of the core laminations and by using the methods used to find θ_2 and θ_3.

5. θ_5 and θ_6 are conduction rises and are calculated by the equation

$$\theta = W \, r_t \lambda$$

where θ = temperature difference (°C)
W = rate of heat flow (W/in²)
r_t = thermal resistivity of insulation, (°C/in)/(W/in²)
λ = length of heat-flow path (in)

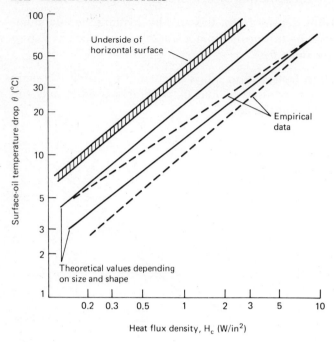

FIGURE 4–22 **Natural convection heat transfer in transformer oil.**

It is usually assumed that all heat flows outward in the coil. Typical values for r_t are:

Material	r_t, $(°C/in)/(W/in^2)$
Kraft paper, oil-impregnated	250
Water	70
Air	1710
Transformer oil (noncirculating)	245
Mica	110
Teflon	170
Nomex (nylon paper)	160–230

The sum of all rises from any point in the coil to the ambient must not exceed the allowable temperature rise for the insulation system being used. For kraft paper the maximum temperature is normally taken to be 105°C for 10,000 h life or 130°C for 2000 h life; oil temperature should be limited to 100°C maximum.

In determining temperature rise, consideration should be given to the expansion of oil with temperature. The coefficient of expansion for oil is 0.073% °C^{-1}; for a 100°C rise, there will be over a 7% increase in oil volume. For small units with moderate temperature rises, the expansion may be accommodated by deformation of the can. Otherwise, the can surfaces may be especially "dimpled" to permit expansion, gas-expansion space may be provided, or an expansion bellows may be incorporated. Sometimes, glass balls or nylon chips (resin) may be added to reduce oil volume; care should be taken that this filler material does not adversely affect the heat-transfer or voltage-breakdown properties of the unit.

Sources of Heat

There are several sources of heat in a pulse transformer, principally:

- Core losses

- Energy stored in stray capacitances

- Losses in conductors

Core losses are calculated by reference to Figure 4–19, and by multiplying the value obtained by the core volume and the PRF to obtain the power dissipated in the core. It is normally assumed that the heat is transferred to the oil only by the exposed core surface.

Energy stored in stray capacitances may contribute significantly to transformer loss. Energy stored is given by the quantity

$$\frac{1}{2} CV^2$$

which when multiplied by the PRF gives the total power. If the load is resistive, much of this energy is dissipated in the load; however, if it is a biased-diode load, this is not the case. In a line-type modulator, the clip-diode circuit may absorb much of the energy in the stray capacitances. Each individual case must be considered separately, and between 10% and 90% of this stored energy may be dissipated in the transformer.

Conductor losses are of two types: those due to pulse currents, and those due to filament current. Filament current calculations may use dc resistance values for power-dissipation calculations. For pulse currents, the situation is somewhat more complex.

The basic equations for determining the effective pulse resistance of conductors are rather complex and are not particularly complete [6,7,11,15]. In many cases, significant simplifying assumptions can be made. For sinusoidal excitation,

$$R_{\text{eff}} = 2.47 \times 10^{-7} \sqrt{f} \times \frac{\text{length of wire}}{\text{bare-wire diameter}}$$

where f is the frequency in Hz. For pulses,

$$R_{\text{eff}} = 1.58 \times 10^{-7} \frac{1}{\sqrt{\tau}} \times \frac{\text{length of wire}}{\text{bare-wire diameter}} \qquad (4\text{--}2)$$

where τ is the pulse length in seconds [10]. These expressions assume that skin effects are important. To check this assumption, assume that skin effects are important and calculate the resistance. Then the dc resistance should be looked up and the larger of the two resistances should be used.

There is a proximity effect that must also be considered [11,10]. If current flows only on one-half of the wire, these values of the resistance must be multiplied by 2. This is the case for the Lord-type transformer-winding configuration. It should be noted that for many pulse transformers, the conductor losses are normally dominated by filament current losses.

4–6 BUSHINGS AND FABRICATION TECHNIQUES

Fabrication Constants

The winding traverse is obtained by using the actual wire width, obtained from wire tables such as Table 4–5, and multiplying by approximately 1.15. Similarly, the radial build is obtained by multiplying the insulation and wire build by 1.25. Specific values for these constants may vary with individual winding technique.

Bushings

Normally, the transformer is hermetically sealed in a container and the leads are brought out through bushings. Some representative high-voltage solder bushings are described in Tables 4–6 and 4–7. In general, the flashover voltage for a bushing is given approximately by $17.5t^{0.63}$kV, where t is the length of the surface creep path in inches; in general, the bushing should be worked at one-third to one-fourth of this stress [21]. If high-altitude operation, or operation under conditions of excessive dust or humidity, is contemplated, voltage ratings

Size (AWG)	Area (cmil)	Bare-wire	1 layer enamel	2 layers enamel or heavy polymer	Turn/in (1 layer enamel)	Ω/1000 ft at 20°C 100% cond.	Lb per 1000 ft, bare
			Diameter				
10	10,380	0.1019	0.1039	0.1056	9	0.999	31.4
11	8,234	0.0907	0.0927	0.0943	10	1.260	24.9
12	6,530	0.0808	0.0827	0.0842	11	1.588	19.88
13	5,178	0.0720	0.0738	0.0753	12	2.003	15.68
14	4,107	0.0641	0.0659	0.0673	13.5	2.525	12.43
15	3,257	0.0571	0.0588	0.0602	15	3.184	9.86
16	2,583	0.0508	0.0525	0.0539	17	4.016	7.82
17	2,048	0.0453	0.0469	0.0482	19	5.064	6.20
18	1,624	0.0403	0.0418	0.0432	21	6.385	4.92
19	1,288	0.0359	0.0374	0.0387	24	8.051	3.90
20	1,022	0.0320	0.0334	0.0346	27	10.15	3.09
21	810	0.0285	0.0300	0.0310	30	12.80	2.45
22	624.4	0.0263	0.0267	0.0278	34	16.14	1.94
23	509.5	0.0226	0.0238	0.0249	39	20.36	1.54
24	404.0	0.0201	0.0213	0.0224	43	25.67	1.22
25	320.4	0.0179	0.0191	0.0201	48	32.37	0.970
26	254.1	0.0159	0.0170	0.0180	54	40.81	0.769
27	201.5	0.0142	0.0153	0.0161	60	51.47	0.610
28	159.8	0.0126	0.0136	0.0145	67	64.90	0.484
29	126.7	0.0113	0.0122	0.0130	75	81.83	0.384
30	100.5	0.0100	0.0109	0.0116	84	103.2	0.304
31	79.70	0.0089	0.0100	0.0105	94	130.1	0.241
32	63.21	0.0080	0.0088	0.0095	104	164.1	0.1913
33	50.13	0.0071	0.0078	0.0085	117	206.9	0.1517
34	39.75	0.0063	0.0070	0.0075	131	260.9	0.1203

TABLE 4-6 SOME LOWER-VOLTAGE INSULATED BUSHINGS [3]

Dimensions (in)		Average flashover (kV rms)	Average corona start (kV rms)	Approx. net weight (oz)
A	B			
0.460	0.094	6.6	6.5	⅛
0.580	0.094	8.1	6.6	⅛
0.460	0.219	6.6	6.5	⅛
0.814	0.188	11.4	6.7	¼

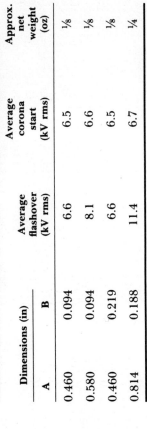

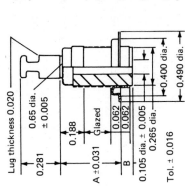

Lug thickness 0.020

0.65 dia. ± 0.005

0.281

0.188

A ± 0.031 Glazed

B

0.062
0.062

0.105 dia. ± 0.005
0.265 dia.

0.400 dia.
0.490 dia.

Tol. ± 0.016

Dimensions (in)		Average flashover (kV rms)	Average corona start (kV rms)	Approx. net weight (oz)
A	B			
0.458	0.031	6.6	4.0	¼
0.562	0.031	8.4	4.9	¼
0.625	0.094	9.5	5.4	¼
0.656	0.031	10.1	5.6	¼
0.741	0.406	11.4	6.1	¼
0.758	0.031	11.7	6.2	½
0.806	0.141	12.5	6.4	½
0.859	0.031	13.3	6.7	½
0.875	0.250	13.4	6.8	½
0.953	0.031	14.8	7.2	½
0.984	0.188	15.2	7.3	½
1.150	0.203	17.5	8.0	½
1.156	0.031	17.5	8.0	½
1.188	1.125	17.9	8.1	½
1.250	0.031	18.8	8.3	½
1.356	0.031	20.0	8.6	½
1.656	0.125	23.6	9.5	¾
1.688	0.312	23.9	9.6	¾
1.957	0.250	26.5	10.3	¾
2.357	0.250	29.0	11.4	1
2.656	0.344	30.8	11.9	1⅛

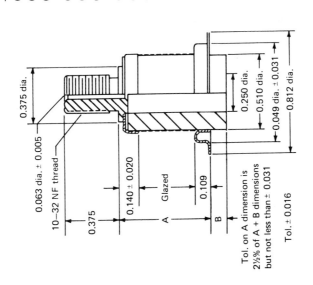

0.375 dia.

0.063 dia. ± 0.005

10—32 NF thread

0.375

0.140 ± 0.020

Glazed

A

0.109

B

Tol. on A dimension is
2½% of A + B dimensions
but not less than ± 0.031

Tol. ± 0.016

0.250 dia.

0.510 dia.

0.049 dia. ± 0.031

0.812 dia.

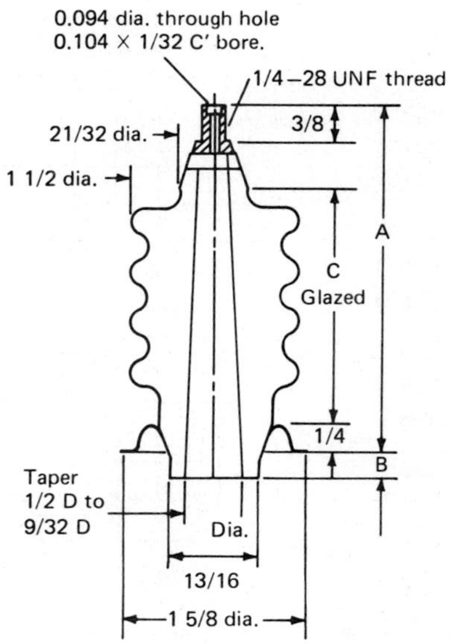

0.094 dia. through hole
0.104 × 1/32 C' bore.

1/4 –28 UNF thread

3/8

21/32 dia.

1 1/2 dia.

A

C
Glazed

B

1/4

Dia.

13/16

1 5/8 dia.

Taper
1/2 D to
9/32 D

TABLE 4-7 SOME LARGE HIGH-VOLTAGE CERAMIC BUSHINGS [1,3]

No. of flutes	A	B	C	Average flash-over (kV)	Approx. net weight (oz)
2	$2\frac{9}{32}$	$\frac{1}{4}$	$1\frac{1}{4}$	25	4
3	$2\frac{25}{32}$	$\frac{1}{4}$	$1\frac{3}{4}$	30	5
4	$3\frac{9}{32}$	$\frac{1}{4}$	$2\frac{1}{4}$	35	6
5	$3\frac{25}{32}$	$\frac{1}{4}$	$2\frac{3}{4}$	40	$7\frac{1}{2}$
5	$3\frac{25}{32}$	1	$2\frac{3}{4}$	40	8

Type	Dimensions (in) B	Average flashover (kV rms)	Average corona start (kV rms)	Approx. net weight (oz)
As shown on drawing	0.500	36.9	16.8	9
With 0.091-in dia. by 5-in long OFHC copper conductors	0.500	36.9	16.8	9½
As shown on drawing	1.250	36.9	16.8	10
With 0.091-in dia. by 5.7-in long OFHC copper conductors	1.250	36.9	16.8	10½

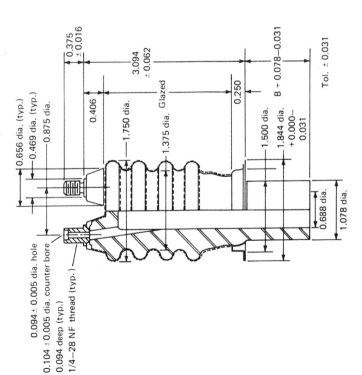

0.656 dia. (typ.)
0.469 dia. (typ.)
0.875 dia.
0.094 ± 0.005 dia. hole
0.104 ± 0.005 dia. counter bore
0.094 deep (typ.)
1/4–28 NF thread (typ.)
0.375 ± 0.016
3.094 ± 0.062
0.406
1.750 dia.
1.375 dia. Glazed
0.250
B ÷ 0.078–0.031
1.500 dia.
1.844 dia. + 0.000 — 0.031
0.688 dia.
1.078 dia.
Tol. ± 0.031

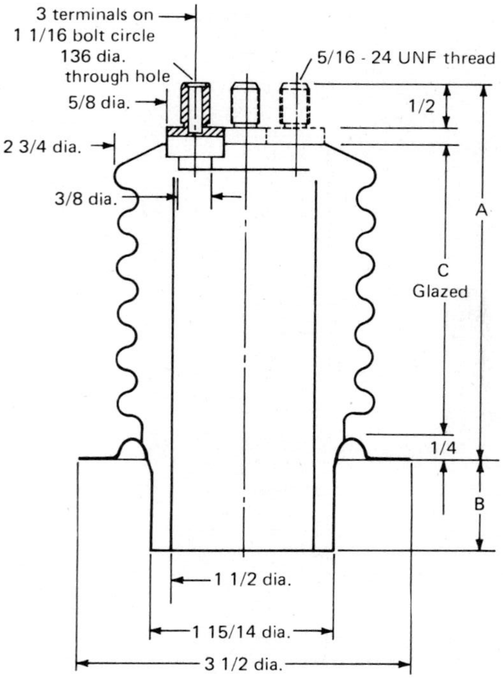

TABLE 4–7 *Continued*

No. of flutes	A	B	C	Average flash-over (kV)	Approx. net weight
2	2³⁄₁₆	½	1¼	26	10 oz
3	2¹¹⁄₁₆	½	1¾	31	13 oz
4	3³⁄₁₆	½	2¼	36	1 lb
5	3¹¹⁄₁₆	½	2¾	41	1¼ lb
6	4³⁄₁₆	1	3¼	45	1½ lb
8	5³⁄₁₆	1¼	4¼	50	2 lb

5/16 - 24 UNF thread

1/2

A

C
Glazed

1/4

B

3 terminals on
1 1/16 bolt circle
136 dia.
through hole
5/8 dia.

2 3/4 dia.

3/8 dia.

1 1/2 dia.

1 15/14 dia.

3 1/2 dia.

should be reduced accordingly. For some applications, cathode bushings of the microwave tube may be inserted into a special ceramic well, eliminating any exposed output bushings. In such cases, care must be used to ensure that the cathode stem is adequately cooled.

Vacuum Impregnation

In order to achieve satisfactory operation at high voltages, the transformer must be thoroughly dried, completely impregnated, and hermetically sealed in a leakproof container. Considerable care is necessary in order to avoid air pockets, or voids, in the insulation system; the presence of voids results in high electric fields and possible breakdown and deterioration of the insulation system. Therefore, voids are to be avoided if at all possible. A typical impregnation sequence is described in the following paragraphs.

Take the component to be impregnated and place it in an oven at 90°C for 4 h minimum. The component should be completely sealed except for one small fill hole.

The oil should be heated under a vacuum for 3 h at 70°C to prepare it. The hot component should then be pumped to less than 1 mmHg for 2 h at 90°C and the oil then allowed to fill the container while maintaining a vacuum of less than 40 mmHg vacuum; the component should remain under a vacuum for 0.5 h. Then it should sit at atmospheric pressure for 0.5 h. Then the component should undergo four cycles of 15 min at 40 mmHg and 15 min under normal atmospheric pressure (or even positive pressure). During all of these procedures the oil should be maintained at approximately 70°C.

While the component is still under oil and the temperature at 70°C, the fill hole should be solder-sealed. The component should then be removed from the oil and thoroughly cleaned (trichlorethylene is useful here). Place the component in a refrigerator to reduce the temperature to 4°C (or some other appropriate temperature) and then place it in an oven at 90°C until thoroughly heated. The component should then be checked to see if any leaks are apparent (powdered talc makes leaks more evident); if no leaks are visible, the unit may be painted.

These procedures are not to be considered inviolate, and variations from these procedures may be made with no dire consequences. This procedure has been used successfully and is based on empirical data from the power-transformer industry.

4–7 Pulse-Transformer Design Procedures

The design of pulse transformers for use in line-type or hard-tube modulators is rather complex, and no single design procedure is applicable for all cases. Rather exhaustive studies of the problems involved are available [5–7,10,12,14–20,24,25], and the serious designer should become thoroughly familiar with these works. For many ordinary transformers (pulse length of 0.2 to 2 μs, maximum output voltage less than 25 kV, turns ratio $\approx$ 5, PRF $\leq$ 5 kHz), a rather simple design procedure will sometimes be adequate.

The design of a transformer involves the selection of suitable core, number of turns, winding configuration, wire size, and insulation thickness. There are many sophisticated design procedures available, but they are all merely ways to make a good first choice of core size and number of turns. In our design procedure, we will assume the transformer will be used in a line-type modulator, utilize a trial-and-error method of core selection, and then calculate the number of turns required to achieve a suitable value of exciting current at the end of the pulse (10% is a reasonable value). A winding configuration is assumed, and a coil is designed by using suitable values for creep and puncture stress for the insulation used and a suitable wire size for the currents involved. The dimensions of the coil are then adjusted to try to achieve "optimum" values of leakage inductance and distributed capacity. The coil is then checked to see that the tail-of-pulse behavior is satisfactory and that the hot-spot temperature is not excessive. If all of these criteria are met, the transformer design is then considered complete. The actual test of any transformer design is how well it operates in the circuit for which it is intended, and the actual operation of the transformer must be considered an integral part of any design procedure.

First, select a core from a list of available 2-mil silicon steel cores (Hypersil, Selectron) [2]. Then assume an initial value of flux density change (using Figure 4–23) and the corresponding permeability (Figures 4–18 and 4–19). The number of turns, the flux density, and the exciting current are related by the equation

$$\frac{V}{N} = \frac{6.45AS\,\Delta B}{t \times 10^8} \tag{4-3}$$

where V = peak voltage of end of pulse (V)
N = number of turns
A = gross core area (in^2)
S = stacking factor (0.89 for 2-mil Silectron)
t = pulse length (s)
ΔB = induction change (G)

and

$$I_m = \frac{2.02\,\Delta B\,l}{N\mu_e} \tag{4-4}$$

where μ_e = effective pulse permeability
I_m = peak exciting current (A)
l = core length (in)

The exciting current should never exceed 10% of the peak pulse current at the end of the pulse.

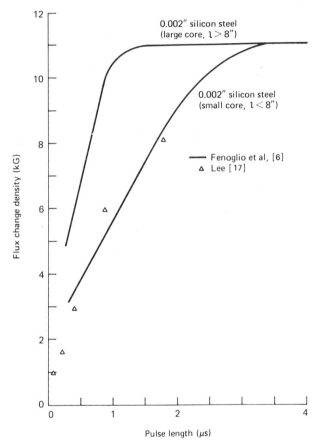

FIGURE 4–23 Suggested initial flux change as a function of pulse length.

The winding configuration most useful for our purposes might be one shown in Figure 4–9 or 4–10. The initial choice of wire size is usually made on the basis of the amount of window available for winding by using a 90% space factor. Experience has shown that if the resulting current density in the wire exceeds 1 A/1500 cmil, the hot-spot temperature may be excessive. The radial build of the finished coil may be obtained by multiplying the sum of the insulation and wire thickness in the radial direction by about 1.25. Paralleling smaller wire sizes should not be overlooked as a favorable alternative to extremely large wire sizes, and the wire sizes should be adjusted until all windings have the same length. The initial choice of insulation thickness should be made on the basis of the allowable stress in the dielectric. Suitable interlayer-insulation stresses under pulsed service are as follows [10]:

Insulation	Puncture stress (V/mil)	Creep stress (V/mil)	Dielectric constant
Kraft paper in oil	200–300	20–30	4.5
Mylar in oil	400	30	3.4
Teflon in oil	300–500	30	2.3

A reasonable stress for core tube insulation is 25 V/mil.

The leakage inductance and distributed capacity of the coil should now be calculated. For the Lord-type winding (Figure 4–10),

$$L_l = \frac{0.032 N_s^2 l_c}{4t} \left(\frac{n-1}{n}\right)^2 \times \left(S_1 + S_2 + \frac{\Sigma d}{3}\right)$$

$$C_d = 0.225 k l_c t \left(\frac{1/12 + 1/4 n^2}{S_2} + \frac{7/12 - 1/2 n + 1/4 n^2}{S_1}\right)$$

where C_d = distributed capacity of high-voltage winding (pF)
  L_l = total leakage inductance referred to the high-voltage winding (μH)
  N_s = total number of high-voltage winding turns in series connection
  l_c = average mean length of turn (in)
  t = wire traverse (in)
  n = ratio of high-voltage winding turns to low-voltage winding turns
  S_1, S_2 = insulation pad thickness (in) (see Figure 4–10)
  d = radial build of the copper of a winding layer, when the winding layer carries pulse current (in)
  k = dielectric constant of coil insulation

The exact values of leakage inductance and distributed capacity desired are not obvious, but if one specifies for a magnetron load that

$$t_r = 1.3 \times 10^{-3} \sqrt{L_l (C_d + C_l)}$$

where t_r = rise time of transformer when source has zero rise time (μs)
C_d = distributed capacity of the transformer (pF)
L_l = leakage inductance of the transformer (μH)
C_l = capacity of the load, including bushing and wiring capacity (pF)

and that

$$R_p = 10^3 \sqrt{\frac{L_l}{C_d + C_l}}$$

where R_p = static resistance of the magnetron (kΩ)

the simultaneous solution of these equations gives

$$L_l = \frac{t_r}{1.3} \times R_p \tag{4-5}$$

$$C_d = \frac{t_r \times 10^6}{1.3 \times R_p} - C_l \tag{4-6}$$

The dimensions of the coil should be adjusted within the limitations of wire size, core size, and properties of the dielectric in an attempt to achieve these values.

The tail-of-pulse response may be checked by the method of Lee [16], which was outlined earlier. The only nonobvious parameters are μ_e, μ_d, and R_e. R_e is usually calculated from the values of core loss (Figure 4-20), and μ_e and μ_d may be obtained from Figures 4-18 and 4-19.

The temperature rise of the coil should now be checked to ensure that it is not excessive, by using procedures described earlier in this section. In making these calculations, one should remember that the pulse current flows on the inner half of the wires and the secondary wire connected to the magnetron cathode carries essentially all of the magnetron current pulse [6]. The values of core loss under pulsed conditions may be found from Figure 4-19, or may be calculated as $(2/3)E_oI_m$ $\times$ duty cycle, in watts.

A final part of the design procedure must include actual operation in the circuit to verify compliance with the design objectives. If any of the objectives are not met, the transformer must be redesigned with either a different core, a different number of turns, a different winding configuration, or all three.

REFERENCES

1. Alberox Corporation, Catalog 775, "High Voltage Bushings," New Bedford, Mass.

2. Arnold Engineering Company, *Arnold Silectron Cores*, Bulletin SC-107B, Marengo, Ill.

3. Ceramaseal, Inc., Catalog 661A, "High Temperature Terminals and Assemblies," New Lebanon Center, N.Y.

4. Crout, P. D., "A Method of Virtual Displacements for Electrical Systems with Applications to Pulse Transformers," *Proc. IRE*, vol. 35, no. 11, November 1947, pp. 1236–1247.

5. deBuda, R. G., and J. Vilcaus, "Limitations of the Output Pulse Shape of High Power Pulse Transformers," in *IRE Nat. Conv. Rec.*, pt. VIII, 1958, 87–93.

6. Fenoglio, P., et al., "High Power-High Voltage Pulse Transformer Design Criteria and Data," Final Report, pt. I of 2 parts, AD No. 28714, Pittsfield, Mass., Feb. 1, 1953.

7. Fenoglio, P., et al., "High Power-High Voltage Pulse Transformer Design Criteria and Data," Final Report, pt. 2 of 2 pts., General Electric, AD No. 21236, Pittsfield, Mass., Feb. 1, 1953.

8. Gillette, P. R., K. Oshima, and R. M. Rowe, "Measurement of Parameters Controlling Pulse Front Response of Transformers," *IRE Trans. Component Parts*, vol. CP-3, no. 1, March 1956, pp. 20–25.

9. Gillette, P. R., et al., "Design Procedures for Pulse Transformers," Final Report, Pt. I, Stanford Research Institute, AD No. 79221, Stanford, Calif., July 1955.

10. Gillette, P. R., et al., "Design Procedures for Pulse Transformers," Final Report, Pt. II, Stanford Research Institute, AD No. 79222, Stanford, Calif., July 1955, pp. 17–19.

11. Glasoe, G. N., and J. V. Lebacqz, *Pulse Generators*, MIT Rad. Lab. series, vol. 5, McGraw-Hill, New York, 1948, pp. 499–562. (Also available in Dover and Boston Technical Publishers editions.)

12. Grossner, N. R., *Transformers for Electronic Circuits*, McGraw-Hill, New York, 1967.

13. Howe et al., "Final Report for High Power, High Voltage, Audio Frequency Transformer Design Manual," General Electric, AD No. 60774, Holyoke, Mass., Aug. 31, 1964, pp. 323–327.

14. Lee, R., "Designing Pulse Transformers for Small Size," in *Proc. 1977 Intermag Conf.*, pp. 7–5.

15. Lee, R., *Electronic Transformers and Circuits*, 2d ed., Wiley, New York, 1955.

16. Lee, R., "False Echoes in Line-Type Radar Pulsers," *Proc. IRE*, vol. 42, no. 8, August 1954, pp. 1288–1295.

17. Lee, R., "Pulse Transformer Design Chart," *Electronic Equipment*, September 1957, pp. 34–38.

18. Lee, R., "Reducing Size of Radar Pulse Transformers," *IRE Trans. Component Parts*, vol. CP-9, no. 1, June 1962, pp. 58–61.

19. Lee, R., and L. Gilman, "Use of Computers in Minimizing Pulse Transformer Weight," *AIEE Trans.*, pt. 1, vol. 81, September 1962, pp. 303–307.

20. Lord, H. W., "Pulse Transformers," *IEEE Trans. Magnetics*, vol. 7, no. 1, March 1971, pp. 17–28.

21. Ludwig, J. T., "Research and Development on Design Method for Reactors," University

of Minnesota, Final Report on Contract No. DA 36–039sc-42573, Minneapolis, 1954, p. 269.

22. Nordenberg, H. M., *Electronic Transformers*, Reinhold, New York, 1964.

23. O'Meara, T. R., "Analysis and Synthesis with the 'Complete' Equivalent Circuit for the Wide-Band Transformer," *AIEE Trans.*, vol. 81, March 1962, pp. 55–62.

24. Smith, J. H., "Simplified Pulse Transformer Design," *Electronic Engineering*, vol. 29, no. 357, November 1957, pp. 551–555.

25. Wilds, C. F. "Determination of Core Size in Pulse Transformer Design," *Electronic Engineering*, vol. 33, no. 403, September 1961, pp. 566–572.

5
PULSE-FORMING NETWORKS

As was pointed out in Chapter 3, the line-type modulator uses an energy-storage element that is similar to an open-circuited transmission line. There are some applications where actual lengths of transmission line are utilized for this element, but this normally is done only for short pulse lengths because of the size and inconvenience of the line length required for longer pulses. In addition, the use of an actual transmission line has other disadvantages, namely its lack of flexibility and inability to adjust for nonideal circuit elements.

In order to circumvent these disadvantages, lumped constant networks are normally utilized rather than actual transmission lines. When line-type modulators were first developed, attempts were made to simulate the transmission line by using the equivalent derived by Rayleigh; however, no matter how many sections were used, overshoots and ringing still existed at the front and leading edges of the output pulse. The reason for these oscillations is Gibbs' phenomenon, associated with the nonuniform convergence of a Fourier series near the discontinuity of a rectangular output pulse. Guillemin realized this difficulty and derived a set of networks that approximate a trapezoidal pulse with nonzero rise and fall time [8]. A number of these networks are summarized in Figure 5–1. One particularly convenient form of the pulse-forming network is the so-called Guillemin E-type network, which has equal-value capacitors and a continuously wound tapped coil whose physical dimensions are chosen so as to provide the proper mutual coupling between tapped sections. The total capacitance and inductance are given by the equations

$$C_n = \frac{\tau}{2Z_0} \qquad\qquad (5\text{--}1)$$

$$L_n = \frac{\tau Z_0}{2} \qquad\qquad (5\text{--}2)$$

where τ = output pulse width
Z_0 = characteristic impedance

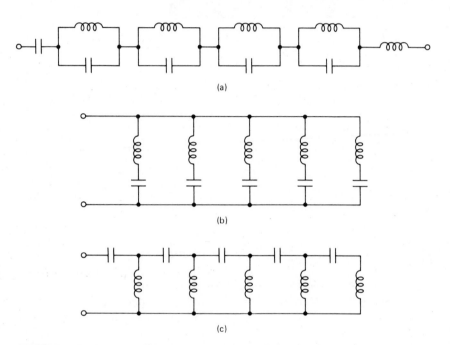

(a)

(b)

(c)

FIGURE 5–1 Some possible, but not rarely used, forms of PFNs: (a) type A, (b) type C, (c) type F.

The number of sections is chosen to provide the desired rise time. The design equations for such a network are summarized in Figure 5–2.

5–1 PFN DESIGN

The design of an E-type voltage-fed Giullemin network [3,4,8] is begun by specifying the number of sections in the network, the impedance of the network, and the pulse width of the network. The pulse width and impedance level are usually specified in the general design

Important relations are:

$$Z_o = \sqrt{\frac{L_n}{C_n}}$$

$$\tau = \sqrt{L_n C_n}$$

$$C_n = \frac{\tau}{2 Z_o}$$

$$L_n = \frac{\tau Z_o}{2}$$

$$\frac{l}{d} = \frac{4}{3}$$

$$\frac{L_c}{L} = 1.1 \text{ to } 1.2$$

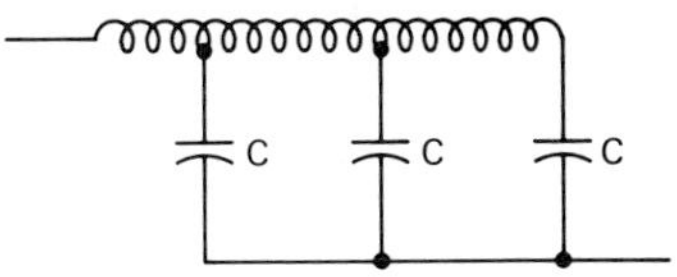

FIGURE 5–2 Guillemin E-type pulse-forming network circuit diagram and critical design parameters.

where C_n = total network capacitance
L_n = total network inductance
τ = pulse width at 50% points
Z_o = characteristic impedance
n = number of sections

L = inductance per section L_n/N
L_c = inductance of section on closed end
C = capacitance per section C_n/n
l = length of coil in one section
d = coil diameter

of the modulator. The number of sections desired is less evident and depends on many factors. For a more complete discussion, see Gillette and Oshima [7].

When PFNs are used to pulse a magnetron through a pulse transformer, the following guideline may be used:

Number of sections	Pulse length
1–3	Less than 0.5 μs
2–5	0.5–2.5 μs
3–8	2.5–5.0 μs

These usually give reasonably good results and generally agree with the results obtained by the methods in Gillette and Oshima [7].

If it is necessary to achieve a specified rise time, the number of sections is given by

$$\frac{0.63\tau}{t_r} + 0.13$$

where τ is the pulse width at the 70% level and t_r the rise time from 10% to 90%. Now we may calculate C_n and L_n using Equations 5–1 and 5–2, and use the design equations given in Figure 5–2.

5–2 COIL DESIGN

The PFN inductor design requires the calculation of a close-wound coil having a length/diameter ratio of 4/3 per section (for close-wound coils having more than one section) and a total inductance L_n. The ratio of length to diameter for single-section coils is not critical.

The "current sheet" inductance of a solenoid is given in Langford-Smith [12] as

$$L_n = \frac{0.1 \; a^2 N^2}{l \, K}$$

where L_n = inductance μH
$\quad a$ = radius of coil (in)
$\quad N$ = number of turns
$\quad l$ = length of coil (in)
$\quad K$ = Nagaoka's constant

or

$$N = \left[\frac{10 L_n \; l}{a^2 K} \right]^{1/2} \tag{5-3}$$

Values of Nagaoka's constant are

Number of sections	Diameter/length	Nagaoka's constant
1	Any	As appropriate
2	0.375	0.86
3	0.25	0.91
4	0.137	0.925
5	0.15	0.94

A usual procedure would be to select a standard-size coil form and then to calculate the length of the coil. Then the number of turns may be calculated. By using a 90% winding-space factor, the allowable wire size may now be calculated. The power dissipated in the wire should now be checked (remember that the pulse current flows only on the inner half of the wire). If the coil is space-wound, Equation 5–3 may be somewhat in error and more exact expressions will be required [12]; however, this is usually not necessary.

Taps are placed at approximately the following places on the coil:

Number of sections	Tap location (% of total turns)				
	1	2	3	4	5
2	60	100			
3	39	68	100		
4	30	52	74	100	
5	25	43	61	79	100

There should be provisions to adjust the position of each coil tap to optimize pulse shape.

For extremely high voltage (pulse voltage greater than 10 kV), it will be necessary to space-wind the coil. For extremely long-pulse coils, bank winding may be convenient. In these cases, the methods given in "Colloquium on PFN's" [4] are appropriate.

There are, of course, a number of networks that have been designed for specific applications to generate unusual waveshapes [3,19].

5-3 VOLTAGE-MULTIPLYING NETWORKS

There are a number of voltage-multiplying networks that can be utilized to increase the output voltage from a discharge pulse generator without the use of a pulse transformer. The simplest of these is the Marx generator, shown in Figure 5–3, consisting of a number of capacitors charged in parallel but discharged in series.

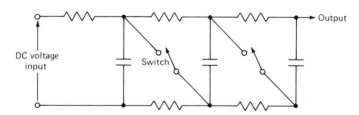

FIGURE 5–3   Marx circuit for generation of high-voltage impulses.

More control over the pulse shape may be obtained by a so-called Darlington line, shown as Figure 5–4, for which the various sections satisfy the relationship that for an n-network system, the impedance of the rth network is

$$Z_r = \frac{R_l r(r+1)}{n^2}$$

and the impedance of the nth network is

$$Z_n = \frac{R_l}{n}$$

The voltage of the output pulse is $n/2$ times the network voltage. The particular case where the Darlington line consists of two sections is called a *Blumlein network;* it is shown as Figure 5–5.

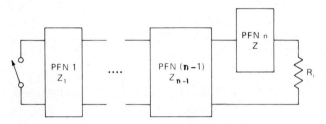

FIGURE 5–4 Block diagram of a Darlington line.

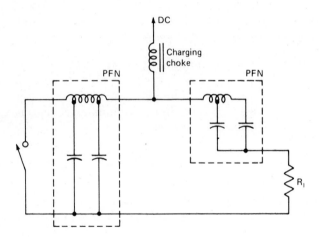

FIGURE 5–5 Blumlein circuit.

5–4 PULSE CAPACITORS

The pulse capacitors in a Guillemin E-type PFN are all of equal value; that value is C_n/n. These capacitors must satisfy a number of different criteria, including having low internal inductance and high stability and being able to withstand high applied voltages and to function reliably for extended periods of time at high recharge and discharge rates.

The design of ac and pulse capacitors involves many factors, a number of which are not clearly understood, and few general statements can be made [2,6,11,16,18]. There are many factors that affect the life of a capacitor in pulse service. These include failure due to corona in the capacitor structure, actual burning of the insulation, deterioration of the insulation due to excessive heat, and failure due to harmful chemicals attacking the dielectric. Obtaining specific information on any portion of the capacitor design or construction process is relatively difficult, and most successful designs are based on extrapolation from earlier known cases.

It has been empirically observed that if the voltage across a single capacitor section exceeds some critical value, it will be very difficult to prevent damaging corona from occurring. For this reason, in a five-section, 1-μs network described in Glasoe and Lebacqz [8], Sprague used four series-connected sections worked at 2 kV peak charging voltage per section. The paper dielectric in each section was stressed at about 210 V/mil. In a four-section, 1.8-μs network charging to 15.2 kV and required to stand 30.4 kV peak charging for 24 h, each section consisted of twelve series-connected capacitors, so that each section was worked 1250 V (2500 V for the 24-h test), with the dielectric (Samica, reconstituted mica paper) worked at about 705 V/mil and stressed at 1410 V/mil for the 24-h test at twice working voltage [15]. Another paper capacitor had 14 series-connected sections for 13.2 kV peak charging voltage, inserted tab construction, and an insulation of five layers of 0.5-mil paper. This resulted in a voltage per section of 950 V, with the insulation stressed at 380 V/mil. A design with 16 kV peak charging voltage had three wound capacitors in series with two floating foils in each section. Insulation was 12 layers of 0.5-mil paper for each section, resulting in a stress per section of 1777 V, with the insulation stressed at 300 V/mil [14]. AMP, Inc., has constructed a network having a peak charging voltage of 10 kV in which each capacitor consists of two series-connected Isomica capacitor sections, with a resulting stress of 5 kV per section [1].

A theoretical basis for the division of high-voltage ac and pulse capacitors into a number of series-connected sections may be found by considering the behavior of laminar voids in the insulation. Consider the situation shown in Figure 5–6, with a laminar void in the insulation between two conductors, or capacitor plates. For electric fields perpendicular to the insulator surface, the stress in volts per mil in the gas constituting the void is equal to the electric field in the insulator multiplied by the dielectric constant of the solid material, assuming that the dielectric constant of the void is 1.0.

For example, if the stress in an insulator of dielectric constant 4.0

is 50 V/mil, the stress in the air between it and the nearby conductor may be as high as 200 V/mil. Since, in general, the gas is the material with the lower breakdown voltage, it will break down at a total applied voltage that the solid dielectric material can easily support.

The voltage across the combination of insulator and void at which incipient breakdown will occur in the voids has been determined by

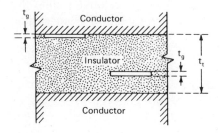

FIGURE 5–6 Idealized voids in solid insulation between two conductors. [17]

Olyphant [17]. For the case of Figure 5–6, assume that a voltage V_t is applied between the electrodes and is given by the sum of the voltage V_g across the gas and V_x across the solid,

$$V_t = V_g + V_x$$

or

$$V_t = E_g t_g + Et$$

where E_g and E are the stresses in the gas and the solid and t_g and t are their respective thicknesses. Thus,

$$V_t = E_g \left(t_g + \frac{t}{k} \right)$$

where k is the dielectric constant of the solid material.

If E_g is set equal to the breakdown strength of the gas, V_t becomes the corona starting voltage, or the voltage at which breakdown first occurs in the laminar void. This corona start voltage has been found to be relatively independent of frequency over the range from 60 Hz to above 1 MHz.

If the values of breakdown strength as a function of air gap at atmospheric pressure are substituted for E_g, a family of curves of corona starting voltage is obtained. Such a family is shown in Figure 5–7. For any value of t/k there is an air gap in which discharges will first occur, and which will give a minimum corona starting voltage. The minimum values of corona starting voltage obtained from Figure 5–7 are replotted as

Figure 5–8. Also shown in Figure 5–8 is a plot of values estimated from Figure 5–7 for the air gap spacing in which discharges will first occur. These spacings are not particularly critical, since corona starting voltage does not vary rapidly with changes in spacing near the minimum.

Approximations for both the minimum corona starting voltage in

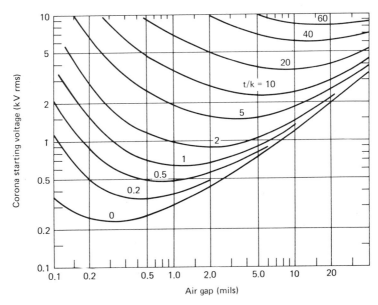

FIGURE 5–7 Calculated corona starting voltages in laminar voids at atmospheric pressure as a function of the void spacing (air gap) for various values of effective insulation thickness (t/k). [17]

laminar voids and the gap for minimum corona starting voltage are given by the following fitted equations:

$$CSV = 0.56 \left(\frac{t}{k}\right)^{0.61} (\text{kV rms})$$

$$t_g = 1.25 \ (t/k)^{0.67} \ (\text{mil})$$

Thus, one can see that for a minimum-volume capacitor, series connections of individual capacitors are desirable, with voltage per section limited to less than from 2 to 4 kV.

The physical design of pulse capacitors must be such that the self-inductance of the capacitors is minimized. In long-pulse units (where lead inductance is not as important), inserted-tab construction is often used if the resulting high-current densities do not cause excessive local heating. Generally a thin piece of some solderable material is inserted into the capacitor to contact the aluminum capacitor foils. While there is only a pressure contact and dissimilar metals are used, both nickel and tin-plated copper have been successfully used as tabs in the capacitor industry. For shorter–pulse-length units, the entire edge of each foil

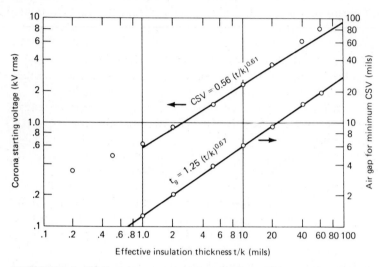

FIGURE 5–8 Minimum corona starting voltage (CSV) as a function of effective insulation thickness. Air-gap spacings for minimum corona starting voltage are also shown. [17]

must be contacted, and the result is either the extended-foil capacitor or the wafer capacitor. The extended-foil capacitor merely extends the foils beyond the edge of the capacitor insulation. The connection is made to the aluminum foil after impregnation of the capacitor. A tin-lead-zinc solder and *no flux* is used to make the solder connection [14]. The solder is applied with a wiping motion of the iron, abrasion alone being used to clean the surface of the aluminum foil. The resulting joint is not very pretty, but it seems to be adequate. Since such techniques are quite expensive, they are usually reserved for exacting applications.

There is no question that the presence of corona does deteriorate the insulation in a capacitor. Also, for otherwise identical capacitors, the one with less corona will usually have the longer life. The correlation between corona levels and life expectancy among *different* capacitors, even those using the same dielectric and impregnants, is rather poor, and corona testing by itself is a poor way to predict capacitor life. For a more extensive discussion of corona testing, see Birks and Schulman [2] and Kreuger [11].

One dielectric that is quite resistant to corona effects is reconstituted mica paper, which is available in several forms. One form that is particularly useful for low-volume pulse capacitors is Isomica, a stage-B resin-impregnated reconstituted mica paper. AMP, Inc., is using capacitors of Isomica to replace its Amplifilm capacitors at high PRFs and high temperatures, and Isomica capacitors are also manufactured by Sprague, Tobe, and Custom. The Isomica is relatively cheap, the capacitors are fairly easy to make, and the Isomica is very heat- and corona-resistant.

Capacitors made from Isomica are stacked-wafer capacitors. The capacitors are stacked and placed in a press, and about 1000 lb/in² of pressure is applied and the temperature is raised to 300°C as rapidly as possible while pressure is still maintained. The capacitor is baked for 20 h at 300°C and 1000 lb/in², and is then cooled and removed from the press and postbaked for 48 h at 150°C [10,21]. After baking, the capacitor must be kept extremely dry, for it absorbs moisture readily. One easy way to do this is to place the capacitor in a mason jar with a desiccant during the postbake and put the lid on the jar while still hot.

The dielectric stress used by commercial companies is one 2-mil sheet of Isomica for each 1000 V of peak charging voltage, with a maximum of 5 to 8 kV per capacitor section. In capacitors constructed at Georgia Tech, about half that stress has been used. The finished capacitors have excellent resistance to heat, many having been operated at 175°C with no ill effects. The capacitors should always be cased and the cases thoroughly impregnated and sealed to prevent absorption of moisture. Suitable impregnants include silicone oil and transformer oil. If desired, wrap and end-fill techniques may be used to exclude moisture.

Because of the difficulties of implementing large capacitances in a stacked-capacitor configuration, and because of limited demand, Isomica has been largely replaced by Samica, which is an unimpregnated reconstituted mica paper. Samica may be used to make wound capacitors by conventional techniques; aluminum-foil electrodes and inserted-tab construction are often used. After winding, the capacitor is normally vacuum-dried and then impregnated. If the capacitor is to be sealed and liquid-impregnated, normally silicone or mineral oils will be used. If a dry capacitor is desired, the capacitor may be impregnated with either a liquid polyester or an epoxy compound and then cured under heat and pressure to produce the finished capacitor. Typical capacitance stability will be better than ±2% from −55 to +105°C, with a dissipation factor less than 0.005 at 25°C and less than 0.008 at +125°C.

5–5 TEMPERATURE-RISE CALCULATIONS

The temperature rise of a pulse-forming network is related to the total energy per pulse and the number of pulses per second passed through the pulse-forming network. Thus, a measure of the losses in watts for a particular type of pulse-forming network is

$$\frac{1}{2} C_n V^2 f$$

where $C_n = $ PFN capacitance
$f = $ PRF

and

$V = $ peak network voltage

and this fact has been used to provide guidelines for initial estimation of case sizes by Graydon [9]. These procedures are summarized below, and can serve as a first estimate for case size selection for both paper and mica capacitors.

Graydon's procedures for case size (or area) selection involve calculating a number of normalized parameters and entering a standard curve. If the parameters

$\tau = $ PFN pulsewidth (s)
$Z_0 = $ characteristic impedance of PFN (Ω)

and the maximum ambient temperature is known, the case selection may be accomplished by the following steps:

1. Calculate $C_n = \tau / 2 Z_0$.

2. Calculate $(1/2) C_n V^2 f$.

3. Calculate C_1 equal to maximum ambient temperature less 20°C.

4. Calculate $C_2 = 31 \left(\frac{1}{2} C_n V^2 f \right)^{0.4}$ (Figure 5–9 may be used).

5. Enter Figure 5–9 to determine the life factor $F(H)$.

6. Calculate

$$C_4 = \frac{K_a F(H)}{0.001 [(\frac{1}{2}) C_n V^2 f] V \sqrt{C_n}}$$

For K_a use 0.035 for V below 15 kV, 0.025 above 20 kV, and 0.0275 above 25 kV.

7. Calculate $Y = A C_2 / C_4$ (see Table 5–1 for A).

8. Calculate $X = B C_1 / C_4$ (see Table 5–1 for B). Using the calculated value of Y, enter Figure 5–10 and determine case area

from the intersection of the calculated Y value and the line corresponding to the calculated value of X.

9. Enter Figure 5–10 to determine case size.

This case area is a preliminary estimate, and more detailed calculations are normally required to determine exact temperature rise. However,

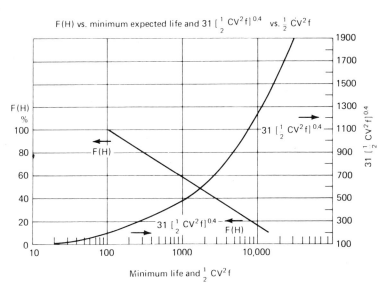

FIGURE 5–9   Guide curves for Figure 5–10. [9]

in a more detailed consideration, individual losses in the various components must be carefully calculated. The principal sources of loss in a pulse-forming network are losses in the capacitor, losses in the coil, and losses in the can itself due to currents induced by the PFN coil. Except for the highest-powered networks, a calculation of losses in the capacitor and in the coil will be sufficient.

Coil losses may be calculated by utilizing the effective wire resistance, which was discussed earlier (Equation 4–2), and by assuming that current flows in only the inner portion of the coil because of proximity effects. The use of litz wire may be somewhat beneficial in reducing the magnitude of these coil losses.

Calculation of the losses in the capacitors may proceed along several distinct lines. The simplest and least accurate approach is to utilize a gross dissipation factor between 0.005 and 0.01 and multiply $(\frac{1}{2})CV^2 f$

TABLE 5–1 COEFFICIENTS OF C_2/C_4 AND C_1/C_4 [9]

Circulation construction	C_2/C_4 coefficient A	C_1/C_4 coefficient B
Natural circulation, internal coil, no fins, no forced air	1	1
Internal coil, either fins or forced air at 400 ft/min	0.38	0.50
Both fins and forced air at 400 ft/min, internal coil	0.215	0.333
Natural circulation, external coil (capacitor section), no fins, no forced air	0.38	0.50
Either fins or forced air at 400 ft/min, external coil (capacitor section)	0.215	0.333

by the dissipation factor to obtain total capacitor losses. However, in higher-power networks, the procedure advocated by Lerner [13] or by Rambo and Gardenghi [20] will usually be required, involving calculation of the Fourier components of the voltage waveforms applied to the capacitor, and the determination of the heating associated with each of these components.

Because of uncertainties in many aspects of PFN temperature-rise calculations, capacitor-loss calculations should be carefully checked experimentally to ensure their correctness. Fortunately, some types of PFN capacitors are used in sufficient quantities that extensive experience is available, permitting quite accurate procedures for estimates of capacitor losses to be developed. One such procedure has been developed by Custom Electronics for use with its wrap-and-fill mica capacitors [5]. For these capacitors, the losses in the capacitor are given by

$$\frac{1}{2} V^2 C f \times \mathrm{DF}$$

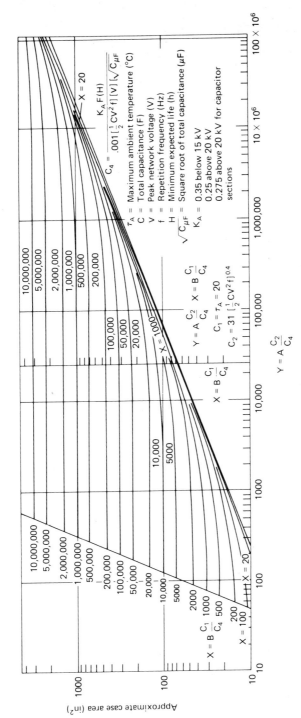

FIGURE 5–10 Estimated PFN case area as a function of known parameters. [9]

193

where V = peak network charging voltage
  C = capacitance
  f = PRF

and the dissipation factor (DF) is a function of pulse width, number of PFN meshes, and PRF. One table for finding DF is Table 5–2.

Once these various PFN losses have been calculated, the temperature-rise calculations outlined in Chapter 4 are completely applicable.

TABLE 5–2 DISSIPATION FACTOR AS A FUNCTION OF PRF AND F, THE RATIO OF NUMBER OF PFN SECTIONS TO PULSE WIDTH, FOR WRAP-AND-FILL RECONSTITUTED MICA CAPACITORS [5]

PRF	Dissipation factor (DF) for various values of F				
	4.0×10^6	6.0×10^6	8.0×10^6	12.0×10^6	16.0×10^6
500	0.020	0.021	0.022	0.024	0.026
1000	0.021	0.022	0.023	0.025	0.027
1500	0.022	0.023	0.024	0.026	0.028
2000	0.023	0.024	0.025	0.027	0.029
2500	0.024	0.025	0.026	0.028	0.030
3000	0.025	0.026	0.027	0.029	0.031
3500	0.026	0.027	0.029	0.030	0.032
4000	0.027	0.028	0.029	0.031	0.033

REFERENCES

1. Ahern, Jack, AMP, Inc., personal communication.

2. Birks, J. B., and J. H. Schulman, eds., *Progress in Dielectrics,* vol. 1, Heywood and Company, Ltd., London, 1959, pp. 5–8, 19–31.

3. "Calculation of PFN's Having Slow Rates of Rise," MIT Radiation Laboratory Report 698, Cambridge, Mass., Mar. 12, 1945.

4. "Colloquium on PFN's," MIT Radiation Laboratory Report 692, Cambridge, Mass., Mar. 14, 1945.

5. Custom Electronics technical staff, "Heat Dissipation and Other Considerations in Custom Electronics' Type "C" Reconstituted Mica Capacitors Used in Pulse Forming Networks," Custom Electronics, Inc., Oneonta, N.Y., August 1978.

6. Drummer, G. W. A., and H. M. Nordenberg, *Fixed and Variable Capacitors,* McGraw-Hill, New York, 1960.

7. Gillette, P. R., and K. Oshima, "Pulser Component Design for Proper Magnetron Operation," *IRE Trans. Component Parts*, vol. CP-3, no. 1, March 1956, pp. 26–31.

8. Glasoe, G. N., and J. V. Lebacqz, *Pulse Generators*, MIT Rad. Lab. series, vol. 5, McGraw-Hill, New York, 1948, pp. 215–221, 655–660. (Also available in Dover and Boston Technical Publishers editions.)

9. Graydon, A., "The Application of Pulse-Forming Networks," *IRE Trans. Component Parts*, vol. CP-4, no. 1, March 1957, pp. 7–13.

10. Hogle, D. H., "Samica/Isomica Dielectrics for Capacitors," *Electrical Shorts*, 3M Company, no. E-PRES-12-1 (45.5) BPH. St. Paul, Minn.

11. Kreuger, F. H., *Discharge Detection in High Voltage Equipment*, American Elsevier, New York, 1965.

12. Langford-Smith, F., ed., *Radiotron Designer's Handbook*, 4th ed., distributed by RCA, Harrison, NJ, 1953, pp. 429–432.

13. Lerner, M., "Which Non-Sinusoidal Voltage May Shorten the Life of a Capacitor?" in *Proc. 1977 Electronic Components Conf.*, pp. 468–474.

14. Lord, Richard, Sprague Electric Company, personal communication.

15. Lord et al., "Development of High Temperature Pulse Forming Network," Final Report, Sprague Electric Company, AD No. 285–305, North Adams, Mass., July 30, 1962.

16. Mabury, R. E., *Power Capacitors*, McGraw-Hill, New York, 1949, pp. 29–38.

17. Olyphant, M., Jr., "Corona and Treeing Breakdown of Insulation: Progress and Problems," pt. I, *Insulation*, vol. 9, February 1963, pp. 35–40.

18. Parkman, N., "Some Properties of Solid-Liquid Composite Dielectric Systems," *IEEE Trans. Electrical Insulation*, vol. EI-13, no. 4, August 1978, pp. 289–307.

19. Perry, A. D., "Pulse-Forming Networks Approximating Equal-Ripple Flat Top Step Response," in *IRE Nat. Conv. Rec.*, vol. 5, 1957, pp. 148–153.

20. Rambo, S. I., and R. A. Gardenghi, "PFN Loss Calculations," in *1978 13th Pulse Power Modulator Symp.*, pp. 43–45.

21. 3M Company, *Processing Instructions for Isomica Capacitors.*

6
DESIGN OF CHARGING CHOKES

The reactor or charging choke utilized in a line-type modulator has a number of unique requirements that must be satisfied:

- Providing a constant inductance with a large ac flux change in the core and an appreciable dc flux
- Freedom from core saturation
- Ability to withstand high voltages
- Freedom from spurious oscillations or resonances
- Reasonable temperature rise

Because of these requirements, the design of charging reactors is somewhat different from the design procedures used in other types of chokes [2,3,4,5,6,7]. The voltages charging reactors are subject to are rather large, and the reactor is usually specified so that its inductance must remain constant within a few percent over a wide range of applied voltages and currents.

6–1 DESIGN PROCEDURE

The formula for the inductance of a reactor is given by Arnold Engineering [1]:

$$L = 3.2N^2A10^{-8}/a + l/\mu_\Delta \tag{6-1}$$

where L = inductance (H)
 N = number of turns
 a = length of effective air gap (in)
 A = gross core area (in²)
 μ_Δ = incremental permeability of core material under conditions of magnetization present in core
 l = length of magnetic path of core (in)

One way to design a reactor whose inductance is approximately constant is to make a much greater than l/μ_Δ. For grain-oriented silicon steel (Silectron or Hypersil), this is satisfied if a/l is greater than 0.6%, the maximum flux in the core is limited to 15 kilogauss (kG), and the ac flux is greater than 100 G. The ac and dc flux may be apportioned as desired, so long as the total flux does not exceed 15 kG.

There are several ways to design reactors to meet our requirements. All of these design methods are essentially ways to select the size of the core to be used and the initial flux density. One rather satisfactory way to select cores and flux densities is to make a series of educated guesses until one finds a suitable design. We shall begin our simplified design procedure by selecting a 4- or 12-mil grain-oriented steel core [1]. The number of turns is determined by an assumed ac flux in the core; 5 kG might be a good starting point [7].

$$N = \frac{4.93 \times 10^6 \, E_{bb} T_r}{AS \, \Delta B_{ac}} \tag{6-2}$$

where ΔB_{ac} = peak ac flux excursion in the core (G)
 E_{bb} = dc supply voltage (V)
 T_r = time to charge network
 A = gross core area (in²)
 S = stacking factor (0.9 for 4-mil Silectron)

Next select the total air gap a by the equation

$$a = \frac{3.2N^2A \times 10^{-8}}{L} \qquad [7] \tag{6-3}$$

and verify that a/l is greater than 0.6%. Next calculate the dc flux in the core by the equation

$$B_{dc} = \frac{0.16NI_{dc}}{a} \qquad [7] \tag{6-4}$$

where B_{dc} = dc flux (G)
 a = effective air gap (in)
 N = number of turns
 I_{dc} = direct current carried by choke ($I_{dc} = \text{PRF} C_n \times 1.9 E_{bb}$)

and verify that $\Delta B_{ac} + B_{dc}$ is less than 15 kG. On the basis of these results, one may wish to revise the initial choice of ΔB_{ac}. An increase in ΔB_{ac} will allow fewer turns, and a reduction in ΔB_{ac} will reduce the maximum flux density. If the air gap is too small or the maximum flux density is too high, it will be necessary to recalculate the reactor, using either a different assumed flux or a different core.

While conventional E-I laminations may be used for core material, C cores of 4-mil grain-oriented silicon steel are often used, because of their high flux density and ease of assembly. A representative group of 4-mil C-core dimensions is given in Table 6–1, where the same nomenclature is used as in Table 4–2.

TABLE 6–1   REPRESENTATIVE SET OF 4-mil C CORES

Core no.	Strip width D (in)	Build E (in)	Window width F (in)	Window length G (in)	Core area $D \times E$ (in²)	Core length $2F + 2G + 2.9E$ (in)
H-1	½	¼	½	1⅛	0.125	3.98
H-5	1	¼	½	1½	0.250	4.73
H-46	¾	⁵⁄₁₆	⅝	1⁹⁄₁₆	0.23	5.28
H-11	1	⁹⁄₃₂	⅝	1⁹⁄₁₆	0.28	5.19
H-51	⅝	⅜	¾	1¹⁵⁄₁₆	0.28	6.46
H-8	1	1½	½	1⁹⁄₁₆	0.50	5.58
H-19	1⅛	¾	¾	2⁵⁄₁₆	0.84	8.30
H-25	1⅜	¹⁵⁄₁₆	¹⁵⁄₁₆	2½	1.29	9.59
H-33	1¾	1	1	3	1.75	10.90
H-34	2	1	1	3	2.00	10.90
AH1430	3	3¼	5½	16½	9.75	53.43

Oil-impregnated kraft paper is usually chosen as the insulation for charging reactors. Reasonable voltage stresses are as follows:

Insulation service	Working stress
Winding core insulation	25 V/mil
Interlayer and wrapping insulation	50 V/mil
Creep stress	25 V/mil

All layer insulation should be at least two layers thick. The overall length of the coil should be $\frac{1}{16}$ in less than the available window. The number of turns per layer may now be calculated by assuming a 90% space factor in winding.

The thickness of interlayer insulation is sometimes determined by the mechanical strength necessary to support the wire.

Wire size (AWG)	Minimum layer insulation (in)
30 and smaller	0.002
26–29	0.003
23–25	0.004
18–22	0.005

The total build of the coil may be obtained by multiplying the sum of the thicknesses of insulating material and wire in the radial direction by a factor of 1.25.

Using this design procedure, we may calculate our coil and check its fit. The number of volts per turn should then be checked, and for Formvar wire should never exceed 300; this limit is almost never exceeded in charging-reactor design. However, when the switch closes, there are impulsive voltage distributions produced in the end windings of the reactor. The impulsive strength of film wire insulation is in excess of 8000 V (10 to 20 kV). For dc power-supply voltages above 4 kV, it is recommended that a shield be used over the outer winding and connected to the thyratron terminal of the reactor, or that the final layers be space-wound, allowing approximately 200 V peak charging voltage per mil of spacing between the wires.

6–2 CALCULATION OF LOSSES

Losses in the reactor now need to be computed to determine the Q of the reactor and the temperature rise of the coil. There are three sources of energy loss we need to consider. The first is the copper loss. Calculation of the equivalent resistance of the wire and the consequent energy loss is covered in Chapter 4. The core loss must then be calculated. Even though there is dc flux present, the core loss may still be found from the ac component of flux as if there were no dc flux, as long as there is no saturation of the core [5]. The values of core loss may be obtained from the manufacturer's data [1], and some are given in the following section. The gap loss, due to fringing flux at the gaps entering the core laminations, is given by the equation

$$W_g = kDaf(\Delta B_{ac})^2 \sqrt{l_e} \qquad [5,8,9] \qquad\qquad (6\text{-}5)$$

where $\quad W_g =$ gap loss in watts
$\qquad k =$ constant (for silicon steel, 3.22 x 10^{-3})
$\qquad D =$ core strip width (in)
$\qquad a =$ total length of air gaps (in)

$$f = \frac{1}{2 \text{ x time to charge network}} \text{ (Hz)}$$

$\quad \Delta B_{ac} =$ peak value of ac flux in core (kG)
$\qquad l_e =$ core lamination thickness (mil)

These three losses are then lumped together and equated to an equivalent resistance by the equation

$$W_t = I^2 R_{eq} \qquad\qquad (6\text{-}6)$$

where $\quad W_t =$ total losses in reactor (W)
$\qquad I =$ rms current in reactor (A)
$\qquad R_{eq} =$ equivalent resistance

and the Q of the reactor is

$$Q = \frac{\omega L}{R_{eq}} \qquad\qquad (6\text{-}7)$$

where $Q = Q$ of charging reactor

$$\omega = \frac{\pi}{\text{time to charge network}}$$

A minimum Q of 10 is considered acceptable.

The heat rise of the reactor should now be checked to see if it is suitable for the insulation system being considered; the procedures outlined in Section 4–4 should be used. There is yet another possible source of heat to be considered: the energy stored in the electric field between the windings. In the event that discharge of the switch occurs at the peak of the charging waveform, this energy is discharged through the switch and does not contribute to heating of the reactor. If a charging diode is used and the triggering of the switch delayed, the choke may "ring," dissipating some or all of the energy in the core of the reactor. Thus, the amount of heating depends upon the interpulse period, the core material, and the capacitances involved.

While any reactor that fits all the above specifications is suitable, the smallest design is usually one of which the coil fills the window completely, of which the total flux is somewhere near the maximum, and which operates close to the maximum temperature. If any one of these criteria is not met, a smaller reactor will generally result if the reactor is redesigned.

6–3   CORE MATERIALS

A number of suitable core materials exist that may be used for charging reactors. Conventional punched laminations of cold rolled steel may be used, and in such a case, the maximum flux should be limited to no more than 11 kG. I have found it most useful to use C or E cores of 4- or 12-mil Silectron for these applications, because of their ease of assembly, rather than to seek the lowest cost; in such a case, a B_{max} of 15 kG may be used. Figure 6–1 is a chart of core loss for 4-

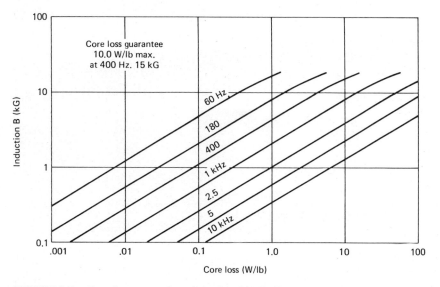

FIGURE 6–1   Core loss vs. ac flux excursion for 4-mil Silectron. [1]

mil Silectron that may be used for heat and Q calculations, as long as saturation is avoided.

6–4   RINGING IN CHARGING REACTORS

The presence of stray capacity associated with the charging choke gives rise to oscillations of the form shown in Figure 6–2. In addition, the steeply falling voltage caused by the switching of the hydrogen thyratron may excite resonances within the transformer or reactor itself, producing extremely high voltages and leading to breakdown of the reactor in extreme cases, or reduction in useful life in less extreme instances. In most cases, satisfactory operation may be obtained by space winding

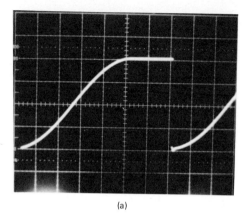

(a)

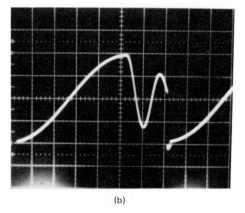

(b)

FIGURE 6–2 Charging voltage waveforms (*a*) on PFN and (*b*) at charging-choke terminal showing ringing due to stray capacity.

of the coil connected to the hydrogen thyratron, and winding all of the coil as a single winding on one leg of the core. However, in some cases, damping of the coil by a parallel *RC* circuit may be required, and in extreme cases, the techniques outlined in Scoles [11] for bisection and damping of the choke may be required. It may be desirable to return the stored energy to the power supply in order to improve efficiency and reduce heating of the reactor.

6–5 DE-QING VOLTAGE REGULATORS

A particular direct method of regulation of the pulse voltage is accomplished by de-Qing of the reactor, as shown in Figure 6–3 [10,12,13]. When a de-Qing regulator is employed, an auxiliary winding is wound on the charging reactor, the pulse-forming network voltage

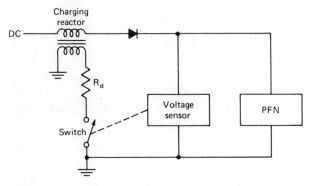

FIGURE 6–3   Basic de-Qing regulator circuit using auxiliary winding on charging choke.

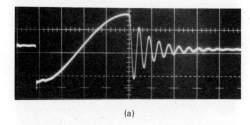

(a)

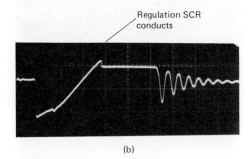

(b)

FIGURE 6–4   Waveforms of the charging choke voltage in a de-Qing regulator (a) with no regulation and (b) with substantial regulation.

sensed, and the auxiliary winding energized at an appropriate time to damp the resonant charging circuit (hence the name *de-Qing*) and terminate the charging process, thus regulating the PFN voltage. Changing waveforms both without and with the de-Qing regulation action are given in Figure 6–4.

There are a number of variations on the de-Qing circuit, as shown in Figures 6–5 and 6–6, including one to return the energy stored in the inductor to the power supply, in order to maximize efficiency. A relatively complete treatment of the design of such a de-Qing regulator is contained in Pickard [10], Voak [13], and Slampyak [12]. A closely

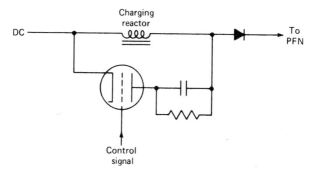

FIGURE 6–5 De-Qing with a series tube and resistor directly across the reactor.

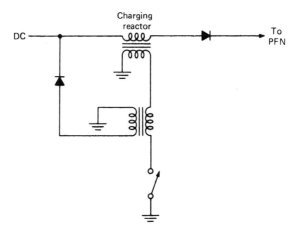

FIGURE 6–6 De-Qing with provisions for return of energy to power supply.

related technique involves the use of a series tube for cutoff of charging current, as shown in Figure 6–7. It should be noted that no shunt or clipping diode is required when a de-Qing network is used, since excessive voltages will not appear on the pulse-forming network in the event of load arcing or other malfunctions.

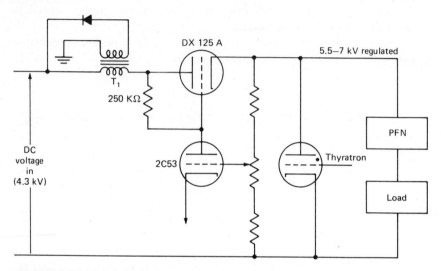

FIGURE 6–7   Charging regulator using series cutoff tube. [10]

REFERENCES

1. Arnold Engineering Company, *Arnold Silectron Cores,* Bulletin SC-107B, Marengo, Ill.

2. Glasoe, G. N., and J. V. Lebacqz, *Pulse Generators,* MIT Rad. Lab. series, vol. 5, McGraw-Hill, New York, 1948, pp. 355–416. (Also available in Dover and Boston Technical Publishers editions.)

3. Grossner, N. R., *Transformers for Electronic Circuits,* McGraw-Hill, New York, 1967, p. 163.

4. Hanna, C. R., "Design of Reactances and Transformers Which Carry Direct Current," *Proc. AIEE,* vol. 46, no. 2, February 1927, pp. 128–131.

5. Howe et al., "Final Report for High Power, High Voltage Audio Frequency Transformer Design Manual," AD No. 607774, Aug. 31, 1964, pp. 298–299.

6. Lee, R., *Electronic Transformers and Circuits,* 2d ed., Wiley, New York, 1955, p. 312.

7. Lee, R., "Linear Reactor Chart," *Electronics,* vol. 28, March 1955, pp. 208–210.

8. Ludwig, J. T., "Research and Development on Design Method for Reactors," University of Minnesota, AD 64525, Minneapolis, September 1954.

9. McElroy, P. K., "Fringing at an Air Gap," *General Radio Experimenter,* vol. 21, no. 8, January 1947, pp. 2–8.

10. Pickard, D. J., "A High Efficiency Charging Regulator for Line-Type Modulators," in *Proc. 5th Symp. Hydrogen Thyratrons and Modulators*, AD650899, May 1958, pp. 223–229.

11. Scoles, G. J., "The Reduction of Unwanted Oscillation (Ringing) in Charging Inductors and Power Transformers," in *Conf. Rec. 1976 12th Modulator Symp.*, February 1976, pp. 124–129.

12. Slampyak, S., "A Unique Regulator by De-Qing Methods," in *Proc. 9th Modulator Symp.*, May 1966, pp. 482–491.

13. Voak, K. F., "Secondary Pulse Voltage Regulator," in *Proc. 9th Modulator Symp.*, May 1966, pp. 465–481.

7
SWITCHES

A common feature of all of the modulators discussed is some means for controlling the transfer of stored energy to the load. A number of devices have been utilized for this purpose, including hydrogen thyratrons, vacuum tubes, silicon controlled rectifiers, reverse-switching rectifiers, saturating magnetic devices, and spark gaps. The characteristics of each of these devices are discussed in some detail in this section.

7–1 HYDROGEN THYRATRONS [7,8,10]

In its basic form, the thyratron is a gas-filled tube containing three electrodes: a cathode, an anode, and a grid. For most modulator applications, the thyratron is filled with hydrogen or deuterium gas in order to prolong cathode life.

The advantages of hydrogen thyratrons for pulse-modulator applications are that they are small and light, require a low-voltage trigger, and have a short deionization time. In practice, their principal disadvantage is that they are a switch that only closes but does not interrupt the flow of current. Such a device is well suited for use in a line-type modulator. Practical hydrogen thyratrons also include a reservoir for replenishment of hydrogen consumed or absorbed within the tube structure.

The thyratron is normally nonconducting with the anode positive with respect to the cathode. A zero or negative voltage exists between the grid and the cathode. Once the grid is driven positive, it initiates gaseous breakdown between the grid, cathode, and anode, and the resulting plasma can handle extremely high peak currents with a relatively low anode-to-cathode voltage.

Proper operation of the tube requires a relatively low-impedance source for the grid-trigger voltage, and a drive circuit whose operation is not adversely affected by large voltages fed back into the output, since at the instant of thyratron firing, the grid may be pulled positive almost to the full anode voltage. Without suitable isolation, such as *LC* despiking networks, this large spike may cause damage to the driver components. Often, negative bias on the grid is desirable in order to promote deionization or rapid recovery of the thyratron and to permit a rapid reapplication of the anode voltage.

Recovery of the hydrogen thyratron may also be enhanced by small negative voltages applied to the anode of the tube immediately after conduction; in order to accomplish this, PFNs are often intentionally slightly mismatched to the load in order to reflect a negative voltage at the anode of the thyratron. However, excessive negative voltages on the anode can permanently damage the tube, and for that reason a clipping diode is often included across the hydrogen thyratron in order to remove large inverse voltages in the event of a load malfunction.

Hydrogen thyratrons may be operated either in series or in parallel, but particular care must be taken to ensure adequate division of voltage or current. For operation in parallel, it is often desirable to incorporate a current-sharing reactor in the anode circuit, as shown in Figure 7–1; and for operation in series, equalization networks should be incorporated

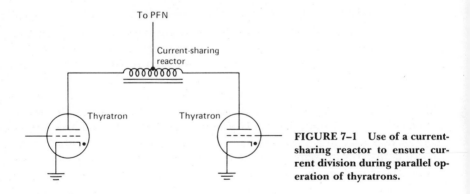

FIGURE 7–1   Use of a current-sharing reactor to ensure current division during parallel operation of thyratrons.

to ensure voltage sharing among the various tubes, as shown in Figure 7–2. For series operation, provisions should be incorporated to ensure that the tubes begin to conduct simultaneously.

Hydrogen thyratrons are made with glass, ceramic, or metal envelopes, either in a triode or in a tetrode configuration, and can operate

with either the grid or cathode at ground potential. Important parameters
of a hydrogen thyratron include the following:

- Power output P_o

- Peak forward anode voltage e_{py}

- Peak anode current i_b

- Average anode current I_b

- RMS plate current I_p

- Plate breakdown factor $P_b = e_{py}i_b \times \text{PRF}$

Other important parameters include reservoir and heater voltages and
current, cathode and heater warm-up time, and grid-drive impedance

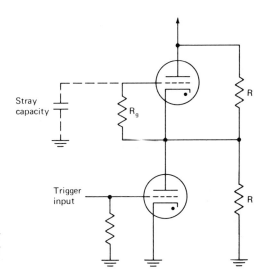

**FIGURE 7–2 Arrangement of
a circuit for series operation of
thyratrons.**

and voltage. The characteristics of a number of representative hydrogen
thyratrons are summarized in Table 7–1.

The principal disadvantages of the hydrogen thyratron are the jitter
between the application of a trigger pulse and the initiation of breakdown
in the tube, which can amount to several nanoseconds on a pulse-to-
pulse basis, and the possibility that the delay will drift tenths of microseconds. The other principal disadvantage is that hydrogen thyratrons
are not well-suited for generating extremely short, very fast rise-time
pulses; the current rise through many hydrogen thyratrons is limited

TABLE 7-1 HYDROGEN THYRATRONS FOR PULSE-MODULATOR SERVICE

Type	Construction	Peak anode voltage (kV)	Peak anode current (A)	P_b factor ($\times 10^9$)
3C45	Triode, glass	3	35	0.30
4C35	Triode, glass	8	90	2.5
5C22	Triode, glass	16	325	3.2
CX1191D	Tetrode	35	500	8.0
CX1193D	Four-gap	140	6000	120
HY-2	Ceramic triode	8	100	2.7
HY-10	Ceramic triode	20	500	10
HY-5	Ceramic triode	40	5000	160
HY 320 2	Ceramic, grounded-grid	35	120,000	
8479	Ceramic triode	50	5000	400

to the 5- to 10-ns range, although tetrode thyratrons are reported to reduce this value somewhat.

7-2 VACUUM TUBES [6,10]

Grid-controlled vacuum tubes have the particular advantage that the grid controls the current through the tube, and therefore they are well suited for utilization in hard-tube modulators. As indicated earlier, hard-tube switches for modulators may be of either the triode, the tetrode, or the pentode configuration, and either thoriated-tungsten cathodes or oxide cathodes may be utilized. In triodes, either conventional wire grids or shielded-grid construction may be utilized.

An oxide cathode consists of a base metal, usually nickel, coated with an oxide layer, which is a combination of barium and strontium oxides. The mixture is typically 60% barium compounds and 40% strontium compounds, which are applied to the cathode in the form of carbonates. During processing of the tube, the cathodes are elevated to a relatively high temperature, reducing the carbonates to oxides and "activating" the cathode. A typical oxide cathode will operate around 1000°K and is capable of emitting approximately 200 to 300 mA/cm² under CW conditions, but may be able to carry as much as 20 A/cm² under pulse conditions.

The life of an oxide-cathode tube is normally limited by evaporation of the cathode material. This evaporation may be minimized by avoiding overheating of the cathode, and may be the significant factor limiting the life of a tube in the field. In order to improve tube life, so-called *dispenser cathodes* have been developed, consisting of a nickel matrix impregnated with suitable oxides; continued evaporation of these oxides at the surface results in movement of oxides from the inner portion of the nickel matrix to the surface, continually replenishing the surface oxide layer and substantially prolonging the life of the tube.

Oxide cathodes are susceptible to damage associated with bombardment of the surface by ions normally present in an evacuated tube under conditions of high applied plate voltages. This characteristic often limits the use of oxide-cathode tubes for high-power modulator applications.

A thoriated-tungsten filament is a tungsten wire coated with a thin layer of thorium. This is typically achieved by adding approximately 1.5% of thoria (thorium oxide) to the tungsten during fabrication of the wire. During processing of the cathode under vacuum, the metallic thorium is reduced and brought to the surface of the filament wire, providing a substantial emitting capability. Typically thorium cathodes operate at temperatures of approximately 1900°K, and while they have a lower emissivity per watt of heating power than oxide cathodes, they are highly resistant to ion bombardment and are thus often utilized in high-power switch tubes.

Oxide cathodes have been utilized in switch tubes with plate voltage ratings up to 75 kV, and for microsecond pulse widths. They offer the significant advantages of smaller size, lower heater power, and better mechanical strength. However, thoriated-tungsten cathodes are widely utilized at higher voltage levels or for the longer-pulse applications.

Grids for pulse-modulator tubes typically consist of meshes or helices wound on vertical stays, as shown in Figure 7–3. The grids are invariably made of tungsten or molybdenum and are coated with platinum or gold in order to reduce secondary emission.

In order to reduce grid current requirements, the shielded-grid construction has been developed, utilizing long strip cathodes set in a focusing groove, as shown in Figure 7–4. The grids consist of large-diameter rods parallel to the emitting strips, spaced on either side of and away from the cathode emitting area so that they are not in the path of the main electron beam. This approach can result in a considerable reduction in grid-drive requirements.

In conventional tetrodes, control-grid dissipation is not often a problem, since grid current requirements are relatively low. In such applications, screen-grid dissipation is often the limiting factor, and is subject to a number of the limitations similar to those which apply to the control grid of a triode.

In tubes with thoriated-tungsten cathodes, the maximum pulse width is often not limited by the emitter itself, but by the control-grid temperature. In such a case, operation at a pulse length shorter than normal test conditions may permit increased peak-grid dissipation. Of course, average grid dissipation cannot be exceeded. It should be noted that

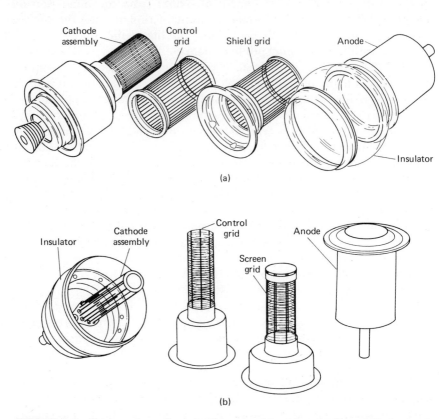

(a)

(b)

FIGURE 7–3 Cutaway views of switch tubes using (*a*) oxide cathodes and (*b*) thoriated-tungsten cathodes. [6]

only conduction current in the various tube electrons contributes to electrode dissipation; therefore, capacitive charging currents for the tube input capacitance do not result in any control-grid dissipation.

It should be carefully noted, however, that the currents required for charging and discharging any capacitances, including stray capacitance, associated with the anode of the tube do directly contribute to anode dissipation. For a number of high-capacitance loads, and for floating-deck modulators, the capacitive charging current may in fact exceed the resistive component of load current. It should be noted that the average plate dissipation depends only on

$$P_d = e_p i_p + 0.5 C_{\text{out}}(E_{\text{bb}}^2 - e_p^2) \times \text{PRF}$$

and is not affected by the rise time of the pulse. Of course, the peak anode dissipation and peak-current requirements associated with the tube are critically dependent upon the rise time and the output capacity.

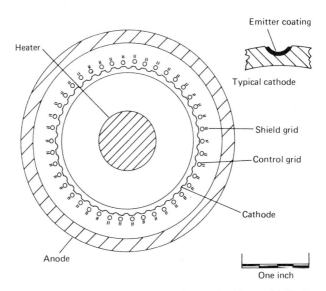

FIGURE 7–4   Cross section of a beamed-grid, or shielded-grid, switch tube. [6]

Typically, ionization of the air outside the tube limits the maximum useful plate voltage, and overvoltage will initiate arcing over the tube envelope with a danger of puncturing the glass or ceramic enclosure. For economy of space, as well as to simplify cleanliness problems, it is typical to utilize oil or enclosed gas insulation when operating above the 50-kV level. In addition, for operation of tubes at voltage levels above 10 kV, the use of corona rings can often improve the ratings of the tubes and reduce arc-over problems. It has been demonstrated that a blower moving air over the tube envelope seems to help reduce ion concentrations, thereby substantially improving high-voltage stability.

Most thoriated-tungsten cathodes are composed of wires, and if they are heated by alternating current, an alternating magnetic field is produced in the vicinity of those wires. This magnetic field may in turn modulate electrons in the vicinity of the cathode, necessitating dc cathode heating if extremely flat-top pulses are required. When dc cathode heating is utilized and long tube life is desired, it may be necessary to reverse the polarity of the heater terminals every thousand hours or so.

In order to increase the ratings of vacuum-tube switches, tubes may be operated either in parallel or in series, or both, but it is necessary to derate the tubes and in some cases incorporate equalization provisions to ensure adequate voltage and current sharing. Typically, when tubes are utilized in parallel, maximum cathode-current and grid-dissipation ratings should be reduced by 5 to 10%.

In addition, tubes in parallel may find it possible to oscillate in a push-pull mode at some relatively high frequency. Usually, appropriate noninductive resistors in the grid and plate leads suffice to prevent such oscillations.

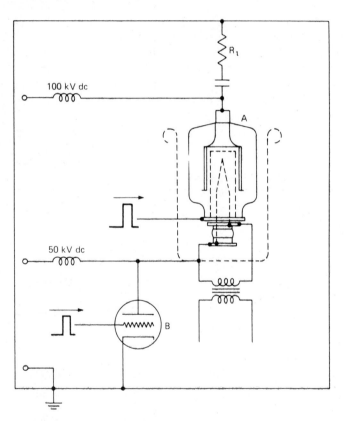

FIGURE 7–5 Use of an electrostatic shield in operating switch tubes in series so tube A does not "see" more than half the applied voltage. [6]

When tubes are utilized in series, the main problem is to see that the plate voltage ratings are not exceeded. This involves the simultaneous turn-on of the tubes, and derating of plate voltage by 80 to 85% of maximum ratings will substantially improve tube life. In addition, grid and plate current should be lowered by approximately 10% to account for variations in individual tubes. Exact values for derating should be worked out in each individual case, depending on the particular circuits used and the tolerances allowed for circuit elements and voltage regulation.

When tubes are operated in series, control of electric-field gradients at tubes operating at elevated potentials may necessitate the use of an electrostatic shield, as shown in Figure 7–5. Care must be taken to keep the lead inductance associated with tubes operated in series to a minimum. If this is not done, large transient voltages may be produced due to lead inductances, generating excessive voltages with consequent damage to modulator components.

Table 7–2 lists a number of representative hard-tube types, while Figure 7–6 is a plot of plate voltage as a function of plate current with various tube capabilities indicated on the chart. Superimposed on this chart are lines of constant switching power that show the range of current and voltage possible for each device by utilization of an appropriate output transformer.

A word of caution should be mentioned at this point. When utilizing

TABLE 7–2   VACUUM TUBES FOR PULSE-MODULATOR SERVICE

Type	Construction	Peak voltage (kV)	Peak current (A)	Average power (W)
4PR60	Tetrode, glass	20	18	60
4PR250C	Tetrode, glass	50	4	250
4PR1000A	Tetrode, glass	30	8	1000
C1149/1	Tetrode, glass	20	18	60
ML-5682	Triode	35	360	120,000
ML-7249	Tetrode	125	2	500
ML-LPT-18	Triode	200	225	30,000
ML-8317	Triode	50	550	60,000
ML-8549	Triode	65	1200	500,000
ML-8495	Triode	160	22	2500

218

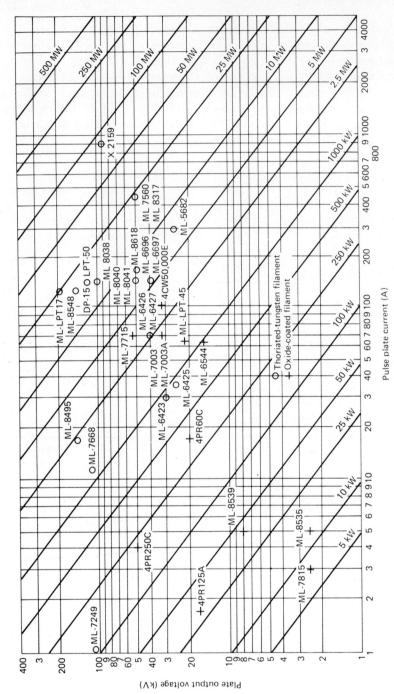

FIGURE 7-6 Voltage and current capabilities of some hard-tube switches, with lines of constant-power capability superimposed.

particular curves from a specific manufacturer, the user should determine in advance whether the curves are typical curves or guaranteed curves. There have been cases where designers have been misled by assuming that published curves were guaranteed when they were but representative data.

7–4 SILICON CONTROLLED RECTIFIERS [5,15,20,21]

The hydrogen thyratron is a quite satisfactory switch, but it suffers from a number of the disadvantages of thermionic tubes, particularly that of relatively short life. With the advent of semiconductor technology, numerous attempts have been made to provide a satisfactory solid-state switching device in order to replace the hydrogen thyratron. The first of these devices to achieve any degree of success was the *silicon controlled rectifier*, called the SCR, or, more correctly and less commonly, the *reverse-blocking triode thyristor*.

The silicon controlled rectifier is a four-layer NPNP device, with connections called the anode, cathode, and gate, as shown in Figure 7–7.

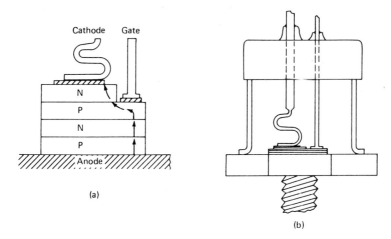

FIGURE 7–7 (*a*) **Semiconductor regions in an SCR, and (*b*) a cross-sectional view of a packaged SCR.** [23]

For zero gate-to-cathode voltage, the SCR appears to be essentially an open circuit in either direction, at least below its forward breakover voltage. If the anode is biased positively with respect to the cathode and the gate current and voltage increased, a point will be reached at which avalanche breakdown of the SCR will be initiated. In this respect, the SCR appears much like a solid-state equivalent to the thyratron.

When SCRs are operated in pulse-modulator service, it is often discovered that failure of the device occurs at much lower than rated currents. The reason for this is that the initial rate of rise of pulse current is an important parameter of a modulator SCR, and one that was not originally recognized as a limitation [23]. Turn-on of the SCR begins at the gate of the SCR and propagates across the junction; under these conditions, the entire current may be passed through a relatively small fraction of the junction area, resulting in unacceptably high current densities and consequent device failure. The slow turn-on gives rise to extremely high dissipation during the switching interval, as shown in Figure 7–8. In

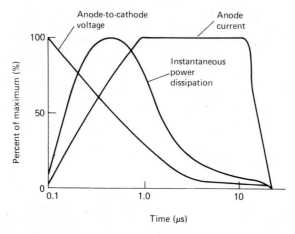

FIGURE 7–8 Dissipation in a pulsed SCR during turn-on, illustrating heating due to excessive rate of rise of current. [23]

extreme cases, this will cause actual melting of the junction, but even if this does not occur, it will significantly reduce life.

A few SCRs, such as the Motorola MCR 729 series [19] have been specifically rated for pulse-modulator service. This series has peak voltages less than 1 kV and turn-on times of 0.2 to 0.4 μs. GE makes a line of inverter SCRs at higher power levels that are suitable for modulator service but have turn-on times of several microseconds. Summary data for several such devices is presented in Table 7–3.

Limitations on the peak voltage in SCRs have been circumvented by series connection of SCRs with appropriate voltage-sharing elements connected in parallel. The problems associated with the limitations in current-handling capacity are solvable in a less straightforward manner. It is possible to operate a number of switches in parallel in order to

TABLE 7-3 CHARACTERISTICS OF SOME INVERTER SCRs SUITABLE FOR MODULATOR USE

SCR type	C124	C141	C159	C358	C384	C444	C712	C457
Peak voltage range (V)	50–600	50–400	500–1200	500–1200	100–800	100–700	1500–2000	500–1400
I_t rms maximum forward conduction, sinusoidal, 1200 Hz (A)	8	26	110	225	500	1000	1500	1800
I_{tsm}, maximum 1-cycle surge (A)	90	200	1600	1600	3500	12,000	20,000	18,700
$R\theta_{j-c}$ thermal impedance junction-to-case (°C/W)	1.8	1.7	0.3	0.135	0.095	0.04	0.023	0.023
Typical turn-on time (μs)	......	3.1	5	5	2	2		
Turnoff time t_q with 120 V/μs reapplied (μs)	20	10	30	30	10–20	10–20	50	40
Rate of rise of current di/dt (A/μs)	100	400	500	500	800	800	800	500
Maximum rate of rise of voltage dV/dt (V/μs)	......	200	200	200	200	200	500	400

share the load; this may be efficiently accomplished by utilizing multiple-primary pulse transformers, with a separate pulse-forming network and SCR switch for each primary winding. The other approach is to utilize a saturable magnetic device in series with the SCR, thus permitting the SCR to completely turn on before large peak currents are carried by the device (see Section 7–5 for design data on such a reactor). Multiple windings in parallel may be placed on this saturable reactor to help ensure current sharing and simultaneous turn-on of all the SCRs. Efficient turn-on of the SCR is enhanced by considerably overdriving the gate; care must be taken to keep the dissipation within safe limits.

As with any semiconductor device, considerable care must be taken in order to keep temperature rise within acceptable limits; care is needed in selection of both peak and rms currents and appropriate heat sinks and mounting. The limiting factor on many SCRs is due to junction heating, which is in turn a function of the level of current, duty cycle, and pulse spacing. The GE SCR manual [11] gives the following relationship for calculating the temperature rise of the junction over the ambient:

$$T_j - T_r = P_0 \left[\frac{t_p R_\theta}{\tau} + \left(\frac{1 - t_p}{\tau} \right) Z_\theta(\tau + t_p) - Z_\theta(\tau) + Z_\theta(t_p) \right]$$

where
T_j = SCR junction temperature
T_r = reference temperature
t_p = pulse duration
τ = interpulse period
P_0 = peak power dissipated in SCR, given as product of peak current and SCR voltage drop
R_θ = steady-state thermal impedance
$Z_\theta(t)$ = transient thermal impedance for time t

In general, the maximum value of T_j is obtained from the SCR data sheet, T_r, t_p, and τ are determined by the application, and P_0 is calculated from the peak current and the device voltage drop, which is also obtained from the SCR data sheet. R_θ is the device thermal resistance if T_r is taken as the heat-sink temperature, and Z_θ is determined from a thermal impedance curve, which is part of the SCR data sheet; one such curve is reproduced in Figure 7–9.

In addition, SCRs evidence a recovery-time problem, and once switching is initiated, considerable time must be allowed in order to sweep carriers from the junction and to permit the SCR to revert to a nonconducting state before voltage is reapplied to the device; if this precaution is not taken, the SCR may conduct continuously. Reapplication of anode voltage must be accomplished with some caution; exceeding the dv/dt rating of the device may result in spontaneous turn-on of the SCR.

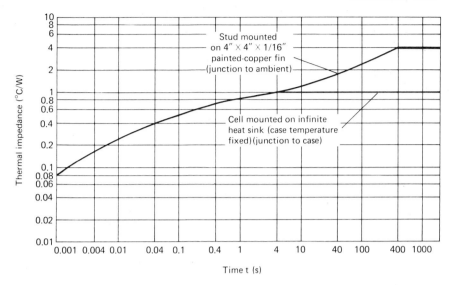

FIGURE 7–9 **Thermal impedance of an SCR as a function of time [11]. Curve defines temperature rise of junction above case temperature for single-load pulse of duration** *t.* **Peak allowable dissipation in thyristor, for time** *t,* **starting from case temperature, equals 100°C (max.** T_C**) minus case temperature divided by transient thermal impedance:**

$$P_{\text{peak}} = \frac{100°\text{C} - T_C}{R_{\theta_{j-c}}(t)}$$

7–4 THE REVERSE-SWITCHING RECTIFIER [2,12]

In order to circumvent some of the turn-on difficulties associated with an SCR in pulse-modulator service, a different class of solid-state device, called the *reverse-switching rectifier* (RSR), or the *reverse-blocking diode thyristor* (RBDT), has been developed. The RBDT is a two-terminal, four-layer PNPN semiconductor switching device designed especially for short, high-energy pulse-generator service. The turn-on mechanism of the RBDT is fundamentally different from that of the SCR, conduction being initiated by a high rate of rise of anode voltage rather than by a trigger applied to a gate. Since conduction is simultaneously initiated over the entire junction area, the RBDT can tolerate a much higher rate of rise of current than can the SCR.

The static *V-I* characteristics of the RBDT are shown in Figure 7–10, the device essentially being nonconducting until a certain critical voltage is reached; once this voltage has been achieved, the device rapidly breaks down, and a large current may then flow with a very small forward drop. The device remains in a conducting condition as long as the current through the device exceeds the holding current.

While it is possible to break down an RBDT in the static mode, RBDTs are invariably operated at less than (typically two-thirds of) the blocking voltage, and breakdown is initiated by application of a rapidly rising

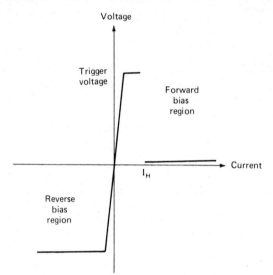

FIGURE 7–10   *V-I* **characteristics of a reverse-blocking diode thyristor (RBDT). [2]**

voltage pulse to the anode. This trigger-voltage pulse should exceed the normal blocking voltage by at least 50%, and should have a dv/dt of 15 kV/μs or greater (25 kV/μs is recommended for many applications). A high rate of rise of trigger voltage is desirable to ensure reliable triggering, to minimize turn-on time, to maximize safe di/dt through the RBDT, and to minimize losses and heating in the device.

The RBDT may be utilized in a pulse modulator as shown in Figure 7–11. An initial rapidly rising trigger-voltage pulse is applied across RBDT$_1$, initiating breakdown, which in turn breaks down RBDT$_2$, discharging the PFN into the load. Provisions are incorporated for resonant recharging of the pulse-forming network.

The characteristics of two available RBDTs are summarized in Table 7–4; critical parameters include the peak forward blocking voltage, which can be 600, 800, or 1000 V, depending on RBDT type. Pulse-trigger voltage is the OFF-state threshold voltage where turn-on begins when a 5000 V/μs trigger pulse is applied. The maximum rate of rise of current di/dt ranges from 2000 to 4000 A/μs for peak-current ratings from 800 to 2500 A. The turnoff time t_q is for a reapplication at the

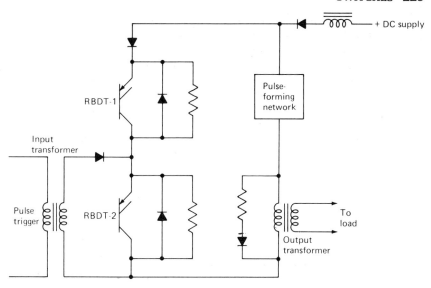

FIGURE 7–11 Modulator circuit using RBDTs. [2]

rate of 20 V/μs, and values of 50 to 100 μs are typical at junction temperatures of 25°C.

RBDTs have been used individually, in parallel, and in series in several pulse-modulator configurations. At the present time, Westinghouse is the principal source for RBDTs.

TABLE 7–4 CHARACTERISTICS OF T40R AND T62R RBDTs

		Typical values	
	Symbol	T40R	T62R
Repetitive peak forward block-ing voltage	V_{DRM}	1000 V	1000 V
Pulse-trigger voltage	V_t	1200 V	1050 V
Rate of rise of current at 1200 A peak	di/dt	2000 A/μs	3000 A/μs
Dynamic forward voltage drop at 4 μs	$V_{tm(dyn)}$	20 V	8 V
Trigger response time	t_{on}	100 ns	
Turnoff time at 20 V/μs	t_q	50 μs	100 μs
Peak forward pulse current	I_{tm}	1200 A	2500 A

7-5 SATURATING MAGNETIC SWITCHES [3,4,13,14,16,17]

An inductor may be made to exhibit a relatively high impedance in an unsaturated condition and a relatively low impedance in a saturated condition, and this property may be utilized in order to switch relatively high power. In actual practice, such inductors are somewhat more complex than might be evident at first glance. Utilization of a dc-bias winding is usually necessary in order to ensure proper core resetting; and in order to provide for a high ratio of unsaturated to saturated permeability, gapless cores such as toroids must be utilized, resulting in a rather complex winding.

In order to examine the operation of such a device it is convenient to refer to a *BH* curve for the core involved, such as the one shown in Figure 7–12. It is assumed that a bias winding is provided on the inductor, as shown in Figure 7–13, and the core is initially biased at point A. If a positive voltage is applied across the inductor, the operating point moves to point B, where the core material has a high degree of

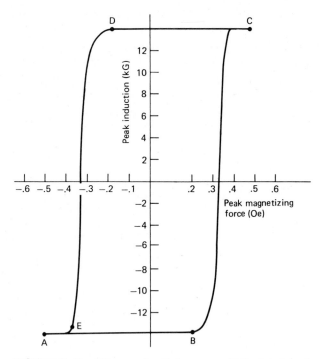

FIGURE 7–12 *BH* curve for Deltamax, a 50% nickel-steel grain-oriented alloy, is shown, illustrating switching action in a saturating inductor. [1]

permeability; at this point the current flowing through the inductor is given by the equation

$$I = I_m + I'_b$$

where I_m is the magnetizing current and I'_b is the bias current referred to the switching winding. The magnetizing current is

$$I_m = \frac{H_c l}{N}$$

where H_c = the magnetizing force corresponding to point B
  l = length of the magnetic circuit
  N = number of turns on the switching winding

Since both I_m and I'_b may be made relatively small, the switching winding may be considered to be in a relatively high-impedance condition. Once the operating point moves along the BH curve to point C, the permeability of the core drops to a low value, I_m increases rapidly, the core becomes saturated, and the switching winding may be represented by a relatively low impedance. After the external voltage is removed, the operating point moves back toward points D and E under the influence of the resetting current, preparing the inductor for the application of the next voltage.

In the saturation region, the inductor appears to have a very low-value inductance, given by the expression

$$L_s = \mu_s N^2 \frac{A}{l} \qquad (7\text{-}1)$$

where μ_s = relative permeability
  N = number of turns
  L_s = saturated inductance (μH)
  A = effective cross-sectional area
  l = length of magnetic path

and since the permeability is very small in this region, the net inductance will be quite low. In the unsaturated region, however, the same expres-

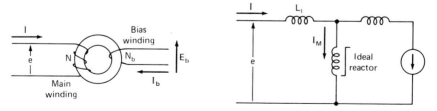

FIGURE 7–13 Winding nomenclature and equivalent circuit for saturable reactor. [4]

sion applies, but in this case permeabilities on the order of 100,000 will be encountered, thus resulting in a very high inductance and a correspondingly low value of current.

Design of a device of this type involves a tradeoff between the saturated and the unsaturated inductance, and holding core and conductor losses to reasonable levels. An initial estimate of core size may be obtained by observing that the volt-time product λ is given by

$$\lambda = 2B_s NA$$

where B_s is the saturation flux density. Rearranging the last two equations to form the equation

$$\text{Volume} = Al = \frac{\mu_s}{4B_s^2} \frac{\lambda^2}{L_s} \tag{7-2}$$

gives the core volume in terms of design parameters. The actual dimensions of the toroid are then chosen so as to minimize copper losses.

In order to achieve satisfactory operation, 50% grain-oriented nickel-iron is usually selected for the core material. This material is commercially known by a number of names such as Deltamax, Square Orthonol, Orthonik, Hypernik V, and 49 Square Mu. Saturation flux densities for this alloy are affected by temperature and by tape thickness, but a reasonable design value is somewhere between 8 and 14 kG. Values of saturated permeability are somewhat variable, but a typical relative permeability

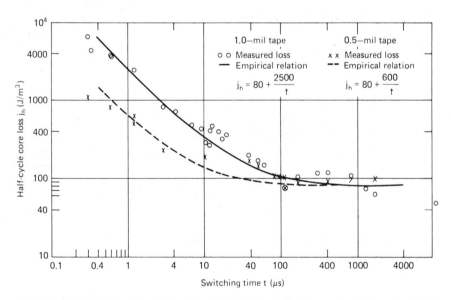

FIGURE 7–14   Half-cycle core loss for Deltamax as a function of switching times. [4]

of approximately 2.3 usually gives satisfactory results. An effective value of coercive force for resetting purposes is somewhat greater than the half-width of the dc or low-frequency loops on the *BH* curve; a value of approximately 28 ampere-turns/m is a reasonable design value.

Core loss is a function of the switching time, material, and temperature. A representative graph of core loss as a function of switching time is given in Figure 7–14; the values here are, in fact, the half-cycle losses, and to compute the total core loss, one needs to take the half-cycle core loss for the switching time and add to it the half-cycle core loss for the resetting time.

Winding and eddy-current losses may be important, and in order to minimize these losses, cores should be ordered with nonconducting casings. Typical winding configurations are single-layer windings that completely fill the core, and a representative configuration is shown in Figure 7–15. It may be that in order to conveniently fill the core utilizing this procedure, several wires must be used in parallel for each winding.

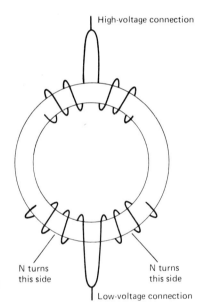

High-voltage connection

N turns this side

N turns this side

Low-voltage connection

FIGURE 7–15 Winding configuration for a saturable reactor. [4]

Since conductor losses may be appreciable, the use of litz wire may be of some benefit in order to reduce conductor losses, particularly for the shorter pulses. Table 7–5 gives a representative set of properties of Deltamax core material, while Table 7–6 lists key dimensions of a set of representative available Deltamax toroids.

TABLE 7-5 PROPERTIES OF DELTAMAX CORE MATERIAL

Property	Value
Specific gravity	8.25
Electrical resistivity	45 $\mu\Omega$/cm
Temperature for heat treatment	1075°C

Magnetic properties	DC	AC frequency (Hz)			
		60	100	400	
Initial permeability μ_i at 20 G	....	....	400–1700		
Maximum permeability μ_m (G/Oe)	70,000–250,000	40,000–100,000			
Maximum differential permeability $\Delta\mu_{max}$ (G/Oe)	....	100,000–400,000	....	55,000–250,000	
Residual induction B_r (G)	12,500–15,000	12,500–15,000	....	12,500–15,000	
Peak flux density B_p (G)	13,500–15,500	13,500–15,500	....	13,500–15,500	
B_r/B_p	....	0.92 minimum	....	0.92 minimum	
Coercive force H_c (Oe)	0.04–0.16	0.20–0.40	....	0.35–0.60	

TABLE 7-6   DIMENSIONS OF SELECTED DELTAMAX CORES

Core designation	Net core area 0.001" tape (cm²)	Mean path length (cm)	Actual core dimensions (in)			Cased core dimensions (nylon case)		
			ID	OD	HT	ID	OD	HT
T 9776	0.057	5.486	0.625	0.750	0.188	0.530	0.845	0.283
T 4168	0.076	8.977	1.000	1.250	0.125	0.900	1.36	0.22
T 6804	0.151	7.980	0.875	1.125	0.250	0.780	1.22	0.345
T 5958	0.171	6.483	0.625	1.000	0.188	0.530	1.095	0.283
T 8485	0.227	6.982	0.750	1.000	0.375	0.645	1.120	0.490
T 7665	0.302	7.980	0.750	1.250	0.250	0.655	1.345	0.345
T 7116	0.454	13.964	1.500	2.000	0.375	1.405	2.095	0.470
T 4178	0.605	17.954	2.000	2.500	0.500	1.840	2.645	0.620
T 9338	0.756	12.468	1.250	1.875	0.500	1.155	1.970	0.595
T 5737	4.535	30.921	3.250	4.500	1.500	3.805	4.665	1.655
T 9260	9.675	39.898	4.000	6.000	2.000	3.790	6.210	2.200

7-6 SPARK GAPS [9,18]

In its simplest form, a spark gap consists of electrodes separated by a gas, which can be hydrogen, nitrogen, air, or SF_6. Initiation of breakdown of the gap can be effected by subjecting the spark gap to overvoltage, ultraviolet radiation, laser illumination, or ionizing radiation.

Spark gaps have been utilized primarily for switches in discharge modulators, and they are still utilized for extremely high-voltage, high-power applications at relatively low PRFs; however, the primary application of spark gaps appears to be for high-energy crowbar diverting circuits in modulators.

The simplest form of a spark gap consists of two electrodes, and such a device will trigger if the applied voltage exceeds some certain critical value; in practice, this is a relatively inconvenient configuration, and multigap arrays are utilized, with breakdown initiated by the application of a trigger voltage to one of the interior elements, which then initiates breakdown of the entire device. A schematic representation of such a device is shown in Figure 7-16. The energy sources shown are to ensure that sufficient energy is available in order to sustain the breakdown across the entire array. Such multiple-gap devices can be fabricated by using a number of spheres, but a more practical approach is to utilize crossed rods or cylinders with their axes at right angles to each other.

Commercial triggered spark gaps are made that contain two primary electrodes and a third trigger electrode, hermetically sealed in a pressurized envelope. Representative of this type of spark gap are those made by EG&G, Inc., which consist of a heavy-wall ceramic cylinder body, brazed on each end to convex metal electrodes. The electrodes are identical except that one has an open area to accommodate the trigger-electrode wire and insulating bushing. The trigger probe is always located in the center of the adjacent electrode and facing the opposite electrode. For that reason the three elements in a triggered spark gap are referred to as the *trigger*, the *adjacent electrode*, and the *opposite electrode*.

Triggered spark gaps typically have peak current carrying-capacity of tens of thousands of amperes, ionization-delay times of a few nanoseconds, relatively low inductance, and a life of thousands to millions of shots, depending upon the application. Table 7-7 gives the principal characteristics of some of the triggered gaps manufactured by EG&G, Inc. Typical current and voltage waveforms for operation of a spark gap are given in Figure 7-17, showing the initiation of breakdown, the conduction region, and the recovery portion. If the minimum trigger voltage required to initiate a complete breakdown is plotted against main-electrode voltage (electrode-to-electrode, or E-E, voltage), a curve typical of all triggered spark gaps, shown in Figure 7-18, is generated.

This curve defines a region on the left where firing does not occur, called the *cutoff region;* a central region, called the *normal operating region;* and a region to the right of the point marked "static breakdown voltage" where the gap self-fires from overvoltage on the two main electrodes. Triggered spark gaps should always be operated above the minimum

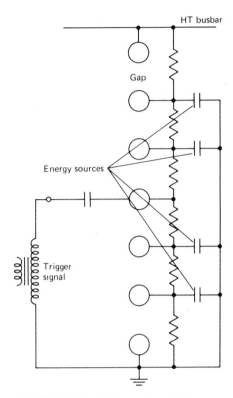

FIGURE 7–16 Triggered multiple gap. [17]

trigger voltage and well above the cutoff voltage portions of the curve to avoid the possibility of random misfire. Similarly they should be operated well below the static breakdown point to avoid the chance of prefire.

The important parts of the transfer characteristic curve include the following:

- Minimum trigger voltage $V_{t(\text{min})}$: the minimum open-circuit trigger voltage for reliable triggering. Spark gaps should be operated well above the minimum trigger voltage, if possible.

TABLE 7-7 CHARACTERISTICS OF TWO-ELECTRODE CERAMIC-METAL TRIGGERED GAPS [9]

E-E range (kV)		SBV (kV)	V, minimum (kV)	Delay time (ns)		Maximum repetitive discharge conditions
Minimum	Maximum			70% SBV	40% SBV	
0.7	2.1	2.6	5	100	1000	3 mC/shot
4.4	10	12.5	7	100	1000	3 mC/shot
8	20	25	10	30	300	4 mC/shot
12	36	42	20	30	300	100 mC/shot
25	69	86	20	30	300	100 mC/shot
40	100	120	20	30	300	100 mC/shot*

* Note: Higher values for single-shot operation. For this gap 4000 J switch energy, 100 kA peak current, and 5 C total charge may be switched.

• Cutoff voltage $(E\text{-}E)_{co}$: the main-electrode voltage marked by a sudden rise in minimum trigger voltage as the electrode-to-electrode voltage is reduced. Operating near cutoff should always be avoided, particularly near the knee of the transfer characteristic curve.

• Minimum operating voltage $(E\text{-}E)_{min}$: the minimum main-electrode voltage for reliable operation. This is equal to approximately ⅓ the maximum operating voltage.

• Maximum operating voltage $(E\text{-}E)_{max}$: typically 80% of self-breakdown voltage (SBV). This is chosen to prevent random prefires.

• Static breakdown voltage SBV: the point where the gap will self-fire with no trigger voltage applied. Pressure fill and electrode spacing determine this point.

• Range: the spread between minimum and maximum operating voltages. The normal gap operating range typically has a 3:1 ratio of maximum to minimum operating voltage. For the most

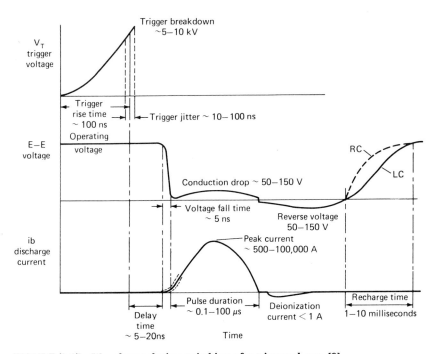

FIGURE 7–17 **Waveforms during switching of a triggered gap. [9]**

reliable operation with minimum delay time and jitter, triggered spark gaps should usually be operated at the high end of the range, between 60 and 80% of SBV.

It is also possible to make a triggered vacuum gap, and such devices have been used for switching applications requiring a wide range of operating voltages. These switches are used primarily in high-energy crowbar systems and are capable of a range of maximum to minimum operating voltage of 100 to 1, and a maximum rating on the order of 100 kV. Typical trigger-circuit requirements for such a gap include a

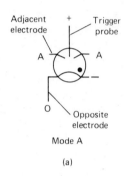

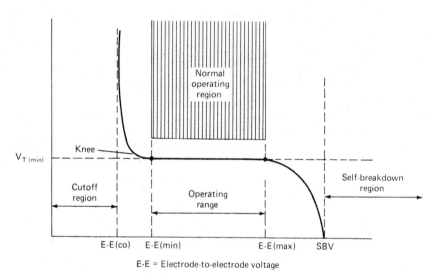

FIGURE 7–18   (*a*) **Schematic representation of a triggered gap, and** (*b*) *V-I* **characteristic for a triggered gap. [9].**

12-kV minimum open-circuit pulse voltage and a loaded current pulse in excess of 40 A.

REFERENCES

1. Arnold Engineering Company, "Tape Wound Cores," Data Sheet no. TC-101C, Marengo, Ill., 1978.

2. Brewster, J. B., and P. F. Pittman, "A New Solid-State Switch for Power Pulse Modulator Applications: The Reverse Switching Rectifier," in *Conf. Rec. 1973 11th Modulator Symp.*, September 1973, pp. 6–11.

3. Busch, K. J., A. D. Hasley, and C. Neitzert, "Magnetic Pulse Modulators," *Bell System Technical Journal*, vol. 34, September 1955, pp. 943–992.

4. Coate, G. T., and L. R. Swain, Jr., *High-Power Semiconductor-Magnetic Pulse Generators*, Research Nomograph 39, MIT Press, 1966. Figures 7–14 and 7–15 were reprinted with permission of MIT Press, Cambridge, Mass. (copyright © 1966 by the Massachusetts Institute of Technology; all rights reserved).

5. Crees, D. E., N. S. Nicholis, and F. Wood, "Thyristors for Pulse Modulation at High Peak and Average Powers," in *Conf. Rec. 1973 11th Modulator Symp.*, September 1973, pp. 12–16.

6. Doolittle, H. D., *Vacuum Power Tubes for Pulse Modulation*, pts. I and II, available from the Machlett Laboratories, Inc., Stamford, Conn.

7. EEV, Ltd., "Professional Electron Tubes," Data Sheet, Chelmsford, England, 1976.

8. EG&G, Inc., "Ceramic-Metal Hydrogen Thyratrons," Data Sheet H5000C-1, Salem, Mass., April 1974.

9. EG&G, Inc., "Ceramic-Metal Triggered Spark Gaps," Data Sheet G6000D-1, Salem, Mass., September 1975.

10. Glasoe, G. N., and J. V. Lebacqz, *Pulse Generators*, MIT Rad. Lab. series, vol. 5, McGraw-Hill, 1948.

11. Grafham, D. R., and F. B. Golden, eds., *SCR Manual, 6th ed.*, General Electric, Auburn, N.Y., 1979, sec. III.

12. Hill, R. A., and W. R. Olson, "Lightweight, High Power Modulator Uses RSR Switch Device," in *Proc. 10th Modulator Symp.*, May 1966, pp. 155–163.

13. Kadochnikov, A. I., I. E. Korobeynikova, and M. A. Kheyfets, "Calculation of the Current Pulse in a Section of a Magnetic Pulse Generator," *Telecommunications and Radio Engineering*, pt. 2, vol. 29, no. 8, 1974, pp. 90–94.

14. Krintz, A., "A Transistor-Magnetic Pulse Generator for Radar-Modulator Applications," MIT Report 7848-R-1, Cambridge, Mass., September 1958.

15. Krueger, T. O., and F. A. Vorwerk, "Modulator Performance of One Kilovolt Thyristors," in *Proc. 9th Modulator Symp.*, May 1966, pp. 294–305.

16. Manteuffel, E. W., and R. E. Cooper, "D-C Charged Magnetic Pulse Modulator," presented at AIEE-IRE Nonlinear Magnetics and Magnetic Amplifiers Conference, September 1959.

17. Melville, W. S., "The Use of Saturable Reactors as Discharge Devices for Pulse Generators," *Proc. IEE,* London, 1951, pp. 185–204.

18. Menown, H., "Gaseous Switches: The Past and Present State of the Art," in *Proc. Intern. Pulsed Power Conf.,* paper IA2, November 1976.

19. Motorola, Inc., Data Sheet MCR 729, Phoenix, Ariz.

20. Pittman, P. F., and D. J. Page, "Solid State High Power Pulse Switching," in *Proc. Intern. Pulsed Power Conf.,* paper IA3, November 1976.

21. Robinson, T. H., "Some Characteristics of Thyristors in High-Power Modulator Circuits," in *Proc. 9th Modulator Symp.,* May 1966, pp. 306–324.

22. Sutherland, R. I., *Care and Feeding of Power Grid Tubes,* Varian, Eimac Div., San Carlos, Calif., 1967, sec. 2.

23. Wechsler, R., "Reducing di/dt Effect Failures in Silicon Controlled Rectifiers," Motorola Application Note AN-173, Phoenix, Ariz., 1965.

8
SPECIFICATION OF TRANSMITTERS

The specifications for a high-power transmitter evolve from a set of system requirements. On the basis of these requirements, the necessary transmitter characteristics are determined, and these in turn determine the requirements for the RF tube and associated modulator. The RF tube and modulator requirements are not independent but interact and determine the requirements for the individual modulator components. A block diagram of this process is shown in Figure 8–1. The process may be an iterative one, selection of a tube or modulator impacting the overall system requirements, which in turn determine tube and modulator specifications.

Some of the types of overall system requirements that may arise include:

- Peak power
- Operating frequency range
- Bandwidth
- Pulse width
- PRF
- Gain
- Stability

- MTI (Doppler) performance
- Reliability
- Prime power
- Size and weight
- Cost
- Environment

and there certainly can be additional ones, depending upon the application.

The system requirements then give rise to requirements for the radar transmitter, which may include features such as:

- Operating frequency
- Bandwidth
- Pulse shape: width, rise, fall, flatness
- PRF
- Gain
- Stability

- Noise performance
- Size and weight
- Cost
- Reliability
- Out-of-band emissions
- Trigger and interface requirements

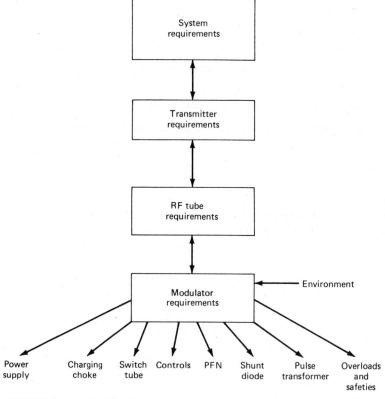

FIGURE 8–1   A block diagram of one approach to the process of setting the requirements associated with a radar transmitter.

These factors then enter into the specifications for the transmitter tube itself, which emphasizes features such as:

- Peak power
- Efficiency
- Operating-point voltage and current
- Filament requirements (surge currents included): filament-heater schedule
- Electromagnetic-compatibility requirements
- Magnetic shielding
- X-ray leakage
- Rise time
- Pushing
- Pulling
- Gain
- Phase and amplitude stability
- Shock and vibration resistance
- Cooling requirements (liquid and air)

- Arc-protection requirements
- Modulator protection required
- Bandwidth
- Duty cycle
- Average power
- Additional electrode or ion-pump voltage required
- Bandwidth
- Electrode capacitance
- Waveguide and electrode pressurization
- Flanges and connectors
- Size and weight
- Voltage- or current-source requirements
- Spurious emissions

Also arising from the general specifications are a number of requirements related to thermal performance, insulation, mechanical features, and the operating environment. Important considerations include:

- Operating ambient (maximum and minimum temperatures)
- Nonoperating ambient (maximum and minimum)
- Altitude (under operating and nonoperating conditions)

- Life expectancy under worst-case conditions
- Maximum hot-spot temperature
- Maximum skin temperature
- Major liquid insulation (mineral oil, askarel, silicone oil, FC-75, gas, other)

- Maximum humidity (is there condensation?)

- Rainfall

- Filling-liquid flash point

- Cooling

    Self-cooled?

    Liquid-cooled? Natural or forced oil circulation? Amount and temperature?

    Forced-air cooling?

- Shock specification

- Vibration specification

- Sealing and leak test requirements

- Operating position (inclination) and oscillating period for mechanical testing

- Finish specification

- Lifting rings (size and location)

- Include block drawing with maximum dimensions that indicates provisions for waveguide, electrical connections, controls, coding, attachment points

- RF interference and leakage

- Presence of salt spray

- Terminal strength

At this point, one can proceed to name the requirements for the individual component parts of the modulator: for a line-type modulator these requirements would cover the power supply, the charging choke, the switch, and the pulse-forming network, as well as the control and monitoring requirements, the safety and overload requirements, the shunt-diode requirements, and finally the pulse-transformer requirements. Similar requirements could be generated for other types of modulators, including hard-tube and magnetic modulators.

Power-supply considerations may include:

- Voltage

- Ripple

- Average current

- Peak current

- RMS current

- Prime power

- Size and weight

- Efficiency

    - Overload circuits: type and speed of action

    - Stored energy

    - Altitude and environmental specifications

The charging-choke, or reactor, requirements emphasize features such as:

- Configuration
- Inductance
- Linearity
- DC voltage
- Possible peak voltage
- Speed of overload action
- Peak current
- Average current

- RMS current
- All environmental and mechanical specifications
- PFN capacitance
- Charging time
- Stray capacities
- Efficiency

The switch for discharging the PFN requires determination of factors such as:

- Peak voltage
- Peak current
- Average current
- RMS current
- Grid-drive requirements
- Heater requirements
- Reservoir voltage and current
- Auxiliary-electrode voltage requirements

while the PFN itself requires a knowledge of:

- Number of sections
- C_n
- L_n
- l/d for coil
- All environmental requirements

- Rise time
- Fall time
- Ripple
- Mismatch
- Z_0

The shunt, or clipping, diode requires that factors such as the following be determined:

- Inverse voltage
- Peak current
- Average current
- Series impedance required
- Discharge characteristics

Particularly important are the pulse-transformer characteristics, including:

- Load type
- Static and dynamic load characteristics
- Total stray capacitance
- Filament requirements
- Pulse voltage and current
- Type of source
- Impedance
- Required rise and fall time connected to load
- Winding configuration
- Resetting currents
- Trigger windings
- Pulse length and PRF
- 10% to 90% rise, maximum and minimum
- Allowable droop and ripple
- Tail-of-pulse requirements: backswing, overshoot
- Special bushings or cathode wells
- Turns ratio

The controls and the provisions for monitoring operation of the transmitter must also be set forth. These may include:

- OFF-STANDBY-RADIATE
- HV RAISE-LOWER
- FREQUENCY TUNE
- HVDC
- SHUNT DIODE I
- TUBE I
- Power-supply current

- Current pulse

- Detected RF

- Radiate and filament time monitors

The proper operation of the transmitter must include a discussion of the safety and overload requirements, which might include:

- PS current

- Tube current

- Temperature

- Coolant flow

- Shunt-diode current

- Tube arcing

- Reflected power

- Waveguide arc

- Solenoid current

The final portion of the modulator specification should include a thorough presentation of the testing requirements that will be used to verify compliance with the various specifications discussed above, and a specification of the condition and place for final acceptance.

The level of specification that is required for a particular modulator or transmitter should be adequate for the intended purpose, but should not be carried to a level that places the designer in a contradictory position (where requirements are such that they may not be simultaneously satisfied). The specification should not overly restrict design choices, but should permit the freedom to utilize the designer's particular resources and capabilities in order to generate an optimum design.

If it is the intention to subcontract the entire transmitter to a transmitter manufacturer, one might, for example, only specify to the modulator requirements level; however, if it is intended to design the modulator in-house, and to manufacture components at one's own assembly facility, one might in that case want to proceed down to the lowest level of specification to help ensure a satisfactory design.

9
SAMPLE DESIGNS

In this chapter, sample designs for a number of different modulator types are presented. In Section 9–1 the component design of a line-type modulator with a hydrogen thyratron switch will be carried out, while in Section 9–2, the design of an SCR-magnetic modulator will be treated in some detail. In Section 9–3, a hard-tube modulator design for a low-powered EIO, which requires unusual flatness and freedom from ringing in order to minimize FM on the pulse, will be described, along with a floating-deck cathode modulator, while in Section 9–4 several approaches to grid-pulsing a TWT will be described. Finally, in Section 9–5 a design for a large, high-power, floating-deck modulator is discussed.

9–1 LINE-TYPE MODULATOR COMPONENT DESIGN

For this representative design a magnetron is selected with an operating point of 20 kV and 22 A and a stray capacitance of 20 pF. The maximum allowable rate of rise of voltage will be 225 kV/μs. Heater (filament) requirements are 12 V at 1.3 A.

General Modulator Characteristics

It is assumed a line-type modulator is specified, using pulse-transformer coupling to the load, and that a hydrogen thyratron is used as a switch tube. It will be designed for a 0.25-μs pulse width and a PRF of 4000 pulse/s. The static operating impedance is then

$$\frac{20 \text{ kV}}{22 \text{ A}} = 910 \text{ } \Omega$$

Assume a pulse-forming network (PFN) impedance Z_o of 50 Ω; then the turns ratio of a transformer to match the load impedance Z_l is

$$n = \left(\frac{Z_l}{Z_o}\right)^{1/2}$$

$$= \left(\frac{910}{50}\right)^{1/2} = 4.26 : 1$$

It may be desirable to mismatch the PFN by approximately 5% in some cases, but that will not be done in this example. This is most common for the high PRFs to promote thyratron deionization. The peak thyratron anode current is then approximately

$$i_b = I_{op} \times M$$
$$= 22 \text{ A} \times 4.26 = 93.7 \text{ A}$$

and the peak anode voltage is given by

$$e_{py} = \frac{2V_{op}}{n}$$

$$= \frac{2 \times 20 \text{ kV}}{4.26} = 9.37 \text{ kV}$$

From the discussion under Recharge Interval in Section 3–2, the required dc supply voltage is then given (assuming a Q of 10 or greater) by

$$E_{bb} = \frac{e_{py}}{1.9}$$

$$= \frac{9.37 \text{ kV}}{1.9} = 4.94 \text{ kV} \approx 5 \text{ kV}$$

Switch-Tube Selection

It has already been shown that

$$e_{py} = 9.37 \text{ kV}$$
$$i_b = 93.7 \text{ A}$$
$$PRF = 4000 \text{ pulse/s}$$

Then, from Section 7–1, the P_b factor is

$$P_b = e_{py} i_b \times \text{PRF} = 3.5 \times 10^9 \text{ W/s}$$

A suitable tube might be a ceramic hydrogen thyratron such as the EG&G, Inc., HY-9 (7782), which has a rating of

$$e_{py} = 16 \text{ kV}$$
$$i_b = 350 \text{ A}$$
$$P_b = 4 \times 10^9$$

PFN Characteristics

From the specifications already given,

$$\tau = 0.25 \ \mu s$$
$$Z_0 = 50 \ \Omega$$

Then the total network capacitance is given by Equation 5–1:

$$C_n = \frac{\tau}{2 Z_0} = \frac{0.25 \times 10^{-6}}{100} = 2500 \text{ pF}$$

and the total network inductance by Equation 5–2

$$L_n = \tau Z_0/2 = \frac{(0.25 \times 10^{-6}) \times 50}{2} = 6.25 \ \mu H$$

Additional design considerations will follow in later sections.

Charging-Choke Parameters

Assume that a charging diode will be used and that it is desired to charge to full voltage in 90% of the interpulse period. Assume 100 pF of stray capacity in all of the anode-connected components; thus, for a resonant period $T_r = 225 \ \mu s$ and total capacity $C_{tot} = 2600$ pF, the value of inductance required from Section 3–2 is

$$L = \frac{T_r^2}{\pi^2 C_{tot}}$$
$$= \frac{(2.25 \times 10^{-4})^2}{\pi^2 (2.6 \times 10^{-9})} = 1.97 \text{ H}$$
$$\approx 2.0 \text{ H}$$

Pulse-Transformer Configuration

There are four transformer configurations that are commonly considered for applications in this power range. These are as follows:

- The single-layer-primary, single-layer-secondary using a low-capacity filament transformer

- The single-layer primary, double-wound- (*bifilar*-wound-) secondary supplying voltage to a filament transformer at magnetron-cathode potential

- A single-layer-primary, single-layer-, bifilar-wound-secondary, the bifilar secondary directly supplying the magnetron filament

- The Lord-type winding, which has windings on both legs of the core, with parallel-connected primaries, partially interleaved primary and secondary windings, and series-connected secondary windings

The first two configurations are used only for high–filament-current applications; this is not the case for the present application. The third configuration has considerable advantages because of its ease of manufacture, but obtaining desired values of leakage inductance and stray capacitance often dictates the use of the Lord winding. A final choice will be made during the detailed component design.

The detailed design of a pulse transformer can proceed along a number of lines; each of these procedures attempts to arrive at optimum values for exciting current, leakage inductance, and stray capacitance in the final design.

Early design criteria (such as those described in the Rad. Lab. series, Vol. 5), attempted to keep exciting current to a reasonable value (say 10%) and match the "impedance" (ratio of leakage inductance to stray capacitance) to both the magnetron and PFN while minimizing the energy stored in the transformer. Such a design procedure results in a design having minimum rise time.

In recent years, it has become more widely recognized that the rate of rise of voltage (or rise time) should fall within a certain range, and that too fast a rise time will result in tube moding and improper operation.

Thus, improved design criteria for pulse transformers are

- Limiting transformer exciting current to a reasonable value (usually 10%)

- Matching the impedance of the transformer to that of the tube

- Achieving the specified rise time

Unfortunately, this approach often results in considerable energy stored in the transformer, with possible heating problems; these will be treated in the detailed design procedure.

This then completes the discussion of the preliminary design of the modulator; of course, the dc power supply, the overload circuits, the thyratron driver, and other components must be designed and the charging and shunt diodes selected, but these are relatively straightforward tasks. A few words of caution are indicated:

- Overloads: The ratings of components such as the power supply, the charging diode, and the shunt diode, and the response time of the overload protection circuits, are closely interrelated. Be sure the overload circuits react rapidly and that components are conservatively rated.

- Thyratron driver: The drive requirements on manufacturer's data sheets are minimum values. Provide a safety margin. Be sure that the drive-circuit impedance remains low under all load conditions; be sure to provide negative thyratron grid bias where necessary.

The remaining sections deal with the detailed design of the principal modulator components: the charging choke, the pulse-forming network, and the pulse transformer.

Charging-Choke Design

The basic design requirement is to have a reactor that has the required value of inductance, has a reasonably high Q (low losses), and will withstand the required voltages. An iterative procedure will be used; i.e., a core will be selected and a trial design made. Usually, some aspect of the trial design will be unsatisfactory and so adjustments will be made and the process repeated until a satisfactory design is achieved.

The basic steps in the design procedure are as follows:

- Select a core.
- Assume an initial flux density.
- Calculate the number of turns in the coil.
- Select an air gap.
- Check the ratio of air gap to core length.
- Design the coil.
- Check the Q of the design.
- Calculate the temperature rise of the coil.

If good engineering practice is violated during the design procedure, an earlier design choice (such as core selection or flux density) must be modified and the intermediate steps repeated.

Magnetic core material of 4% silicon steel in 4-mil strips formed into a cut C core will be used. Because of the high operating voltage involved, oil-impregnated kraft paper will be utilized for insulation, and the finished choke will be hermetically sealed in an oil-filled container. A cross-sectional view of the type of construction normally used for charging chokes is shown in Figure 9–1, along with names of the principal parts of the choke.

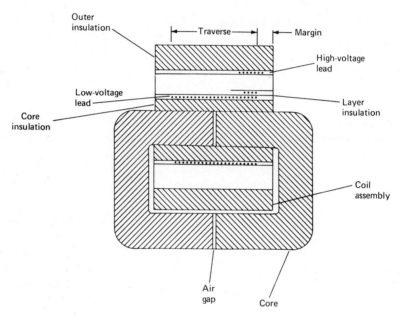

FIGURE 9–1 Cross-sectional view of a charging choke, showing major features and nomenclature.

A large number of standard cores are available, but the choice can often be limited by the available window (the opening in the middle of the core) space for the coil. The insulation from the first winding to the core must withstand 5 kV; at 25 V/mil this will require 0.2 in. The outer wrap must stand 10 kV; at 50 V/mil this will also require 0.2 in of insulation. Thus, 0.4 in of insulation is required, without any allowance for windings. Since several thousand turns may be required, window heights less than ¾ to 1 in will not normally be considered. Also, a relatively long window is desirable in order to efficiently package the windings, because of the coil margins required to keep creep stress at a reasonable value.

After an examination of catalogs of standard magnetic cores, a tentative selection of H-25 is made (this core has a $^{15}\!/_{16} \times 2\!\frac{1}{2}$-in window). As an initial guess, assume a maximum ac flux of 7 kilogauss (kG); then the number of turns is given by Equation 6–2,

$$N = \frac{4.93 \times 10^6 E_{dc} T_r}{AS \, \Delta B_{ac}}$$

Using a stacking factor S of 0.9 and a value of A of 1.29 in², one obtains

$$N = \frac{4.93 \times 10^6 \times 5000 \times 225 \times 10^{-6}}{1.29 \times 0.9 \times 7000}$$

$$= 682 \text{ turns}$$

Then the air gap is given by Equation 6–3,

$$a = \frac{3.2 \times N^2 \times A \times 10^{-8}}{L}$$

or, for a 2-H inductance,

$$a = \frac{3.2 \times 682^2 \times 1.29 \times 10^{-8}}{2}$$

$$= 0.0096 \text{ in}$$

The length of the magnetic core for the H-25 core is given by

$$l = 2F + 2G + 2.9E$$

then from Table 6–1

$$l = 2(0.938) + 2(2.5) + 2.9(0.938) = 9.596 \text{ in}$$

The ratio of air gap to core length is given by

$$\frac{a}{l} = \frac{0.0096}{9.596} = 0.1\%$$

Since this value is smaller than the smallest allowable value (0.6%), increase the turns by $\sqrt{6} \approx 2.5$; the resulting values will be

$$N = 1705 \text{ turns}$$
$$B_{ac} = 2800 \text{ G}$$
$$a = 0.06 \text{ in}$$

Note that the particular value of a is usually adjusted to obtain the desired value of L during assembly. The value of I_{dc} is given by

$$I_{dc} = \text{PRF } C_n \ (1.9 \ E_{dc})$$
$$= (4000)(2.5 \times 10^{-9})(1.9 \times 5000)$$
$$= 95 \text{ mA}$$

and from Equation 6–3

$$B_{dc} = 0.16 \frac{NI_{dc}}{a}$$

$$= 0.16 \times 1705 \times \frac{0.095}{0.06}$$

$$= 432 \text{ G}$$

Since $B_{dc} + B_{ac}$ is considerably less than 15 kG, the core will definitely not saturate.

The next major step is to design the coil; assume the use of #30 wire with heavy Polythermaleze insulation (diameter = 0.0116 in). The available window is 2.5 in; subtracting 0.1 in for mechanical spacing leaves 2.4 in for the coil. Margins for 10 kV voltage at 25 V/mil are 0.4 in at each end, leaving 1.6 in for winding. Assuming a 0.9 space factor for windings, this allows

$$\frac{1.6}{0.0116} \times 0.9 = 124 \text{ turns/layer}$$

Then the required number of layers is

$$\frac{1705}{124} = 14 \text{ layers}$$

The maximum voltage across each insulating layer is given by the voltage at the end of the coil winding and is equal to twice the voltage developed across each coil winding. The voltage per coil layer is

$$2 \times \frac{5000}{14} = 714 \text{ V/layer}$$

The required interlayer insulation is stressed at 50 to 100 V/mil, and 14 mils is required if a stress of 50 V/mil is selected.

The radial build of the coil can now be summarized as

Core insulation	0.2 in
14 layers of 0.014-in paper and 0.0116 in wire	0.358
Outer wrap	0.2
	0.758 in

$$\times 1.2 \text{ build factor} = 0.910 \text{ in}$$

which will fit in the window available. It should be emphasized that the last (outer) winding should be space-wound to accommodate the impulsive voltage stress that occurs upon thyratron switching.

The next step is to check the Q of the choke. The core loss component is, from the manufacturer's data sheet in Figure 6–1 for 2.8 kG and 4 kHz PRF

$$3 \text{ W/lb} \times 3.08 \text{ lb} \approx 9\text{W}$$

The copper losses are next calculated by first determining the mean turn length to be approximately 11 in, or the total wire length to be 1563 ft. From wire tables, the resulting resistance of the #30 wire is 156 Ω. For an rms current of 0.1 A, the resulting power loss is 1.56 W.

The fringing loss is given by Equation 6–5, with

$$k = 3.22 \times 10^{-3}$$
$$D = 1.38 \text{ in}$$
$$a = 0.06 \text{ in}$$
$$f = 2222, \text{ corresponding to a charging period of 225 } \mu\text{s}$$
$$W_g = 3.22 \times 10^{-3} \times 1.38 \times 0.06 \times 2222 \times (2.8)^2 \times 2 = 9.3 \text{ W}$$

Then, the total power is 19.86 W, and for the rms current of 0.1 A, from Equation 6–6

$$R_{eq} = 1986 \text{ } \Omega$$

or from Equation 6–7,

$$Q = \omega L/R_{eq} = \frac{(2\pi)(2000)(2)}{1976} \approx 13$$

an acceptable value.

The remainder of the design procedure involves the calculation of the hot-spot temperature. The total losses in the core are 18.3 W. This heat is conducted to the oil through the edges of the core laminations, which are not covered by the coil. This area is calculated by subtracting the coil length from l (length of the magnetic circuit) and multiplying the resulting figure by twice the core buildup; i.e.,

$$(9.6 - 2.4) \times 2 \times 0.938 = 13.51 \text{ in}^2$$

The resulting power density is 0.74 W/in², and according to Figure 4–22, the rise of core over oil is 18°C.

The copper losses were earlier calculated to be 1.56 W; this is distributed over an area given by the product of the mean length of turn and the winding traverse. The resulting area is

$$11 \times 1.6 = 17.60 \text{ in}^2$$

and the heat flux is 0.09 W/in². This flows through ½ in of insulation. The resulting temperature rise is

$$(250)(0.09)(0.5) = 11.25°C$$

The total power dissipated by the choke is 19.86 W; assume the choke is to be enclosed in a 3- x 3- x 4.5-in can. The internal area of the can is then

$$2 \times 3^2 + 4 \times 3 \times 4.5 = 72 \text{ in}^2$$

and the resulting heat flux is

$$\frac{19.86}{72} = 0.28 \text{ W/in}^2$$

From Figure 4–22, using the upper side of the empirical curves, it can be seen that the drop from case to oil is approximately 6°C.

Assume the can is mounted on the 3- x 3-in base; then the area available for transfer of heat to the air is 63 in² (72 − 9), and the heat flux is

$$\frac{19.86}{63} = 0.32 \text{ W/in}^2$$

As seen in Figure 4–21, the rise from case to ambient is approximately 42°C.

The hot-spot temperature will thus occur at the core surface; summing the drops from core to ambient, one obtains,

Core to oil	18°C
Oil to case	6°C
Case to ambient	42°C
Drop from core to ambient	66°C

Thus, the design can operate in a 39°C ambient without exceeding a calculated hot-spot temperature of 105°C. If operation at higher temperatures is desired, fins or forced-air cooling might be used, or a design with a lower flux density might be attempted. It should be noted that these calculations are somewhat conservative, since heat loss through the base is ignored; this extra caution is used to provide a greater margin of safety in the final design.

The remaining steps in the design procedure involve high-voltage bushing selection, and detailed design of the core mounting fixture and the case. Since these procedures are relatively straightforward and will differ greatly depending upon the application, they will not be treated in detail here.

A charging choke was built in accordance with this design with 0.030-in Teflon spacers in each core gap. Initial measured inductance was 1.98 H at 1000 Hz, but when all was assembled and finally banded, a value of 1.85 H was measured. The choke resonated with its own capacity with approximately a 100-μs period; measured capacity from case to coil was 66 pF. The charging time of the network remained essentially unchanged for variations in voltage and average current from maximum values down to essentially zero current. The measured charging period to back-biasing of the charging diode was approximately 245 μs, slightly longer than the design value, but still acceptable, and charging efficiency was greater than 95%.

Pulse-Forming Network Design

There are two basic aspects of PFN design: capacitor design and coil design. The design assumes an E-type network with equal-value capacitors; these capacitors may be either fabricated or purchased. A constant-diameter tapped coil will be used; since the coil is usually tuned (i.e., tap positions are adjusted) to optimize the waveform, and since the coils are relatively easy to make, coils are normally fabricated in-house.

The network values are

$$C_n = 2500 \text{ pF}$$
$$L_n = 6.25 \text{ μH}$$

To follow the discussion in Chapter 5, a three-section network is initially assumed.

For the three-section network, the ratio of coil diameter to length is 0.25, and Nagaoka's constant is .91. If a 0.5-in diameter form is chosen, then the length will be 2 in. The required number of turns is given by Equation 5–3:

$$N = \left(\frac{(10)(6.25)(2)}{(0.5^2)(0.91)} \right)^{1/2} = 24 \text{ turns}$$

The resulting coil can be close-wound with #13 wire, or space-wound with a smaller-diameter wire. The use of space winding on a threaded form is probably more satisfactory, because of the ease of adjusting the taps. Suitable initial taps are at 9, 16, and 24 turns.

The network will contain three equal-value capacitors, each approximately 830 pF; either paper or reconstituted-mica paper can be used. Often the capacitors are purchased from outside sources, but they can also be fabricated; if it is desired to fabricate the capacitors, the following observations may be useful. If paper is used, one might select for each capacitor five series-connected sections with 14 to 20 layers of 0.5-mil paper for insulation for each section. If reconstituted mica is selected, one might use two series-connected sections with 5 to 10 sheets of 2-mil mica between foils. As with all other high-power components, the temperature rise of the resulting design must be checked.

Later in the design procedure, the initial choice of a three-section network will be found unsuitable, since this results in too rapid a rise time. Thus, a two-section network will be used in the final design. The total inductance will remain at 6.25 μH, but a ratio of diameter to length of 0.375 or a Nagaoka's constant of .86 will be required, and this will be realized as 45 turns of #28 wire space-wound on a 0.375-in diameter coil 1 in long. The total network capacitance will still be 2500 pF, but it will now consist of two 1250-pF capacitors; all other earlier comments on capacitor design will still apply to this two-section network.

Pulse-Transformer Design

The approach to be followed in pulse-transformer design has been briefly discussed in Chapter 4, and it is worth repeating that considerable emphasis will be placed on achieving a specified value of rise time, *not* on minimizing the rise time. The basic procedure to be followed is:

- Select a core.
- Calculate the number of turns, assuming an initial flux density.
- Check the exciting current.
- Design the coil.
- Calculate L_l and C_d.
- Check the temperature rise of the design.

If any of these steps produces results that fall outside the expected range, one of the earlier assumptions must be modified and the process repeated.

The initial choice of winding configuration will be the single-layer primary, single-layer, bifilar-wound secondary (two identical single layers, one on top of the other, separated by minimum insulation, constitute the secondary) with an oil-paper insulation system. Figure 9–2 shows a cross-sectional view of such a pulse transformer, with the principal components identified. Longer pulse lengths or faster rise times might require selecting some other configuration, such as the Lord winding.

Again, the initial choice of a core is somewhat arbitrary, but certain cores can be rejected on the ground that the available window will be too small. After an examination of a list of standard cores, an L-19

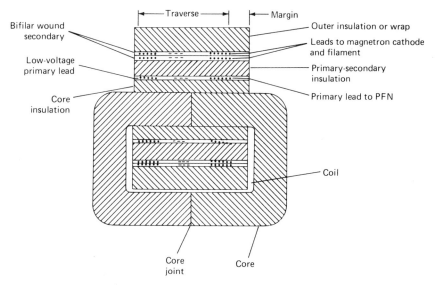

FIGURE 9–2 **Cross-sectional view of a typical simple (single-layer-primary, single-layer-, bifilar-wound-secondary) high-voltage pulse transformer, showing major features and nomenclature.**

core is selected for an initial trial. A 4-kG initial choice of flux-density change is assumed (see Figure 4–23); then, from Equation 4–3,

$$V/N = \frac{6.45 AS\,\Delta B}{t \times 10^8}$$

$$= \frac{6.45 \times 0.5 \times 0.89 \times 4000}{0.25 \times 10^2} = 459 \text{ V/turn}$$

For 20 kV voltage this requires

$$\frac{20,000}{459} = 44 \text{ turns}$$

Then the exciting current is given by Equation 4–4 ($l = 5.83$ in):

$$I_m = \frac{2.02\,\Delta B\,l}{N\mu_e} = \frac{2.02 \times 4000 \times 5.83}{44 \times 440} = 2.43 \text{A}$$

where μ_e is obtained from Figure 4–17. The desired value of I_m is 2.2 A, so increase the number of turns to

$$44 \sqrt{\frac{2.43}{2.2}} = 46 \text{ turns}$$

The next step is to begin design of the coil. The window length is $1\frac{9}{16}$ in, less $\frac{1}{16}$ in for mechanical fit; thus 1.5 in is the coil length. Allowing 0.1 in at the low-voltage end for support and 0.6 in at the high-voltage end for creep stress (30 V/mil) leaves 0.8 in for winding 46 turns. This would require #28 wire, but even if a 100% space factor could be used, this wire size would have a current density much larger than would be acceptable.

Thus, one might be led to select a core with a longer window. Consider an L-24 core. For an initial choice of flux change of 4 kG, the turns required will be

$$\frac{V}{N} = \frac{6.45 \times 0.625 \times 0.89 \times 4000}{0.25 \times 10^2} = 574 \text{ V/turn}$$

For 20 kV voltage,

$$N = \frac{20,000}{574} = 35 \text{ turns}$$

The magnetizing current ($l = 7.96$ in) is given by

$$I_m = \frac{2.02 \times 4000 \times 7.96}{35 \times 400} = 4.59 \text{A}$$

Since this exciting current is too large, the turns should then be increased to

$$35 \sqrt{\frac{4.59}{2.2}} = 51 \text{ turns}$$

Allowing $\frac{1}{16}$ in for mechanical tolerance leaves 2.25 in of coil length. Allowing 0.1 in for low-end margins and 0.6 in at the high end permits a 0.0273-in diameter wire (use #22, with a diameter of 0.0267 in, assuming a space factor of 0.9. This gives 2A/(1000 cmil), a value somewhat high, but one that will yield an acceptable temperature rise in later calculations.

The primary winding should be the same length as the secondary. The required 12 turns will have the correct traverse if three #19 wires are used in parallel for the conductor.

The detailed build calculations for the core are as follows:

Core insulation	0.200 in
Primary (#19 wire, three in parallel)	0.038
Insulation pad (15 kV at 300 V/mil)	0.050
Secondary 1 (#22 wire)	0.027
Insulation	0.004
Secondary 2 (#22 wire)	0.027
Outer wrap	0.070
	0.416 in

$$\times 1.25 \text{ build factor} = 0.52 \text{ in}$$

which should fit the window with room to spare. Actually, it might be more desirable to take more care in winding to be able to fit #21 wire into the available window, to reduce current density in the wire even further, but this will not be necessary.

The next step requires calculation of the distributed capacity and leakage inductance of the coil, which are in turn related to the rise time and the tube impedance. The desired rise time of the entire modulator is approximately

$$\frac{20 \text{ kV}}{225 \text{ kV}/\mu s} = 0.09 \text{ } \mu s$$

The rise time of the three-section PFN itself is approximately 0.04 μs, and so the pulse transformer rise time will be given by

$$(0.09^2 - 0.04^2)^{1/2} = 0.08 \text{ } \mu s$$

Assume 2 pF of stray capacitance for bushings and 2 pF for leads; when combined with the load stray capacitance, this results in a total

$$C_l = 24 \text{ pF}$$

The desired value of leakage inductance is from Equation 4–5

$$L_l = \frac{t_r}{1.3} \times R_p = \frac{0.08 \times 10^{-6}}{1.3} \times 910 = 56 \text{ } \mu H$$

and from Equation 4–6, the distributed capacitance

$$C_d = \frac{t_r}{1.3 R_p} - C_l = \frac{0.08 \times 10^{-6}}{1.3 \times 910} - 24 \times 10^{-12} = 44 \text{ pF}$$

In order to calculate values of L_l and C_d for the transformer, a few parameters need to be calculated (see Figure 4–9).

$N_s = 51$ turns

$S_1 = 0.050 \times 1.25 = 0.0625$ in

$\Sigma a = \dfrac{0.0359 + 0.0263}{2} = 0.05$ (Note: Pulse current flows in only one-half the wire.)

$t = 2.24 - 0.1 - 0.6 = 1.6$ in

$k = 4.5$ (oil-paper insulation)

$l_c = 2(1.0 + 0.625 + \pi \times 0.26) = 4.9$ in

$n = 4.26$

In calculating l_c it is assumed the mean length of turn goes through the middle of the 0.050-in insulation pad; thus l_c is the sum of the core cross-section perimeter and the circumference of a circle having a radius equal to the distance from the mean turn to the surface of the core.

Then, from Figure 4–9,

$$C_d(\text{pF}) = \frac{0.225 \times 4.5 \times 4.9 \times 1.6}{0.0625}$$

$$\times \left(\frac{1}{3} - \frac{2}{3(4.26)} + \frac{1}{3(4.26)^2}\right) = 24.8 \text{ pF}$$

$$L_l(\mu\text{H}) = \frac{0.032 \times 51^2 \times 4.9}{1.6}\left(0.0625 + \frac{0.03}{3}\right) = 18.5 \ \mu\text{H}$$

These values are not even close to the desired values; i.e., the rise time will be much too *fast;* one approach to use in this case is to reduce the number of PFN sections in order to increase PFN rise time, thus permitting a faster transformer rise time.

If a two-section network is assumed, its rise time will be about 0.0625 μs, and the desired transformer rise time will be

$$(0.09^2 - 0.0625^2)^{1/2} = 0.06 \ \mu\text{s}$$

The desired value of leakage inductance becomes

$$L_l = \frac{0.06 \times 10^{-6}}{1.3} \times 910 = 42 \ \mu\text{H}$$

and that of distributed capacity becomes

$$C_d = \frac{0.06 \times 10^{-6}}{1.3 \times 910} - 24 \times 10^{-12} = 26.7 \text{ pF}$$

The capacitance, then, is slightly too small, but still within tolerances (10%). The desired inductance is somewhat larger than achieved; this adjustment is best accommodated by adding a small external inductor of value

$$\frac{(42 - 18.5)}{(4.26)^2} = 1.3 \ \mu\text{H}$$

in the pulse-transformer primary circuit.

If, on the other hand, the value of L_t for the transformer is larger than desired, one of the winding configurations should be selected to have a portion of the secondary interleaved with the primary. If the capacitance needs to be reduced, the primary-secondary spacing can be increased or a different insulating material (such as Teflon) used.

With the use of a two-section network along with the 1.3-μH additional inductance in the primary circuit (placed in series with thyratron anode), the electrical parameters will be considered satisfactory.

The remaining calculations involve the thermal performance of the transformer. Sources of heat include the following:

- Energy stored in the core

- Energy stored in the stray capacitance

- Energy stored in the leakage inductance

- Power dissipated by pulse currents

- Power dissipated by filament current

Experience has shown that the third and fourth items are usually rather small compared with other contributions. If a shunt diode and resistor are used, most of the energy in the stray capacitance and that stored in the core will be dissipated in the shunt diode and resistor.

The power in the distributed capacitance is given by

$$\frac{1}{2} C_d V^2 \times \text{PRF} = \frac{1}{2} (24.8 \times 10^{-12})(2 \times 10^4)^2(4000) = 19.9 \ \text{W}$$

thus showing the desirability of using a shunt diode. In our design, the use of a shunt diode and resistor will be assumed; the shunt will absorb approximately 75–90% of this power (an empirical factor), leaving about 4 W converted to heat within the transformer from this source.

The power stored in the core due to magnetizing current is given by $(2/3)E_oI_m \times$ duty cycle (W), or

$$\frac{2}{3} (2 \times 10^4)(2.2)(0.001) = 29 \ \text{W}$$

The power dissipated by the filament current is obtained by calculating the wire length as

$$51 \times 4.9 \times 2 = 500 \text{ in} = 41.7 \text{ ft}$$

and the wire resistance as 0.53 Ω, for a dissipated power of 0.9 W.

The maximum temperature rise will occur at the core surface; the core dissipates 33 W. The area of the exposed edges of the core available for heat transfer (not covered by the coil) is approximately 7.14 in² (calculated as the core length of 7.96 in less the coil coverage of 2.25 in multiplied by the core edge thickness of 0.625 in, multiplied by 2). The resulting heat flux is 4.6 W/in², which from the upper bound of the empirical data from Figure 4–22 should produce a temperature rise from core to oil of about 40°C.

The total power dissipated in the case is approximately 34 W. Assume that a 4- x 4- x 5-in can is used, corresponding to a total area of 116 in², or a heat flux of 0.3 W/in²; thus, an 8°C rise will occur from case to oil.

The area available for heat transfer to the air is approximately 100 in² (assuming a 4- x 4-in base); the corresponding heat flux is approximately 0.34 W/in². Thus, the case-to-ambient rise is approximately 25°C (see Figure 4–21).

The temperature rise from ambient to core is approximately 73°C, permitting operation to an ambient temperature of approximately 32°C.

The remaining tasks involve the design of the mechanical mounting and the selection of bushings; as before, this is strongly application-dependent and will not be treated in detail here. The final design step is actual operation of the transformer, with particular attention to the tail-of-pulse performance. A transformer was fabricated in accordance with this design and operated on both resistive and magnetron loads. On a 7208B magnetron load, the rise time from 10% to 90% of full output voltage was slightly less than 100 ns, and the backswing voltage was approximately 5 kV; there was no recrossing of the axis either close to or distant from the output pulse.

9–2 SCR-MAGNETIC MODULATOR

There are a number of different forms of magnetic modulators that may be utilized in order to achieve different design objectives. In order to present the principles of the design of a saturating reactor for use in a magnetic modulator, the relatively straightforward configuration shown in Figure 9–3 has been selected for analysis. This modulator was designed to pulse a resistive load; it also incorporates multiple windings on the reactor L_2 and saturating transformer T_1 to ensure current sharing among the multiple SCRs used to handle the required current. The specific modulator design is adapted from Coate and Swain [1]. In this configuration, the switching of the charging SCR initiates charging of the low-voltage storage capacitor from the dc supply. Once the storage capacitor has been completely charged, the switching SCRs are triggered,

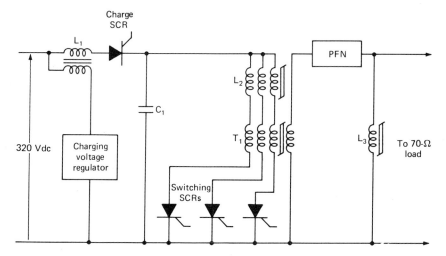

FIGURE 9–3 Simplified schematic diagram of SCR-magnetic modulator used in the design example.

applying the storage-capacitor voltage across the primary of saturating transformer T_1, charging the pulse-forming network through the saturated inductance of L_2 and L_3. Once the pulse-forming network has been completely charged, T_1 saturates, discharging the PFN into the load. Inductor L_3 is biased to saturation to provide a low-inductance charging path around the load. Auxiliary windings on L_2, T_1, and L_3 are utilized in order to provide suitable magnetic bias for the cores.

The design of an SCR-magnetic modulator can be carried out in a number of different ways. The particular design procedures may be dependent upon the specific modulator configuration considered, including the number of compressive stages employed. Because of certain inaccuracies and approximations in the equations employed in the design of SCR-magnetic modulators, along with the variability of the magnetic core materials, analytical design approaches are used primarily as guidelines, and the actual design is refined on the basis of experience obtained by operating these initial designs in test circuits. For this reason, the design of SCR-magnetic modulators is often quite expensive, and usually justified only where the manufacture of a large number of items permits the distribution of the initial development costs over a large production run.

One representative design procedure may be broken down into a number of separate steps, similar to the following:

- Define load parameters: voltage, current, RRV, pulse width, duty cycle, stray capacity.

- Select dc supply voltage.

- Make a trial PFN design.

- Estimate the transfer efficiency.

- Make an initial selection of turns for T_1.

- Determine the value of C_1.

- Select a charging interval.

- Calculate the value of L_1.

- Design charging choke L_1.

- Select a hold-off interval based on SCR turn-on characteristics.

- Select the charge-transfer interval from C_1 to C_n.

- Determine the saturated inductance of L_2.

- Compute the volume of L_2 and select the core.

- Determine the number of turns and the winding configuration for L_2.

- Select the saturated inductance for T_1.

- Compute the volume and select the core for T_1.

- Compute the number of turns and the trial winding configurations for T_1.

- Calculate the winding and core losses for L_2 and T_1, and recompute the design if necessary.

- Make a trial design for L_3.

- Calculate the core resetting.

- Do the thermal design.

- Operate the trial design in a representative circuit.

• Refine or modify the design as indicated on the basis of operating performance.

It is desired to produce a 9.1-kV pulse across a 70-Ω resistive load; a pulse length of 1.5 μs is desired, and a dc supply voltage of 320 V is specified.

The PFN will have a 70-Ω impedance and a 1.5-μs length; thus from Equation 5–1

$$C_n = \frac{\tau}{2Z_o} = \frac{1.5 \times 10^{-6}}{2 \times 70} \approx 10^{-8} \text{ F}$$

The modulator efficiency is estimated at 70%; i.e., approximately 85% of the voltage across C_1 will be transferred to C_n through T_1. The turns ratio is thus

$$n = \frac{E_o}{E_{dc} \times 0.85}$$

$$= \frac{9.1 \times 10^3}{(320)(0.85)} = 33$$

where the common factor of 2, which would appear in both numerator and denominator, has been omitted. Then C_1 may be calculated as

$$C_1 = (10^{-8})(33^2) = 10 \ \mu\text{F}$$

by conservation of the stored energy of the two capacitors, assuming that all charge is transferred from C_1 to C_n.

Next, the charging interval for C_1 may be established, and the design of charging choke L_1 proceeds as in Chapter 6.

The next step involves the design of switching inductor L_2. The peak charging voltage on C_1 is 1.9 $\times$ 320, or 608 V. An SCR with a 5-μs turn-on time is selected, giving a required volt-time integral product of

$$\lambda = (5 \times 10^{-6})(608) = 3.04 \times 10^{-3} \text{ V} \cdot \text{s}$$

It is desired that L_s for L_2 be an appreciable portion of the inductance controlling the transfer of charge from C_1 to C_n. The network inductance L_n is 210 μH (from Equation 5–2), and if one selects the saturated inductance of L_3 to be around 10% of this value to minimize the voltage developed across the load during charging, say 30 μH, the total inductance on the secondary of T_1 will be 210 + 30 or 240 μH. Transforming this to the primary of T_1, an equivalent L of 0.24 μH is obtained. Thus, the combination of 0.24 μH and the saturated inductance of L_2 should resonate with the series combination of C_1 and C_n (referred to the primary of T_1). If a 5-μs charge-transfer interval is selected, then from Equation 3–2

$$5 \ \mu s = \pi \ \sqrt{(0.24 \times 10^{-6} + L_s)(5 \times 10^{-6})}$$

or

$$L_s \approx 0.3 \ \mu H$$

for L_2. Thus, the design parameters for L_2 are

$$\lambda = 3 \times 10^{-3} \ V \cdot s$$
$$L_s = 0.3 \ \mu H$$

From Equation 7–2, with

$$B_s = 1.0 \ \text{tesla (T)}$$
$$\mu_s = 2.9 \times 10^{-6} \ H/m$$

the core volume is

$$Al = \frac{(2.9 \times 10^{-6})(3 \times 10^{-3})^2}{(4)(1^2)(0.3 \times 10^{-6})} = 2.18 \times 10^{-5} \ m^3$$

After examination of available cores it is decided to use two 4178 Delta-max cores side by side; together these have $A = 1.21 \times 10^{-4}$ m^2 and $l = 1.8 \times 10^{-1}$ m and are in nonmetallic cases. Then by rearranging Equation 7–1, the required turns can be found:

$$N = \sqrt{\frac{l}{A} \frac{L_s}{\mu_s}} = \sqrt{\frac{(1.8 \times 10^{-1})(0.3 \times 10^{-6})}{(1.21 \times 10^{-4})(2.9 \times 10^{-6})}} = 12 \ \text{turns}$$

At this point the validity of the design may be checked by using the biased inductor to discharge a charged capacitor and measuring the voltage hold-off and discharge characteristics. It will be determined that a reduction in turns to 10 gives the following values:

$$\lambda = 3.3 \times 10^{-3} \ V \cdot s$$
$$L_s = 0.32 \ \mu H$$

When the inductor was fabricated, solid copper wire was used, although litz wire might have reduced losses somewhat. It is not surprising that turns should be removed, since only the iron area was used in the above calculation. If the net case area had been used instead, the turns would have been more nearly correct. It also might appear that a B_s of 1.0 T may be a little small, and experience has shown that a value of 1.4 T may be more appropriate for some situations.

The design of T_1 now begins with the specification of a 5-μs transfer period of charge from C_1 to C_n and a 0.5-μs guard interval to accommodate changes in material properties with temperature. If all circuit values are referred to the secondary of T_1 and it is remembered that the voltage across T_1 will be sinusoidal, with an average value one-half the peak voltage, then

$$\lambda = \frac{(608)(33)}{2}(5.5 \times 10^{-6}) = 5.5 \times 10^{-2} \text{ V} \cdot \text{s}$$

Then a value of L_s is chosen that is small compared to L_n, say 30 μH. Then core volume

$$Al = \frac{(2.9 \times 10^{-6})(5.5 \times 10^{-2})^2}{(4)(1^2)(30 \times 10^{-6})} = 7.3 \times 10^{-5} \text{ m}^3$$

A type 50261 core with a volume of 6.91×10^{-5} m^3 and a length of 0.23 m was selected. The turns were

$$N = \sqrt{\frac{(0.23)(30 \times 10^{-6})}{(3.02 \times 10^{-4})(2.9 \times 10^{-6})}} = 88 \text{ turns}$$

Actual measurements resulted in a reduction to 66 turns, at which point T_1 exhibited $\lambda = 6 \times 10^{-2}$ V $\cdot$ s and $L_s = 32$ μH.

The shunt inductor should support the output pulse with a little to spare; thus it is designed for 2 μs and 10 kV, or $\lambda = 2 \times 10^{-2}$ V $\cdot$ s. Then if one assumes $L_s = 30$ μH,

$$Al = \frac{(2.9 \times 10^{-6})(2 \times 10^{-2})^2}{(4)(1)(30 \times 10^{-6})} = 9.6 \times 10^{-6} \text{ m}^3$$

A 4180 core was selected with a volume of 1.32×10^{-5} m^3 and a length of 0.219 m. The turns are then

$$N = \sqrt{\frac{(0.219)(30 \times 10^{-6})}{(6.05 \times 10^{-5})(2.9 \times 10^{-6})}} = 193 \text{ turns}$$

The test operation had the result that 118 turns were used, which resulted in $\lambda = 2.04 \times 10^{-2}$ V $\cdot$ s and $L_s = 29.3$ μH.

The bias supply was selected as 3 Volts 1 A, and a series choke of value 50 mH was used to isolate the supply and to supply constant bias current. The bias windings of L_2, T_1, and L_3 were connected in series, 21 turns on L_2, 8 on T_1, and 10 on L_3.

The final steps include thermal design by procedures outlined before, and actual operation in the circuit. In actual operation, the saturation time of L_2 was approximately 5.2 μs, the transfer interval from C_1 to C_n was 5.2 μs, and the modulator produced a 9.1 kV pulse 1.6 μs long across the 70-Ω resistive load. The overall modulator efficiency was 69.7%.

9–3 HARD-TUBE MODULATORS

Hard-tube modulators have a number of desirable characteristics, including the ability to operate at high pulse-repetition rates, to generate closely spaced pulse bursts, and to carefully control the shape of the output pulse generated. The design of a conventional hard-tube modulator involves the selection of a suitable switch tube, determination of the coupling capacitor to provide the desired pulse droop, and the selection of suitable recharge and isolating elements. A reasonable design for a conventional hard-tube modulator is set forth in Volume 5 of the Rad. Lab. series. Two less conventional designs are discussed in this section; one is a hard tube modulator for a millimeter-wave EIO, while the other is a switch driver for a high-power floating-deck modulator.

EIOs typically exhibit a large frequency change for a relatively small change in cathode voltage (see Section 2–2); thus, an extremely flat top on the cathode voltage pulse is required if frequency changes during the pulse are to be minimized. This requirement led to the selection of a hard-tube modulator, operated in the unsaturated region, with a capability for an extremely precise control of the drive pulse applied to the switch tube.

The modulator can be conveniently divided into three sections: a pulse shaper, a driver, and an output stage. The output stage, which is shown in Figure 9–4, consists of a Y690 switch tube operating in the unsaturated mode. The output stage is driven by the driver, consisting of a bifilar-wound inverting transformer driven from the plates of three 5687 tubes. The grids of the 5687 tubes are driven through a bifilar-wound inverting transformer by a power FET, which in turn is driven by the pulse shaper.

The pulse shaper is shown in Figure 9–5 in simplified form. An input trigger generates a basic pulse which is longer than the desired transmitter pulse and which is used to drive a tapped delay line. The output of each delay-line tap is buffered and goes to a NAND gate and through an inverter to an adjacent NAND gate.

A drawing of a single combination of these gates is given in Figure 9–6, showing the NAND of the delayed and undelayed waveforms causing the output to go low for a time interval equal to the delay-line spacing. This action causes current to flow through transformer T_1 to transistor Q_1, and directly through transistor Q_2. The ratio of these currents is adjusted by the potentiometers, and the difference in the two currents either charges or discharges capacitor C_1 during the appropriate interval. In this manner the pulse shaper can generate an output pulse whose shape is adjustable in increments equal to the spacing of the delay-line taps. The voltage on C_1 is buffered by the emitter follower Q_3 and sent to the FETs of the output stage. A voltage that is the average of the peak current through the EIO is fed back to the emitter power

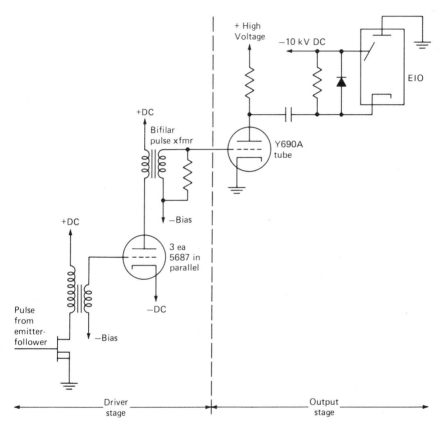

FIGURE 9–4 Simplified schematic diagram of the driver and output stage of the hard-tube modulator used to pulse a millimeter-wave EIO.

supply of Q_3 in order to stabilize the peak EIO current. In the particular version that was constructed, the spacing of the delay-line taps was 10 ns, and so each adjustment potentiometer controlled a 10-ns section of the driver pulse. In order to terminate the pulse, the outputs of the delay lines were multiplexed and a selected tap was monitored; when the signal reached this preselected tap, the MOD PULSE OFF signal was

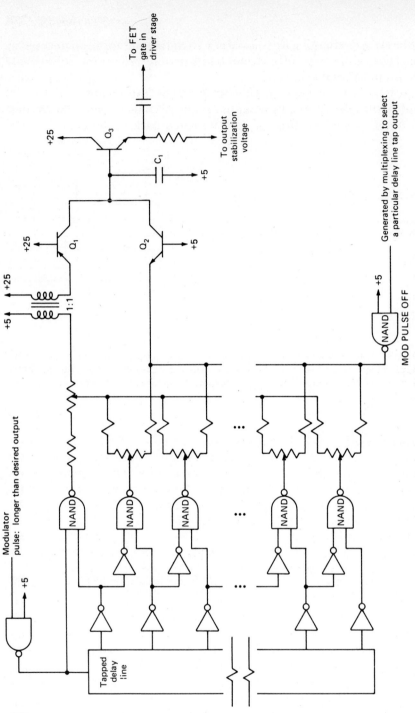

272

FIGURE 9-5 Simplified schematic diagram of pulse-shaper circuit used with EIO modulator.

generated, discharging the capacitor C_1 and terminating the driver pulse. Selection of the tap to be multiplexed permitted ready adjustment of the output pulse width.

A relatively low-value resistor for the plate load for the Y690 triode switch tube was chosen in order to properly discharge the stray capacity

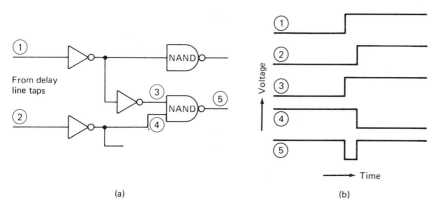

(a) (b)

FIGURE 9–6 **Simplified circuit diagram and waveforms for one section of pulse-shaping logic used to generate the incrementally adjustable drive pulse.** (*a*) **Simplified diagram of pulse logic used in pulse shaper;** (*b*) **idealized waveforms at points in** (*a*), **above.**

associated with the EIO to achieve the desired rapid fall time. Unfortunately, this resulted in a reduction in modulator efficiency, but for this application pulse fidelity and pulse-shape control were more important than efficiency. Capacitive coupling to the cathode was utilized, and a bifilar-wound choke provided heater current for the EIO from a dc filament supply floating at the -10-kV bias level.

By using this design approach, it was possible to generate a voltage waveform to pulse an EIO with a high degree of flatness; Figure 9–7(*a*) shows the voltage waveform on the cathode of an EIO operating at 140 GHz. The extreme flatness achieved is shown in Figure 9–7(*b*), an expanded view of the same waveform, illustrating that a voltage flatness of less than 50 V was achievable by this method.

The second hard-tube modulator example is the grid driver for a floating-deck hard-tube modulator for a system that generates 25-A, 50-kV pulses that must be instantaneously variable in width from 1 to 100 μs at pulse rates up to 200,000 pulse/s [6]. In order to satisfy these requirements, a high-power floating-deck modulator was fabricated; a simplified block diagram of such a system is given in Figure

9–8, and one for the grid-drive circuit is given in Figure 9–9. In Figure 9–10 are shown the idealized waveforms for plate voltage, plate current, grid voltage, and grid current for the switch tubes. Note the initial spike in the waveform used to provide the plate current to discharge the stray capacitance of the circuit. In addition, it is also desirable to be able to

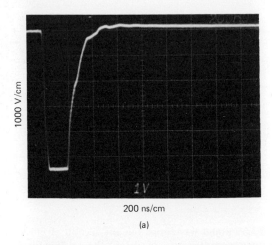

200 ns/cm

(a)

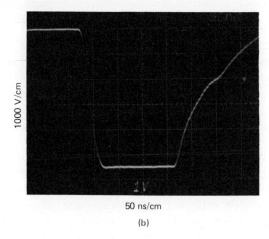

50 ns/cm

(b)

FIGURE 9–7 Modulator output waveforms at cathode of EIO for hard-tube modulator, showing the flat top of the output pulse. (*a*) Cathode voltage pulse; (*b*) expanded cathode voltage pulse showing flatness of pulse top.

"ramp" the top of the drive pulse in order to compensate for droop in the energy-storage capacitor bank.

A schematic diagram of a suitable grid-drive circuit is given in Figure 9–11, and waveforms in this circuit are shown in Figure 9–12. The timing of the output pulse is controlled by transformer-coupling ON and OFF triggers across the high-voltage interface. Tube V_1 acts as a cathode

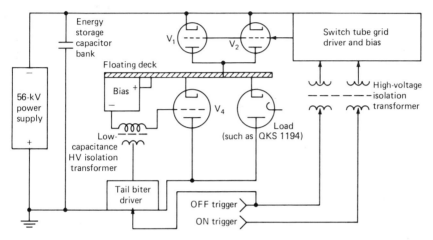

FIGURE 9–8 **Floating-deck modulator block diagram (filament and power isolation omitted for simplicity). [6]**

follower to establish a reference voltage across capacitor C_1. V_2 acts as a constant-current source providing approximately 10 mA of current. Tube V_3 is initially biased slightly positive with its plate near the reference potential across the tube. Once the ON trigger is received, the ON blocking oscillator generates a pulse equal in width to the spike required at the output; the pulse is fed to both the grid of the tube V_5 and the spike amplifier. The plate of V_5 pulls the grid of V_3 negative, charging capacitor C_2 and cutting off tube V_3. The time constant R_2C_2 is selected so that V_3 will remain cut off for a time greater than the width of the longest desired output. The output of the spike amplifier is transformer-coupled through T_1 and CR_2 to the plate of V_3, forming the spike portion of the output signal. After the spike has been removed, the plate voltage of V_3 is clamped to the reference potential across C_1. Once the OFF trigger is applied, the OFF blocking oscillator pulses the grid of tube V_3 and V_4 positive, reducing the output voltage to zero. The voltage at the plate of tube V_3 is buffered by the 7403 cathode followers to

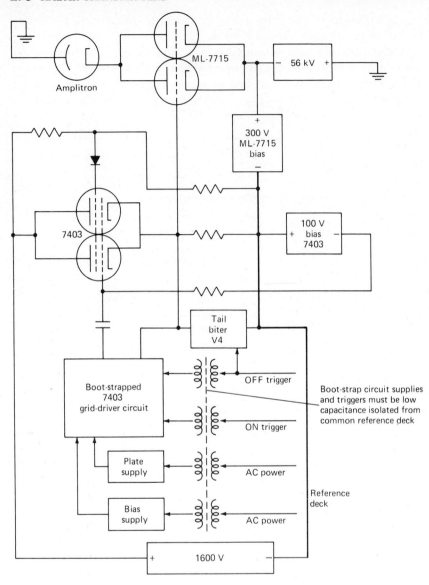

FIGURE 9–9 Block diagram of grid-drive circuit used in Figure 9–8 (heaters and supplies are omitted). [6]

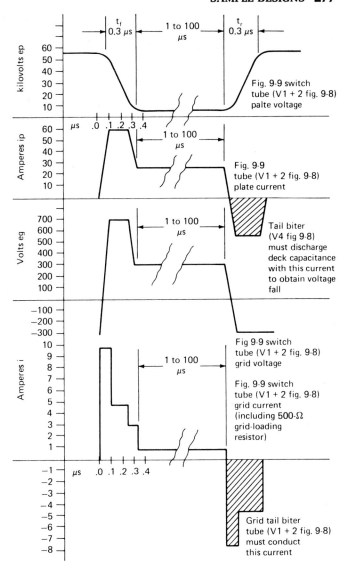

FIGURE 9–10 Switch tube waveforms for the circuit shown in Figure 9–8. [6]

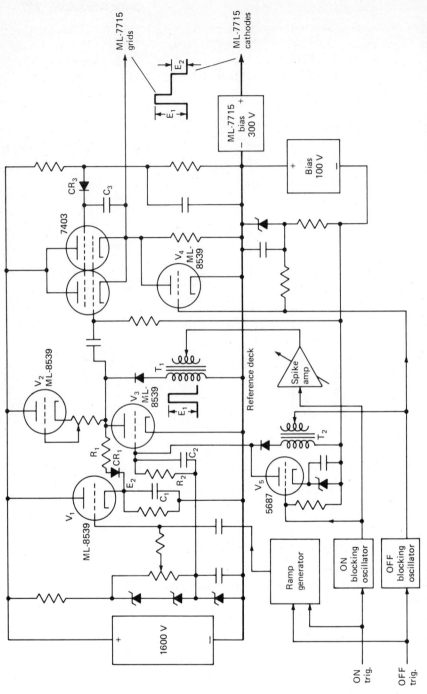

FIGURE 9–11 Details of grid-drive circuit used to generate waveforms shown in Figure 9–10 (heaters and heater supplies are omitted). [6]

278

drive the final switch-tube grid. The tube V_4 is required to discharge the input capacitance of the switch-tube grids in order to achieve fast fall time. Ramping of the output is accomplished by feeding a portion of the output of the ramp generator to the grid of tube V_1, thus ramping the clamp level across C_1. The operation of the ramp generator is syn-

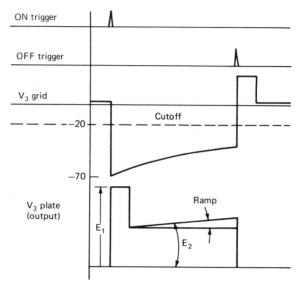

FIGURE 9–12   **Waveforms of modulator shown in Figure 9–11. [6]**

chronized by the ON and OFF triggers, which are transformer-coupled across the high-voltage interface.

9–4   GRID-PULSE MODULATORS

In a grid-pulse modulator, a constant dc voltage is applied from the anode to the cathode of the tube, the grid is biased negative with respect to the cathode during the OFF condition, and the grid is pulsed positive with respect to the cathode in order to turn on the RF tube. In this section, possible designs for several TWT modulators grid-pulsed for low power (1 to 10 kW) will be discussed.

There are a number of different approaches that may be utilized in order to provide the dc cathode power supply for the tube. Conventional rectifying or voltage-multiplying circuits may be utilized in order to provide this dc voltage, but in many cases the amount of ripple or the regulation of the supply is not adequate. If an inverter-type power supply is utilized, a high switching frequency may be selected, permitting low ripple while using filter components small in size and weight. it is also possible to incorporate feedback within such a switching regulator in order to improve circuit regulation. However, a more straightforward approach to achieve low ripple and good regulation is to incorporate regulator circuitry between the rectifier output and the tube. Series vacuum-tube regulators are almost universally employed for such an application.

A simplified schematic diagram of a straightforward series regulator is given in Figure 9–13. The key to operation of this circuit is the utilization of the high-voltage corona-discharge-voltage reference tube, which can provide up to tens of thousands of volts reference voltage with relatively low currents. This circuit arrangement works well for applications where extreme regulation is not required.

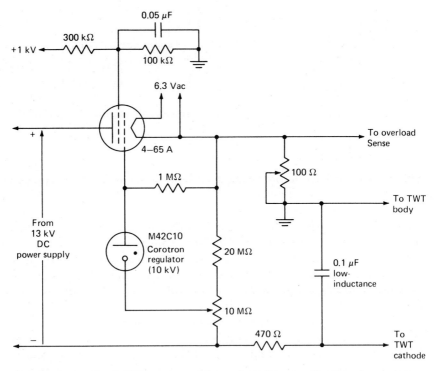

FIGURE 9–13 Simple TWT power-supply regulator for an application where extreme regulation is not required.

For applications where more exacting regulation requirements exist, additional loop gain must be provided in the regulation loop [5]. Figure 9–14 shows the simplified schematic diagram for such a TWT dc power-supply regulator, which provides a high degree of regulation coupled with relatively small size achieved by the use of a miniature series regulator tube. The instantaneous load current is provided by the storage

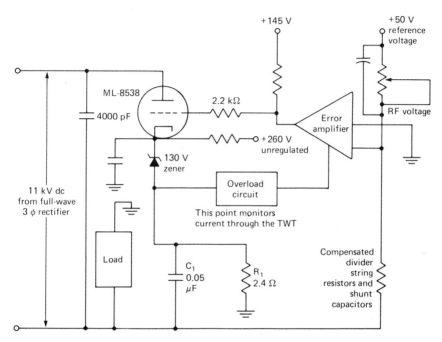

FIGURE 9–14   Diagram for TWT cathode-voltage regulator for a −8.3-kV supply. [5]

capacitor C_1. In order to achieve good regulation, a compensated divider string samples the tube voltage, compares it with a reference, and drives the series regulator tube in order to keep the output voltage constant. Any arcs through the tube are sensed as an increase in voltage across R_1, which initiates a cutoff of the series regulator tube for approximately 70 ms.

A key to the small size of the overall power supply is the use of the miniature triode tube. This tube is encapsulated as shown in Figure 9–15 in order to ensure connection reliability. An extremely thin layer of efficient dielectric separates the base of the heat sink, an aluminum block, from the chassis.

The low-frequency open-loop gain of the regulator is approximately 113 dB, and attenuation in the feedback string is approximately 44 dB, the resultant loop gain being approximately 69 dB. The frequency for a 0-dB loop gain has been measured as 144 kHz. For operation at 15 mA, 8300 V, line regulation was measured to be 0.025%, ripple and noise totaled 3 V peak-to-peak, and regulation over the temperature range was 0.288%.

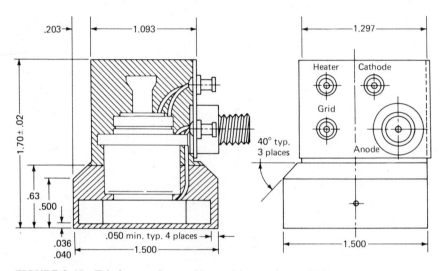

FIGURE 9–15 Triode potted assembly used in regulator of Figure 9–14. [5]

The pulsing of the grid may be approached in several ways, including utilizing a small floating deck for the grid driver, utilizing a pulse generator that floats at cathode potential, and generating an appropriate pulse at ground potential and transformer-coupling it to the grid. Under no circumstances should direct capacitive coupling of the pulse to the grid be utilized, since an arc within the TWT would then result in excessive grid-to-cathode voltages and the discharge of the stored energy in the coupling capacitor through the grid, with its subsequent destruction.

Figure 9–16 is a simplified schematic diagram of a grid-modulator pull-up and pull-down circuit designed to provide an extremely flat pulse to the TWT grid; a flatness of 2 V was typically achieved, and rise and fall times on the order of 15 to 20 ns were observed for the RF output pulse [2]. The entire modulator floats at grid potential, and trigger pulses are coupled across the high-voltage interface through transformer T_1 [4]. A similar configuration is shown in Figure 9–17; this resulted in a rise time of the detected RF signal of less than 5 ns. A small line-type modulator that floats at cathode potential may be used to pulse the grid, as shown in Figure 9–18.

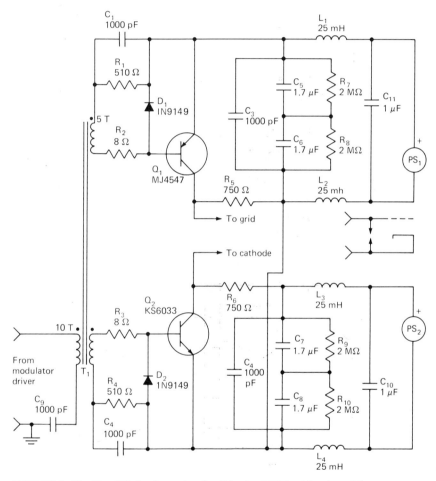

FIGURE 9–16   Simplified schematic of solid-state TWT grid pulser. [2]

An approach that results in reduced circuit complexity at high voltage involves transformer coupling of the pulse directly to the grid of the TWT, as shown in Figure 9–19. A high-voltage, high-power vacuum-tube blocking oscillator was utilized to generate the pulse at ground

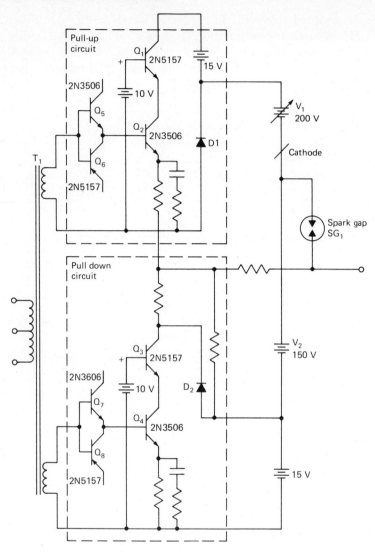

FIGURE 9–17 Simplified schematic diagram of another solid-state TWT grid pulse. [4]

potential. The selection of this approach was at least partially influenced by the availability of a 1-kV supply near ground potential and the utilization of ML-7209 tubes in other portions of the system. A view of the plate voltage of the blocking oscillator is shown in Figure 9–20, and a view of the detected RF output pulse for this modulator is shown in Figure 9–21.

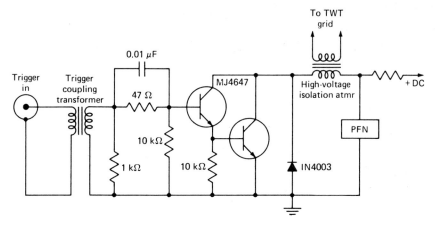

FIGURE 9–18 Simplified schematic diagram of a PFN discharge TWT grid pulser.

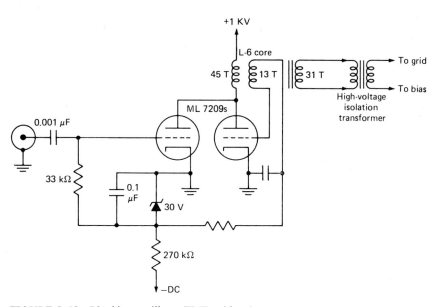

FIGURE 9–19 Blocking-oscillator TWT grid pulser.

9–5 FLOATING-DECK MODULATOR

Floating-deck modulators are typically utilized in high-power linear-beam tubes and often require extremely large voltage swings with relatively low beam-intercept current. Because such high-power tubes are not commonly encountered, few design examples of large, high-power

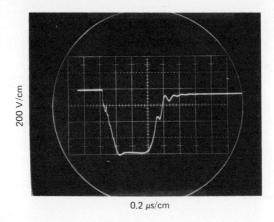

200 V/cm

0.2 μs/cm

FIGURE 9–20 Blocking-oscillator plate voltage for circuit of Figure 9–19.

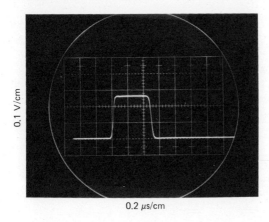

0.1 V/cm

0.2 μs/cm

FIGURE 9–21 Detected RF output of a TWT grid-pulsed by the circuit of Figure 9–19.

floating-deck modulators are encounted in the literature. An article by Glen Grotz, which was originally presented at the Ninth Modulator Symposium, is probably the best summary of techniques and performance associated with large, high-power floating-deck modulators, and this design example is based on the reprint of his article in *Cathode Press* [3].

The specific application was to pulse a large klystron, which was to be the transmitter for a radar to study the characteristics of reentry vehicles. Such a modulator, while not required to switch an appreciable portion of the beam current, nevertheless needs to have a high current capability in order to charge and discharge the stray capacitance rapidly to achieve good pulse shape. The modulator must be insulated for the full klystron beam potential, and all control and adjustment functions must bridge this high-voltage barrier. As is the case with any high-voltage, high-power application, the possibility of arcing or breakdown in either the switch tube or the klystron itself must be accommodated to prevent damage to the switch tubes, the klystron, or associated circuitry.

The floating-deck modulator accommodated both a single-pulse and a pulse-burst mode, and the individual pulses could be either relatively long or short. The klystron operated at 180 kV of beam voltage and 220 A of beam current when the modulating anode was driven to ground potential. The modulating-anode current was typically less than 1 A, but requirements for charging and discharging the stray capacitance can result in considerably higher peak-current requirements for the modulator.

A simplified schematic diagram of the modulator klystron and the power supply is shown in Figure 9–22. Switching of the modulating anode is accomplished by a pair of ML-LPT-17 switch tubes, rated at 200 kV and 200 A peak current. Light beams are utilized to conduct the start pulses to the floating modulator deck, which floats at −195 kV dc.

During the flat top of the pulse, where no charge or discharge current is required, the drive requirements of the switch tubes are reduced to a level commensurate with the continuous conduction currents, in order to reduce grid dissipation in the switch tubes. At the end of the flat top of the pulse, a light-beam stop pulse turns off the drive, clamping the modulating anode back to the cathode. Once the deck has been returned to the cathode for at least 2 μs, the drive to the second tube is removed, and a bias power supply prevents conduction of the klystron during the interpulse period.

In order to ensure a constant voltage on the klystron during the transmitted pulse, elements C_5, R_6, C_6, R_7, L_1, R_8, and R_9 were included in order to provide appropriate damping and a voltage source impedance which is constant over a wide range of frequencies.

A simplified schematic diagram of the driver stage is shown in Figure 9–23. The starting light beam is generated by a neon lamp and conducted through a Lucite rod to the photomultiplier tube, which generates the start pulse for the switch tube. This is then amplified and transformer-coupled to the ML-7003 driver tube, which in turn is coupled to the grid of the LPT-17. A few features of this driver are worthy of note, including first, the incorporation of the circuit that centers about the motor-driven delay line DL_1, which determines the width of the initial grid-drive spike. Control for the motor drives that determine both the width and the amplitude of this initial spike is accomplished by utilizing a long Lucite rod to actuate microswitches, which in turn control the rotation of the motor. The second interesting feature associated with this driver circuit is the inductor Z_1 incorporated in the grid circuit of

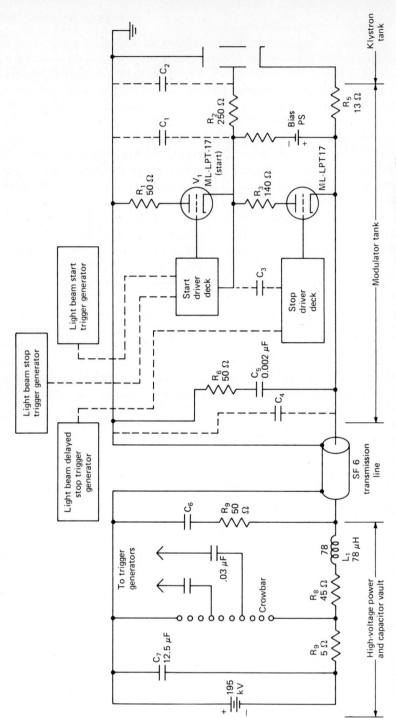

FIGURE 9–22 Simplified schematic of klystron, modulator, and power supply for floating-deck modulator. [3]

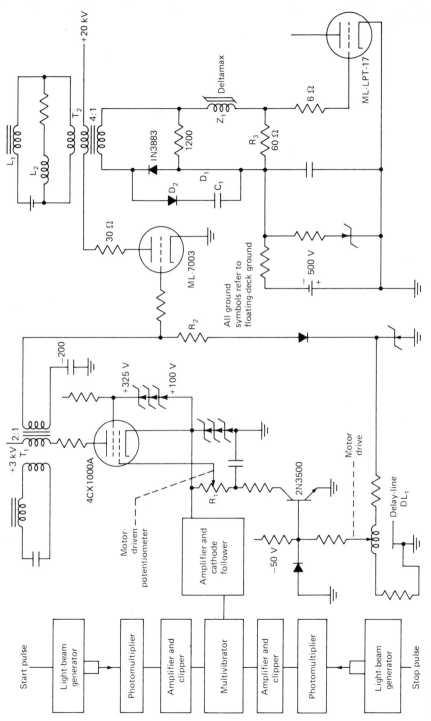

FIGURE 9–23 Simplified grid-driver schematic diagram for modulator of Figure 9–22. [3]

289

the LPT-17. This is a biased saturable inductor, arranged so that normal pulses are transmitted through with little attenuation but large voltage spikes produced by arcing within the LPT-17 cause the inductor to come out of the saturated region, presenting a high impedance and protecting the diodes associated with the driver tube. Figure 9–24 shows a view of the driver output waveforms generated by this circuit. It should be

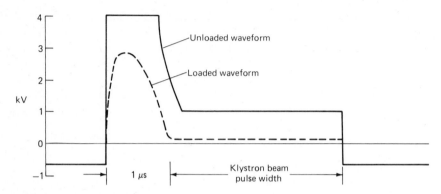

FIGURE 9–24   Driver output waveform produced by the circuit of Figure 9–23. [3]

noted that extremely low impedances are utilized in the klystron drive circuit, in order to prevent loss of control of the tube current by the grid circuit due to secondary grid emission in the event of modulator malfunction.

The modulator is contained in an oil-filled steel tank, the oil providing both a cooling and an insulating function. Most of the electronic equipment is contained within two large corona shields, which are supported on insulating legs and whose sides are perforated in order to permit the passage of cooling oil. The oil is continuously pumped through a heat exchanger, filtered externally, and returned to the tank through the cooling jackets for the anodes of the switch tubes. AC power for each of the floating decks is provided by an electrostatically shielded isolation transformer, insulated by oil-impregnated kraft paper surrounding the electrostatic shield. Critical voltages are controlled by motors, which are in turn controlled by the push-rod arrangements described earlier. Critical voltages are monitored by meters, which are visible through conducting glass panels provided for electrostatic shielding.

An integral part of the design of a high-power modulator is the consideration of conditions that may occur in the event that one of the high-voltage devices should arc. An acceptable design must establish two conditions: first, all components must be protected so that an occasional arc will not destroy the component in which the arc occurs; and second, an arc in one component must not result in the overvolting and failure of another component. In order to ensure the second condition, the distributed inductance and stray capacitance of all components must be damped so as to preclude an oscillatory condition in the event an arc occurs at any point in the circuit.

The modulator equivalent circuit shown in Figure 9–25 can be used

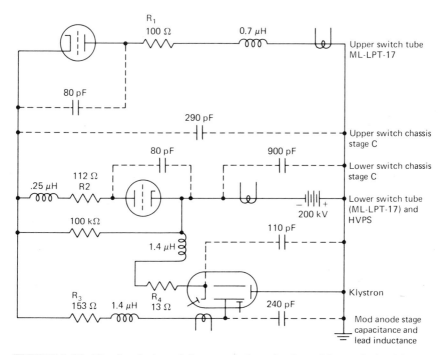

FIGURE 9–25 **Floating-deck modulator equivalent circuit used for analysis of damping during faults and crowbar firing. [3]**

to analyze the effects of various transients that occur because of arcs at various points in the circuit; appropriate damping resistances are incorporated to ensure that oscillatory discharges do not take place. As an example, if an arc should occur in the upper switch tube, the discharge of the upper-chassis stray capacitance through the upper switch tube will cause a polarity reversal on the upper chassis. Such a reversal will result in an overvoltage condition on the lower switch-tube anode unless the circuit is critically damped so that such a voltage reversal does not take place. Therefore, a resistor was placed in the anode of the upper switch tube to critically damp the distributed inductance and stray capacitance of the circuit. In a similar manner, combinations of arcs were analyzed and appropriate resistances incorporated to ensure that oscillatory discharge conditions did not exist.

Prevention of damage to either switch tubes or the klystron is accomplished by means of a spark-gap crowbar circuit, which senses the peak current drawn from energy-storage capacitor C_4 and discharges the power supply in the event of excessive current associated with an arc in any portion of the floating-deck modulator. The discharge characteristics of all of the capacitances in the various portions of the circuit must be such that the allowable energy per pulse dissipated in either the klystron or the switch tubes is not exceeded. A somewhat arbitrary limit of 30 J per arc for the klystron was established, and calculations of the various energy-storage elements indicated that a maximum of 24 J per arc would be dissipated. Primary contributors are the energy stored in stray capacitance C_2, damping capacitors C_3 and C_4, and the discharge of the 12.5-μF energy-storage capacitor C_5 through the klystron in the event of an arc from the cathode to the modulating anode to the tube body.

In a similar manner, switch-tube dissipation can be calculated and will be substantially less than for the klystron, since peak currents in the switch tube are significantly reduced by the series damping resistors in the anode of each switch tube.

Several of these modulators have been built and delivered, and two were operated for nearly three years, accumulating a total of over 3000 high-voltage hours without any switch-tube failures occurring except for initial failures during shakedown. One tube failed as a result of crowbar logic-circuit failure, while another failed because of an anode ceramic puncture. The ceramic thickness was increased and no further punctures occurred.

REFERENCES

1. Coate, G. T., and L. T. Swain, Jr., *High-Power Semiconductor-Magnetic Pulse Generators,* MIT Press, Cambridge, Mass., 1966.

2. Feil, M. J., "A Solid-State TWT Modulator," in *IEEE Conf. Rec. 1976 12th Modulator Symp.,* February 1976, pp. 179–181.

3. Grotz, G., "Design Considerations for a 180 kV Floating Deck Modulator," *Cathode Press,* vol. 25, no. 2, 1968, pp. 16–27. (Also presented at 9th Modulator Symp.)

4. Ishikawa, K. Y., C. T. McCown, and G. E. Stronks, "A Modulator for the SEASAT-A Radar Altimeter," in *Conf. Rec. 1978 13th Pulse Power Modulator Symp.*, June 1978, pp. 235–241.

5. "−8.3 kV TWT Power Supply Uses Miniature Planar Triode as Series Regulator," *Cathode Press,* vol. 25, no. 2, 1968, pp. 10–15.

6. O'Loughlin, J. B., "The Planar Triode ML-8539 Is Used to Drive High Power Switch Tubes," *Cathode Press,* vol. 24, no. 2, July 1967, pp. 2–6.

APPENDIX
A
PULSE-MEASUREMENT TECHNIQUES

In order to evaluate the performance of high-power-pulse radar transmitters, specialized measurement techniques are required. These measurements fall into two categories: measurement of the voltages and currents associated with the pulse modulator, and measurement of the transmitted-pulse power, frequency, and spectrum.

High-voltage probes and dividers are required to reduce modulator-pulse and charging-waveform voltages to safe levels that can be viewed on an oscilloscope. High-voltage pulse measurements can also be made with peak-reading voltmeters. The measurement of pulse currents in magnetrons and thyratrons requires specially constructed pulse-viewing resistors and transformers. The high voltages and currents encountered in pulse modulators can cause problems with capacitive and inductive pickup, as well as differences in ground potential, or ground loops, which result in undesired signals in the pulse-viewing system. The transmitted RF pulse can also produce unwanted electromagnetic interference in oscilloscopes and peak-reading voltmeters.

Knowledge of the transmitted-pulse peak power, center frequency, and power spectrum is needed to achieve optimum system performance. Thermistors, bolometers, calorimeters, and diode detectors are used in measuring average RF power. Peak-power meters using diode detectors or integrating bolometers are also commercially available. The pulse spectrum can be measured with commercially available spectrum analyzers up to 40 GHz. As with high-voltage viewing, care must be exercised to reduce the peak and average microwave power to safe levels.

A-1 VOLTAGE AND CURRENT MEASUREMENTS
Oscilloscopes

Modulator pulse and charging waveforms, as well as the detected RF pulse, are viewed on cathode ray oscilloscopes. The principal consideration in the selection of an oscilloscope for pulse viewing is the oscilloscope bandwidth. The bandwidth of the oscilloscope determines the fastest pulse rise time that can be viewed without distortion. For a pulse with an exponential rise time, the rise time t_r as measured from the 10% to the 90% amplitude point is related to the oscilloscope bandwidth by the equation

$$t_r = \frac{2.2}{f}$$

where f is the oscilloscope bandwidth. The rise time as viewed on the oscilloscope screen can be determined by the equation

$$t^2_{r(\text{viewed})} = t^2_{r(\text{pulse})} + t^2_{r(\text{scope})}$$

where $t_{r(\text{pulse})}$ is the actual pulse rise time. Real-time measurements with oscilloscopes can be made at frequencies up to 500 MHz. Sampling oscilloscopes are available with bandwidths up to 18 GHz (for example, the Hewlett-Packard Model 1811A, which uses a remote feed through sampling head Model 14300, thus eliminating the need for high-frequency interconnecting cables).

Radar transmitters often produce RF pulses of less than 1 μs in width at a repetition rate in the kilohertz range, which may produce a very dim oscilloscope trace when viewed in real time. Oscilloscopes with variable-persistence storage CRTs permit easy viewing of low–repetition-rate pulses. The Tektronix Model 7834 storage oscilloscope has a stored writing speed of 2.5 cm/ns, enabling one to capture a single-shot rise time of 1.4 ns, 3.5 cm high. Digital-storage oscilloscopes may also be useful in such measurement situations.

High-Voltage Dividers [5]

High-voltage dividers are required to reduce modulator voltages to levels compatible with the input range of the oscilloscope. In general, the input impedance of a voltage divider must be so high that it produces negligible effects on the circuit being measured. The divider must have a uniform transient response over a wide band of frequencies so that it produces negligible distortion of the measured waveforms. In the usual case where a coaxial cable is used to connect the output of a divider to the input of an oscilloscope, the output impedance of the divider should be matched to the characteristic impedance of the cable to avoid unwanted reflections. Electrical characteristics of the divider should not vary with voltage, temperature, and time. The divider should be capable of precise calibration by standard laboratory techniques.

High-impedance voltage dividers are constructed of noninductive resistors and high-frequency, low–dissipation-factor capacitors. There are three types of voltage dividers: the parallel RC divider, the resistive divider, and the capacitance divider. The circuit for a parallel RC divider is shown in Figure A-1. The general solution for the response of this circuit to an applied step voltage V is found to be

$$\frac{V_2}{V} = \frac{R_2}{R_1 + R_2} + \left(\frac{C_1}{C_1 + C_2} - \frac{R_2}{R_1 + R_2}\right) e^{-t/R'C'}$$

where $R' = \dfrac{R_1 R_2}{R_1 + R_2}$

and $\quad C' = C_1 + C_2$

If $R_1 C_1 = R_2 C_2$, then

$$\frac{R_2}{R_1 + R_2} = \frac{C_1}{C_1 + C_2}$$

and

$$\frac{V_2}{V} = \frac{R_2}{R_1 + R_2} = \frac{C_1}{C_1 + C_2}$$

giving a perfect voltage divider whose ratio is the same for all values of t, i.e., whose response is the same at all frequencies.

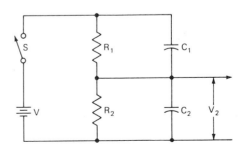

FIGURE A-1   Parallel RC **compensated voltage-divider circuit.**

If R_1C_1 is less than R_2C_2, then V_2 builds up exponentially, with a time constant equal to $R'C'$, as shown in Figure A-2, and if R_1C_1 is greater than R_2C_2, then V_2 decreases exponentially. The stray capacity of the cable and the scope and the scope-input resistance can be allowed for in the design and calibration of the divider. Because of the conflict

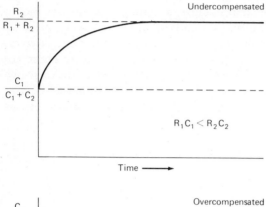

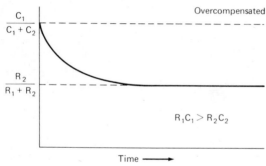

FIGURE A-2 *RC* divider response curves for step input voltage showing overcompensated and undercompensated conditions.

between dissipation ratings and high-frequency characteristics in R_1, *RC* voltage dividers generally have much higher pulse ratings than their dc or rms rating. Tektronix high-voltage probes P-6013 and P-6015 are basically *RC* dividers with additional compensation networks, as shown in Figure A-3, where the various circuit elements affect different areas of the pulse. The characteristics of the P-6015 probe are given in Table A-1.

The resistance divider is a special case of the *RC* divider in which two noninductive resistors are connected in series to form a voltage divider where the stray capacities are given by C_1 and C_2. If these capacities are kept small, this divider will have good pulse response. Excellent high-frequency response can be obtained if the divider is made low

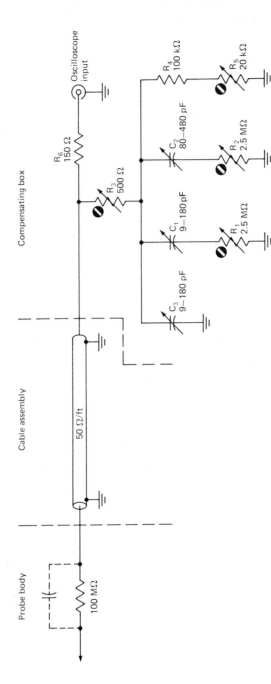

FIGURE A-3 Schematic diagram of Tektronix 1000:1 high-voltage probe usable to 40 kV pulse voltage.

TABLE A-1   TEKTRONIX P-6015 PROBE CHARACTERISTICS

Attenuation ratio	1000:1 (variable by about 9%)
Bandpass (complete assembly)	DC to 50 MHz (flat within 2%)
Rise time (complete assembly)	Approximately 4 ns
Temperature range	10 to 55°C
Cable center-conductor resistance	50 Ω/ft
Input resistance	100 MΩ (±3%)
Input capacitance	Approximately 3 pF
Maximum input voltage (dc or rms)	20 kV (for frequencies above 100 kHz)
Maximum input voltage (pulse)	40 kV peak (maximum duty factor 10%; maximum pulse duration 0.1 s)

enough in resistance that the value of R_2 is less than or equal to the cable characteristic impedance. It is desirable that the cable be properly matched to avoid reflections. If R_2 equals the cable characteristic impedance, Z_0, the cable is properly matched to the circuit and no reflections occur. For the case where R_2 is less than Z_0, there are two methods of termination: (1) a shunt resistor of value $R_0 = Z_0$, and (2) a series resistor of value $R_m = Z_0 - R_2$, as shown in Figure A-4.

The voltage-division ratio is given by the equations

$$\frac{V_s}{V} = \frac{R_2 R_0}{R_1 R_2 + R_2 R_0 + R_0 R_1}$$

for the shunt resistor and

$$\frac{V_s}{V} = \frac{R_2}{R_1 + R_2}$$

for the series resistor. The low impedance of this type of voltage divider may cause excessive loading of the pulse generator and is, in general, too low for observing dc or charging waveforms.

The capacity divider was the first to be commonly used in pulse work because of the availability of high-voltage vacuum capacitors. The capacity divider has a high input impedance, but the low-frequency response is very poor because of the leakage of the low-voltage capacitor, making the divider inadequate for viewing charging waveforms. Since the capacity divider is reactive, it tends to form a resonant circuit with the inductance of the connecting leads and may produce high-frequency oscillations on the leading edge of the voltage pulse, limiting the high-frequency response of the divider. Shunt termination of the connecting cable cannot be used with the capacity divider, because this produces an unbalanced RC divider, which will differentiate the pulse. The series termination of $R_t = Z_0$ works well if the reactance of C_2 is small compared with R_t at the cable ringing frequency. To avoid accidental pickup of

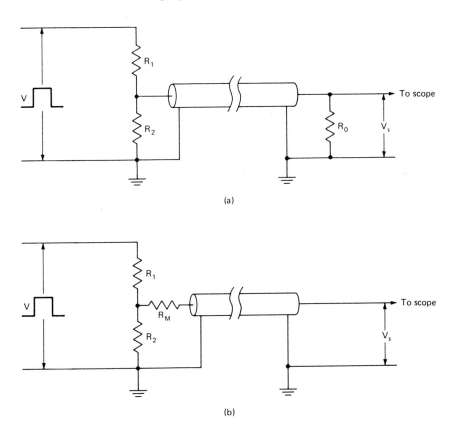

(a)

(b)

FIGURE A-4 (*a*) Shunt and (*b*) series terminations for resistive voltage dividers.

undesired signals, the voltage point between R_1 and R_2 or C_1 and C_2 must be well shielded. The choice of the divider ratio must often be a compromise between the need for a low-impedance output and the need for a large output signal level to avoid sensitivity to stray pickup.

Peak-Reading Voltmeters [15]

Peak-reading voltmeters measure pulse voltages by rectifying the pulse signal and reading the resulting dc current or voltage. Figure

A-5 shows three basic types of peak-reading voltmeters: the peak-above-average type, the peak-to-peak type, and the peak-above-zero type.

The peak-above-average voltmeter consists of a capacitive divider in which the signal across the low-voltage capacitor is rectified and then read by a sensitive dc voltmeter. The input of the capacity voltmeter must be well shielded to avoid stray pickup. Sensitive dc voltmeters are also prone to RF pickup. In order to find the pulse voltage with respect to ground, the dc voltage level must be accounted for. If the

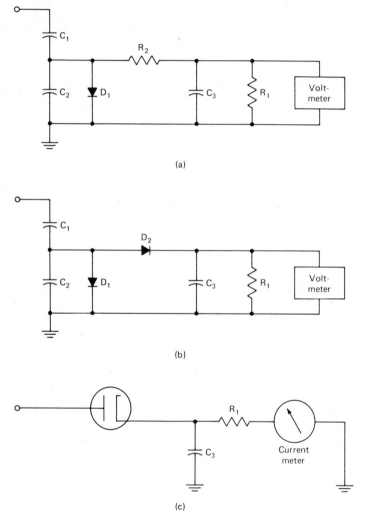

FIGURE A-5 Various types of peak-reading voltmeters: (*a*) peak-above-average, (*b*) peak-to-peak, (*c*) peak-above-zero.

dc level can be measured or calculated, then it can simply be added to the peak-above-average reading. If the dc level is trivial, it can be ignored, as would be the case for a low–duty-cycle pulse waveform. Since there is no dc voltage across an inductor, the output of a pulse transformer will have a zero average level. The average voltage of the output terminal of a charging choke will be close to the dc supply level.

The peak-to-peak voltmeter is a variation of the peak-above-average voltmeter but has limited usefulness in pulse-modulator circuits, since the peak-to-peak voltage is of little interest, except for unidirectional pulses where one is at ground. The peak-above-zero voltmeter is best for modulator work, since it reads the true peak voltage; however, it is more difficult to construct since it requires a high-voltage rectifier, capacitor, and resistor. Because of the long recovery time of high-voltage silicon diodes, the rectifier must be a high-voltage vacuum diode. For negative voltages, an isolated filament transformer is required, which adds to the input capacity. The peak-above-zero voltmeter can be directly calibrated on high-voltage dc and has no sensitive circuits that can be affected by RF pickup. The peak-above-average and peak-to-peak voltmeters can be calibrated by the peak on a sine wave.

In all types of peak-reading voltmeters, errors will unavoidably be introduced in the measurement of peak voltages at very low duty cycle because of the droop of C_3 between pulses. The meter will read the average of the ripple across C_3 rather than the peak voltage. The resulting error is:

$$\frac{1}{2R_1C_3 \times \text{PRF}}$$

This linear approximation of the exponential decay across C_3 is correct to less than 1% if the time constant R_1C_3 is 50 times the longest interpulse period.

Pulse-Current Measurement [15]

The pulse currents in thyratrons and magnetrons can be viewed by inserting a small resistor in the ground return of the pulse current and observing the voltage across the resistor, as shown in Figure A-6, where the small value of resistance is achieved by connecting several resistors in parallel.

Thyratrons and magnetrons have pulse currents from less than 10 A to several hundred amperes which can rise to full value in less than 10 ns. For such high rates of rise of current, small inductances can produce large voltages across the viewing resistor. A carbon resistor 1 in long has enough self-inductance to produce a di/dt voltage comparable to its IR drop. In order to reduce inductive effects to 1%, the self-inductance L_r of the viewing resistor must be

$$L_r = 0.01 \, R t_r$$

where R is the resistance of the viewing resistor in ohms and t_r is the pulse rise time. Ordinary wire has an inductance greater than 0.5 μH/ft; thus, special care must be exercised to reduce the inductance of

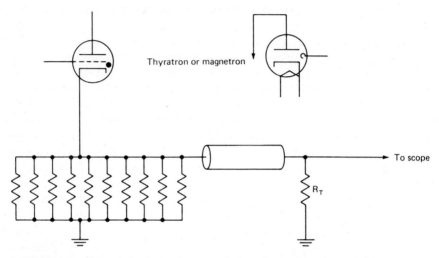

FIGURE A-6 Current-viewing resistor consisting of a number of composition resistors in parallel. Often the resistors are arranged in a coaxial configuration.

the viewing resistor. The most common solution is to provide a large number of current paths that have as large a diameter and as short a length as practical. Coaxial construction of the ground return can cancel out much of the inductance. Low-inductance viewing resistors can also be constructed by folding a thin Nichrome sheet back on itself to cancel the inductance.

Since the resistance of the viewing resistor is generally very low, the viewing cable can be matched with either a series or a shunt termination. If the internal impedance of the pulse generator is low, a series matching resistor should not be used, since the sudden increase in voltage across the viewing resistor that occurs when the initial wave front returns from the open end of the cable at the oscilloscope can effect an appreciable change in load current; therefore, best results can be obtained with a shunt termination at the oscilloscope.

When the pulse current is viewed in the ground lead of a magnetron, the output flange of the magnetron must be insulated from the waveguide. This can be done by using a choke flange, nylon screws, and a thin Mylar sheet between the flanges. For short pulses, the inductance of the waveguide to ground may be high enough that the magnetron can be connected directly to the waveguide without causing severe distortion of the current pulse.

The average current in a pulse circuit can be measured by connecting a conventional current meter in parallel with a large capacitance that bypasses the pulse current. A resistor should be connected in parallel with the meter to ground to provide a dc return in case of meter burnout. A resistance or an inductance or both can be placed in series with the meter to protect the meter against surge current.

Another method of viewing pulse currents is with a pulse-current transformer. The secondary of the transformer is closely wound around a high-permeability core. The one-turn primary is the wire that carries the pulse current and passes through the center hole of the core. The primary must be adequately insulated to withstand the pulse voltage. The pulse-current transformer may be placed anywhere in the pulse circuit. Figure A-7 shows the equivalent circuit of such a current-viewing transformer.

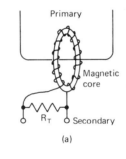

(a)

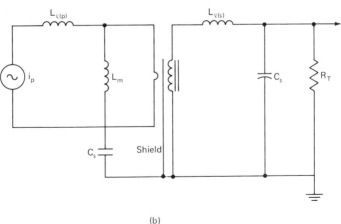

(b)

FIGURE A-7 (a) **Pulse-viewing current transformer and** (b) **equivalent circuit.**

The loosely coupled primary and tightly coupled secondary give the current transformer an accurate current transformation, although not necessarily an accurate voltage transformation. For a high-μ core and a low value of the output load R_t, very little magnetizing current is required, and the secondary current develops a voltage output across the load that is an accurate representation of the primary current, although the voltage ratio is not accurate, because of the loose coupling. The leakage inductance of the secondary is minimized by the tight coupling of the secondary to the core, giving the pulse transformer good high-frequency response. Loose coupling of the primary produces a high leakage inductance that presents a high reactance to the pulse circuit. The cable connecting the transformer to the oscilloscope can be terminated at either end, as in the pulse-viewing resistor. The low-frequency response of the current transformer is improved by making the magnetizing inductance large by using a larger core with a high μ. The high-frequency response is improved by minimizing the effect of the leakage inductance and distributed capacity in the secondary. To avoid stray pickup caused by capacitive coupling between the secondary and the primary, the secondary is usually completely enclosed by a shield, with a gap to prevent a shorted-turn effect. The shield conducts the capacitive currents directly to ground. Double shielding of the transformer and cable may be required to avoid ground-loop problems. Although it is usually not a problem, the transformer can saturate with very large-amplitude or long-duration pulses. If the average dc current flowing through the transformer primary is large, the transformer may tend toward saturation over many pulses. This problem can be avoided by resetting the core with a bias current through the secondary. The Tektronix Model CT-5 current transformer has a bandwidth of 0.5 Hz to 20 MHz and maximum current ratings of 50 kA and 700 A. The transformer rise time is 17.5 ns.

Stray Pickup [5,15]

There are three types of stray pickup associated with high-voltage modulators: capacitive, inductive, and RF pickup. Undesired voltages can be coupled into the measuring circuit through stray capacitances. For example, 1 pF of stray capacitance to a thyratron anode falling from 20 kV to ground in 50 ns will couple 20 V into a 50-Ω circuit. Capacitive pickup can be avoided by using coaxial cable. In severe cases, a double outer shield may be required along with shielding of the source end.

Inductive pickup is caused by a time-varying magnetic field. The voltage induced between the signal and return leads depends on the net flux between them and its rate of change; thus inductive pickup can be eliminated by having the signal and return leads equidistant from the source of the magnetic field. The outer shield of the coaxial cable averages the field over its diameter, making its induced field equal to that of the center conductor. Since the magnetic field falls off inversely with the distance from its source, the average of these fields over the outer diameter of the coaxial cable may not be equal to that of the field at the center conductor if the cable is close to the source of the magnetic field, so that the cancellation of the induced voltage will be incomplete.

RF pickup can be a problem with high-powered microwave transmitters. The leakage RF energy may be rectified in sensitive instruments, primarily in oscilloscopes and sensitive voltmeters. The problem can be solved by removing the instrument as far as possible from the RF source or by using shielding. RF on signal cables can be eliminated by using low-pass filters. In high-power modulators, different ground points can have pulse differences in potential caused by the large currents flowing through the finite resistance and inductance of the ground path. Capacitive and inductive pickup can also produce differences in ground potential. For an oscilloscope with different ground points, such as a safety ground and a trigger ground return, the different ground potentials will result in ground loops that can cause stray pickup. Two tests can be made to determine if circulating ground current is causing stray pickup. If the coaxial cable is disconnected from the input of the oscilloscope and only the ground is connected, then the residual signal on the oscilloscope will be preamp pickup. If the coaxial cable is reconnected to the scope and the source end disconnected from the measurement point and connected to a shielded termination with the outer conductor touched to the ground at the measurement point, cable pickup will be observed.

Circulating ground current can be eliminated by using pulse baluns, as illustrated in Figure A-8. The balun has the effect of introducing

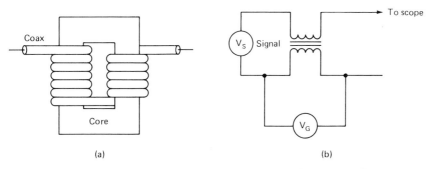

(a) (b)

FIGURE A-8 **Pulse balun used to reduce effects of circulating ground currents on waveform measurements: (*a*) balun construction; (*b*) ground-loop voltage.**

an inductance in the ground loop which impedes the flow of circulating ground currents. Since the ground resistance is generally very low and the pulse differences in potential occur at high frequencies only, a small amount of inductance is required to eliminate circulating ground current. The pulse balun consists of a coaxial cable wound about a magnetic core. Usually only a few turns are required. The balun can be considered a bifilar choke that presents a high impedance to common mode voltages but a low impedance to differential mode signals between the center and outer conductors, which cause equal currents to flow in opposite directions, resulting in no net flux in the balun.

A-2 AVERAGE-POWER MEASUREMENT [2,4,7,9,12,14]

A knowledge of average RF power is often important in characterizing CW transmitter and low-power CW drives; in addition, average-power measurements may sometimes be used to infer peak power, as will be discussed in Section A-3. There are five types of average-power sensors: bolometers, thermistors, thermocouples, calorimeters, and diode detectors, thermistors being the most commonly used.

Bolometers and Thermistors

Bolometers and thermistors are power sensors that operate by changing their resistance with temperature when RF power is dissipated as heat in the sensor. The bolometer is a thin piece of wire that has a positive temperature coefficient of resistance. The thermistor is a semiconductor device that has a negative temperature coefficient. Bolometers are very susceptible to burnout, since they are operated with a dc bias to balance the Wheatstone bridge that measures the resistance of the bolometer. The high operating power is near the burnout point, making them easily destroyed.

Thermistors are generally favored over bolometers for average-power measurement. The thermistor is a small bead of metallic oxides, typically 0.4 mm in diameter with 0.03-mm wire leads. A graph of resistance versus power for a typical thermistor is shown in Figure A-9. The lines are nonlinear and vary greatly from one device to the next. Power measurement based on the shape of these curves would be very difficult. Instead, a method is used to maintain a constant resistance in the thermistor by maintaining constant power dissipation with a dc or low-frequency bias current. As the RF power increases, the bias power is decreased by the proper amount required to maintain a constant resistance. The amount of bias power decreased is equal to the RF power and is displayed on a meter.

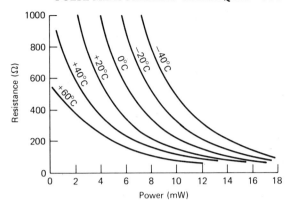

FIGURE A-9 **Resistance as a function of power for a typical thermistor.** [7]

Thermistors are mounted in waveguide or coaxial structures, and are designed to be well-matched to the waveguide or coaxial transmission line. Modern thermistor mounts have an additional thermistor with matched temperature characteristics to compensate for changes in ambient temperatures.

Figure A-10 shows the simplified diagram of an HP 478 coaxial thermistor mount. This mount contains four thermistors, each biased to a resistance of 100 Ω. To the RF power the R_d thermistors appear

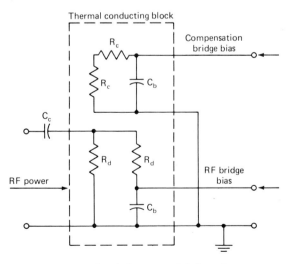

FIGURE A-10 **Circuit for a coaxial thermistor mount showing thermistors used for thermal compensation.** [7]

in parallel through the coupling capacitor C_c and the bypass capacitor C_b. Thus, the thermistor pair provides a 50-Ω termination. To the bias power, the thermistors appear in series (giving 200 Ω).

Figure A-11 shows a waveguide thermistor mount. The detecting thermistor R_d is mounted on a glass epoxy bar so that it is thermally isolated from the waveguide. Electrical contact to the thermistor is made by a thin gold plating on the epoxy. A block of polystyrene foam is inserted in the waveguide to protect the thermistor from air currents, which might change its temperature, and to keep out foreign material. Waveguide thermistors are available to 95 GHz.

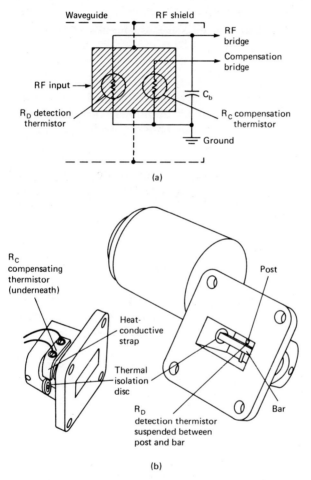

FIGURE A-11 (a) Circuit and (b) disassembled view of a waveguide thermistor mount. [7]

Thermocouples

Thermocouples generate a voltage due to a temperature gradient along the thermocouple. This voltage can be produced in two ways. One is the *Thomson emf*, where a voltage is produced between the hot and cold ends of a metal rod by the diffusion of electrons freed by thermal agitation. The other phenomenon is the *Peltier emf*, where a voltage is produced across the junction of two different metals when the junction is exposed to heat. Thermocouples use both the Thomson emf and the Peltier emf to produce a net thermoelectric voltage.

Modern thermocouples use thin-film and semiconductor technologies. A thin-film resistor of tantalum nitride converts the RF energy to heat. The thermocouple consists of a layer of N-type silicon, and the thin-film resistor (see Figure A-12). As with the coaxial thermistor mount,

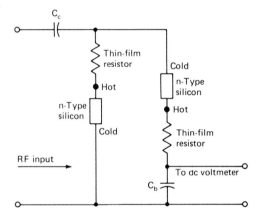

FIGURE A-12   Circuit diagram of a thermocouple power-measuring circuit. [7]

the two thin-film resistors form a 50-Ω termination to RF frequencies through the coupling and bypass capacitors. For dc voltage the two thermocouples are in series and their voltages add. The dc voltage is measured and is proportional to the microwave power at a sensitivity of about 100 μV/mW. Thermocouples' average power is limited to 300 mW.

The thermocouple chip is attached to a transmission line deposited on a sapphire substrate, as shown in Figure A-13. The thin-film resistors in this structure form a very low-reflection termination.

Diode Detectors

Diodes can convert high-frequency energy to dc by their rectification properties. An ideal diode obeys the diode equation

$$i = I_s(e^{\alpha V} - 1)$$

where i is the diode current, V is the voltage across the diode, I_s is the saturation current, and $\alpha = q/nkT$, where k is Boltzmann's constant, T is the absolute temperature, q is the charge of an electron, and n is an empirical constant. The value of α is typically 40 V^{-1}. Expanding

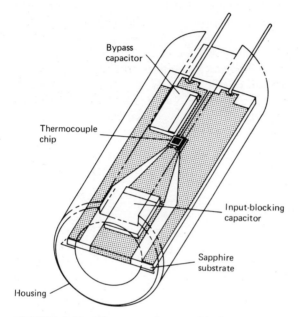

Bypass capacitor

Thermocouple chip

Input-blocking capacitor

Sapphire substrate

Housing

FIGURE A-13 Thermocouple assembly for measurement of power. [7]

the diode equation to a power series gives:

$$i = I_s \left(\alpha V + \frac{(\alpha V)^2}{2!} + \cdots \right)$$

For small signals, only the first two terms are significant, and the second-order term provides signal rectification which results in signal detection; such a diode is said to be operating in the *square-law region.*

Figure A-14 shows a simplified diagram of a source and a diode detector. Maximum power is transferred when the parallel combination of the diode resistance R_d and the matching resistance R_m equals the source resistance R_s. R_d is a strong function of temperature. R_d is made larger than R_s to reduce the temperature dependence of the reflection coefficient. However, a large value of R_d results in decreased sensitivity. A good compromise for R_d is 2.5 kΩ. This requires I_s to be about 10 μA.

I_s for an ordinary silicon pn junction diode is quite large. The low value of I_s is achieved in Schottky diodes, which have the desired low barrier potential. Originally, these were point-contact diodes, which are

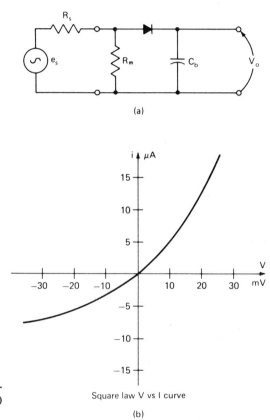

FIGURE A-14 (a) Diode detector equivalent circuit and (b) V-I curve. [7]

Square law V vs I curve

(b)

mechanically very fragile. Also, they were easily burned out because of their small junction area, which results in very high current densities. Now, however, Schottky diodes can be built with photometallurgical techniques to be much more suitable for power measurements, and they can give good performance to 18 GHz. These diodes can measure power from −20 dBm (10 μW) to −70 dBm (100 pW), making them about 3000 times more efficient than thermocouple power sensors. At −70 dBm the diode detector output is about 50 nV, requiring highly sensitive metering circuitry.

Calorimeters

Calorimeters are capable of directly measuring high power levels. Calorimeters generally consist of a water load where the microwave power is absorbed in a matched-impedance section of transmission line or a waveguide filled with a stream of water. The temperature rise of the water is measured by calibrating thermocouples or thermistors, and it is then related to the microwave power level.

A-3 PULSE-POWER MEASUREMENTS [6,7,10]

Units and Definitions

At frequencies from about 30 MHz through the optical spectrum, the direct measurement of power is much more accurate and easier than the measurement of voltage, and at frequencies above 1 GHz, power becomes the fundamental unit of measurement. One reason for this is that the voltage and current vary with position along a transmission line but the power remains constant. Also, in waveguides the voltages and currents are difficult to define and are dependent on the waveguide geometry.

The watt is the fundamental unit of power. One watt is one joule per second, or the rate of energy transfer. In many cases, one is interested in measuring the ratio of two powers, or relative powers. Relative power is a unitless quantity and is expressed in decibels (dB). The power ratio in decibels is defined as follows:

$$P(dB) = 10 \log \frac{P}{P_{ref}}$$

where P_{ref} is the reference power. The advantage of using decibels is that the gain of several cascaded devices can be found by simply adding the gain in decibels of all the individual devices. It should be noted that attenuation is expressed as a negative number of decibels.

Absolute power is popularly expressed in dBm, where $P_{ref} = 1$ mW:

$$P(dBm) = 10 \log \frac{P}{1 \text{ mW}}$$

For example, 13 dBm is 20 mW. A positive value of dBm means "decibels above one milliwatt," and a negative value of dBm means "decibels below one milliwatt."

All power-measurement devices measure power by averaging the instantaneous microwave power $p(t)$ over some period of time T. Mathematically this is expressed as follows:

$$P = \frac{1}{T} \int_0^T p(t) \, dt$$

The term *average power* means that the power is to be averaged over many periods of the lowest frequency involved. For a CW signal, the lowest frequency and the highest frequency are the same; thus the average power is equal to the instantaneous power. The lowest frequency of a pulse-modulated signal is the PRF; thus the integration period $T = n/\text{PRF}$, where n is a large number. Typically, integration times from a few hundredths of a second to several seconds are required.

For pulse power P_p, the instantaneous power is averaged over the pulse width τ. For a trapezoidal pulse, the pulse width is taken at the 50% amplitude points. The relationship between pulse power and average power is given by

$$P_p = \frac{P_{\text{avg}}}{\text{duty cycle}}$$

where duty cycle $= \tau \times \text{PRF}$

It should be noted that the value for τ for a nonrectangular or nontrapezoidal pulse is measured at some point other than the 50% point. This value of τ is referred to as the *equivalent rectangular* pulse width.

Envelope power is measured by making T less than $1/f_m$, where f_m equals the highest modulation-frequency component. The envelope power is what is detected by a square-law detector. The peak envelope power is the maximum value of the envelope power. For a rectangular pulse, the pulse power and peak envelope power are the same, and both may be referred to as peak power.

For a CW signal, the average, instantaneous, and peak powers are identical; thus, CW signals are usually used in calibrating power meters.

Peak-Power Measurement

If the pulse to be measured is trapezoidal, the average power may be measured and the peak power calculated if the pulse width and duty cycle are known; the relationships discussed in the preceding paragraphs are used.

The calculation of peak power from a measurement of average power suffers from the disadvantage that nontrapezoidal waveforms cannot be easily measured. One approach to the problem of measuring such nonrectangular waveforms is the notch wattmeter, shown in block diagram form in Figure A-15. In this concept, a low–duty-cycle RF pulse is measured by pulsing off a reference CW power source during the

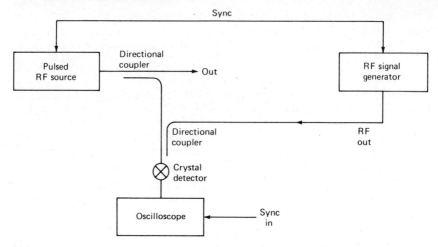

FIGURE A-15   Simplified block diagram of a notch wattmeter. The RF signal genera-tor is "notched" off during the time the signal to be measured is present.

interval in which the pulse source being measured is turned on. By adjustment of the notching signal to the same PRF, amplitude, and duration as the pulse under measurement, it is relatively easy to make the reference CW signal power equal to the peak power being measured.

Another approach to peak-power measurements involves the use of a calibrated crystal detector, as shown in Figure A-16. The reference-

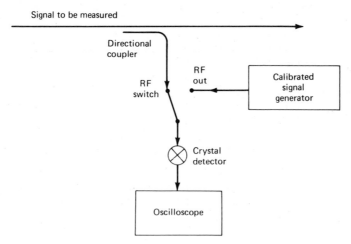

FIGURE A-16   Block diagram of equipment for measurement of peak power using a calibrated-crystal detector.

signal generator is modulated with some known waveform, such as a square wave, and its detected output adjusted to be equal to that produced by the signal to be measured. Then the peak power of the square-wave signal is determined by conventional techniques; the square wave power is equal to the peak power being measured.

Another method of measuring the peak envelope power by using a diode peak detector is shown in Figure A-17. A portion of the RF pulse

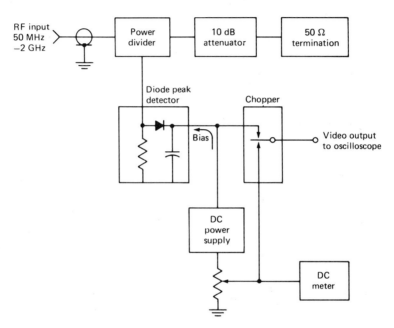

FIGURE A-17   Simplified block diagram of a diode peak detector for measurement of peak RF power. [7]

is fed to a diode peak detector, which develops a dc voltage proportional to the peak voltage of the RF pulse. This voltage is compared to a reference voltage, which is displayed on a meter calibrated in power units. The dc and the pulse envelope are alternately displayed to an oscilloscope by a switch. The dc voltage is adjusted until it is coincident with the envelope peak viewed on the oscilloscope; the equivalent peak envelope power is related to this dc voltage. Of course, sample-and-hold ("boxcar") techniques could also be used to measure this peak detected voltage.

The calibration service currently available at the National Bureau of Standards for calibration of peak RF pulse power meters makes use of the *sampling-comparison* method shown in Figure A-18. This technique uses a specially constructed diode switch to extract a sample of RF power from the pulse to be measured, and also from a CW signal of known value. The CW signal is adjusted to obtain identical readings of the pulse and CW samples on the oscilloscope, and the CW level is then

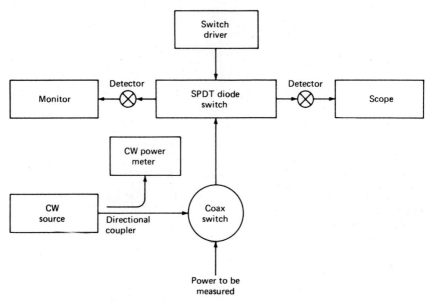

FIGURE A-18 Sampling-comparison method of measuring peak power used by the National Bureau of Standards. SPDT = single-pole, double-throw.

equal to the peak pulse power to be measured at the input of the coaxial switch.

The pulse power as defined in the first part of Section A-3 can be measured directly by the technique of bolometer integration and differentiation. The bolometer's long thermal time constant integrates the RF power and then cools off (see Figure A-19). If this signal is differentiated, the original envelope shape is obtained, enabling the detection of peak envelope power. The pulse widths capable of being integrated range from about 0.25 μs to 10 μs, with maximum peak power of about 300 mW. A simplified block diagram of such a peak-power measurement system is given in Figure A-20. Of course, the bolometers used with such a system must be carefully calibrated if accurate absolute-power measurements are to be performed. Calibrated mounts are available for the radar bands L through X.

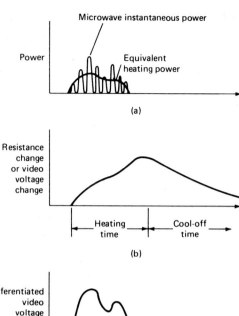

(a)

(b)

FIGURE A-19   Use of bolometer integration and differentiation for measurement of pulse power. (a) microwave pulse; (b) signal at bolometer; (c) bolometer signal after differentiation.

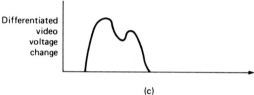

(c)

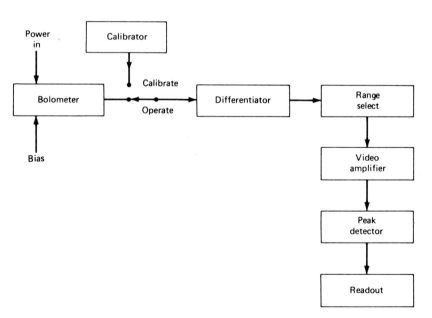

FIGURE A-20   Simplified block diagram of a peak-power meter using a bolometer integration-differentiation measurement system.

319

A-4 SPECTRAL ANALYSIS [1,3,8,11,13]

A considerable amount of information concerning the characteristics of a transmitted RF pulse is included in its frequency spectrum. The frequency spectrum of a pulsed RF signal consists of a central line at the carrier frequency surrounded by a number of discrete lines spaced at the pulse-repetition frequency. The amplitude of these lines is determined by the characteristics of the RF transmitted pulse. Figure A-21 shows the spectrum of a rectangular transmitted pulse, with a

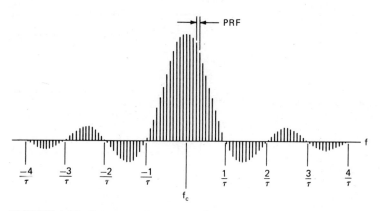

FIGURE A-21 Spectrum of a rectangular-envelope RF pulse of width τ and a fixed PRF. [8]

central line whose amplitude is given by the peak transmitted power times the duty cycle, or the average power, surrounded by lines spaced at the PRF and modulated by a $(\sin x)/x$ envelope. Figure A-22 illustrates the effects of changes in pulse width and pulse-repetition frequency, changes in pulse width affecting the shape of the envelope and the position of the nulls of the envelope, while changes in PRF affect only the spacings of the individual frequency lines.

Deviations from ideal behavior result in modification of the spectrum of the pulse, which is a sensitive measure of these deviations. Figure A-23 illustrates the effects of frequency modulation and amplitude modulation on the spectrum of an RF pulse. It should be noted that combined FM and AM on the pulse, as shown in Figure A-23, is usually representative of magnetron pulse spectra, because of the coupling between frequency and amplitude associated with pushing phenomena in magnetrons.

If, however, there are FM or AM modulations on a pulse-to-pulse basis, the individual spectral lines will be broadened; this effect is particularly important in pulse-Doppler or MTI systems, as was shown in the example given in Chapter 1.

The measurement of the spectral characteristics of an RF pulse may be accomplished by a number of different means, depending on the type of information to be extracted. The information concerning the

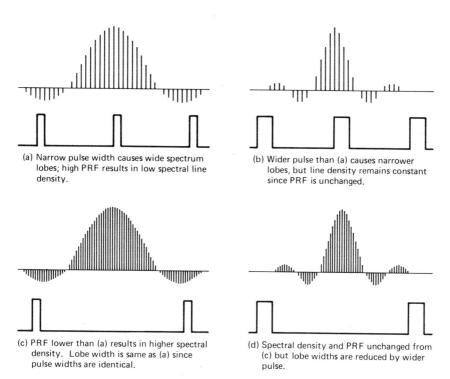

(a) Narrow pulse width causes wide spectrum lobes; high PRF results in low spectral line density.

(b) Wider pulse than (a) causes narrower lobes, but line density remains constant since PRF is unchanged.

(c) PRF lower than (a) results in higher spectral density. Lobe width is same as (a) since pulse widths are identical.

(d) Spectral density and PRF unchanged from (c) but lobe widths are reduced by wider pulse.

FIGURE A-22   Effects of pulse width and PRF on pulse spectra. [8]

envelope of the spectrum can be readily extracted by the use of spectrum analyzer techniques, but examination of the broadening of the individual spectral lines presents a much more difficult measurement problem.

A simplified block diagram of the basic elements that constitute a spectrum analyzer is given in Figure A-24. A sawtooth generator generates both a frequency control for the local oscillator and a drive for the horizontal deflection on a CRT. The local oscillator output is mixed with the incoming RF signal. The resulting signal is amplified in an IF amplifier, detected, and displayed on the vertical axis of the screen.

The response of the IF amplifier may be either linear, square-law, or logarithmic in order to achieve the desired vertical display; and the amount of frequency scanning (dispersion), the rate at which the frequency is scanned, and the bandwidth of the IF amplifier (resolution) are normally selectable to achieve the desired characteristics.

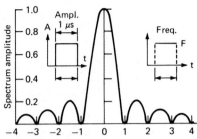

Spectrum of rectangular pulse without AM or FM occurring during pulse. Shape is that of $\dfrac{\sin \omega \frac{\tau}{2}}{\omega \frac{\tau}{2}}$ function.

(a)

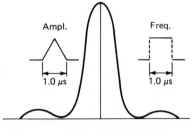

Triangular pulse spectrum without FM during pulse. Effective pulse width is shorter than (a) causing minima to occur at wider intervals of frequency.

(b)

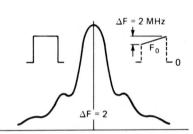

Spectrum of rectangular pulse with linear FM resulting in increased side-lobe amplitude and minima not reaching zero.

(c)

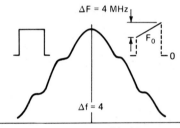

Same pulse spectrum as (c) with more severe FM.

(d)

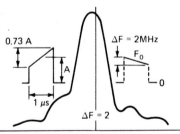

Effect of linear AM and FM during pulse. Note loss in symmetry due to pulse amplitude slope.

(e)

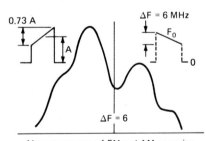

More severe case of FM and AM occurring during pulse.

(f)

FIGURE A-23   Some pulse spectra. [8]

If individual spectral lines are to be resolved, the IF bandwidth B must be less than the spacing between spectral lines; that is,

$$B < \text{PRF}$$

and preferably

$$B < 0.3 \times \text{PRF}$$

In order to avoid errors, the scan width and scan time must satisfy the following relationship:

$$\frac{\text{Scan width}}{\text{Scan time}} < B^2 \qquad [8]$$

where scan width is in hertz per division, scan time is in seconds per division, and B is in hertz.

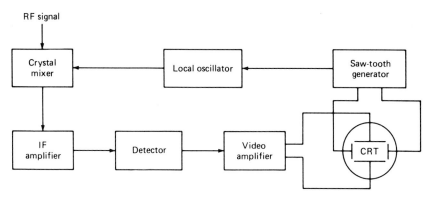

FIGURE A-24   Simplified block diagram of a spectrum analyzer.

If the IF bandwidth cannot meet this requirement and cannot achieve reasonable scan times and sensitivity, the individual spectral lines cannot be resolved. This is not necessarily an undesirable situation, since considerable information can be obtained from the envelope of the spectrum, which is obtained by utilizing an IF bandwidth that encompasses a number of the spectral lines of the pulse spectrum. It should be emphasized that such a display is not a true frequency display, but it does combine both time and frequency. The lines that are displayed under this condition are not the true frequency component lines, but represent the energy that enters the IF bandpass at each transmitted pulse. A certain indication that this condition exists is that the amplitude of these displayed lines and the number of lines displayed change as the IF bandwidth is varied.

In the event that operation in this so-called envelope mode is desired, for good spectral resolution, a reasonable rule of thumb for the selection of IF bandwidth is that

$$B < \frac{0.2}{\tau_{\text{eff}}}$$

and for resolution of lobe minima, it is recommended that

$$B < \frac{0.3}{\tau}$$

It is suggested that bandwidth in the range

$$\text{PRF} > B > 0.3 \text{ PRF}$$

be avoided, and that the scan time satisfy the following relationship:

$$\text{Scan time (s/div)} \geq \frac{10}{\text{PRF (Hz)}}$$

which will ensure that at least 100 lines are visible on any display.

Another important factor to consider in spectral analysis of low–duty-cycle pulses is the so-called desensitization of the spectrum analyzer. The maximum signal that can be accommodated by a spectrum analyzer is limited by the capability of the mixer or spectrum analyzer front end, typically on the order of -10 dBm. There is a pulse desensitization factor α given by

$$\alpha_p = 20 \log \tau_{\text{eff}} \, Bk$$

where $k \approx 1.5$ [8]

The equivalent noise "floor" of the spectrum analyzer is related to the selected IF bandwidth. Thus, the maximum dynamic range of the signal that can be accommodated by the spectrum analyzer is given by the maximum input power in dBm, less the desensitization factor in decibels, less the equivalent noise level for the selected bandwidth (typically on the order of -100 dBm). For short pulses, low duty cycles, and the resultant large IF bandwidths, this pulse desensitization may severely limit the ability to examine low-level frequency side lobes associated with a particular spectrum, and may represent a limiting factor in the use of conventional spectral analysis techniques.

The other type of measurement condition that is of interest to the transmitter engineer is an examination of the broadening of each individual spectral line associated with pulse-to-pulse frequency and amplitude instabilities. The particular requirements of large dynamic range, a high order of frequency stability, and an ability to measure with a high degree of resolution require special techniques to perform such measurements.

The spectrum of a signal is broadened by the presence of AM or FM modulation of the signal. Effects of FM noise are often displayed as a plot of frequency deviation as a function of modulation rate, with the frequency deviation expressed in either peak or rms hertz for a given measurement bandwidth. Effects of AM noise are usually displayed as the single side-band–to–carrier power ratio in dB measured in a specified bandwidth as a function of the frequency separation from the carrier. For small FM modulation indices, these measures of AM and FM noise are related by

$$\frac{P_s}{P_c} = \left(\frac{2 f_m}{\Delta f}\right)^2$$

where P_s = total noise power in a specified bandwidth centered f_m Hz
  from the carrier
  P_c = carrier-signal power
  f_m = modulation rate or separation from carrier (Hz)
  Δf = rms frequency deviation (Hz) in specified bandwidth

The particular techniques utilized for accurate measurement of these noise levels depend upon whether the noise to be measured lies between the central line and the first spectral line, between higher-order spectral lines, or at a distance from the pulse center frequency.

A simplified block diagram of a test setup for measuring spectral power between the first two spectral lines is given in Figure A-25. A sample of the RF drive and a sample of the tube output pulse are compared in a phase-sensitive mixer, after introduction of a delay and gating of the drive signal to compensate for the characteristics of the tube. The output of the phase-sensitive mixer is then sent through a low-pass filter and amplifier before being sent to a wave analyzer for spectral analysis. This approach is utilized in order to employ available equipment, specifically wave analyzers having the required dynamic range in excess of 100 dB, and measurement bandwidths of a few hertz.

In the event that noise measurements beyond the frequency region between the center frequency and the first spectral line are required, one of the inputs to the phase-sensitive mixer is offset in frequency, as shown in Figure A-26. This approach has a lower sensitivity due to the introduction of additional frequency-noise components in the reference channel.

A critical component in this measurement approach is the phase-sensitive mixer, and considerable care must be utilized in order to avoid nonlinear operation and generation of spurious intermodulation products [3,11,13]. With care, it has been possible to reduce spurious components to levels below 100 dB relative to the carrier component. In most

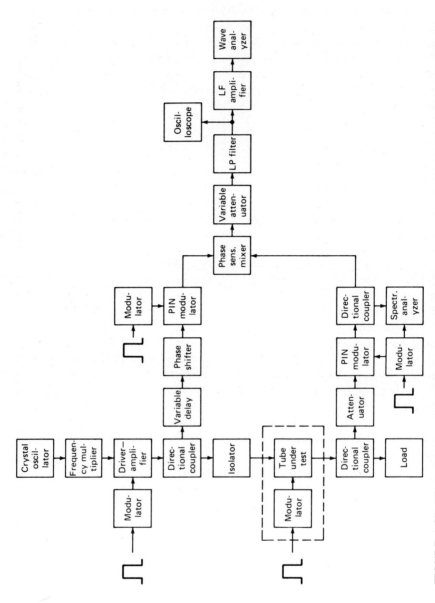

FIGURE A-25 Block diagram of measurement equipment for measurement of spectral components close to the carrier frequency. [13]

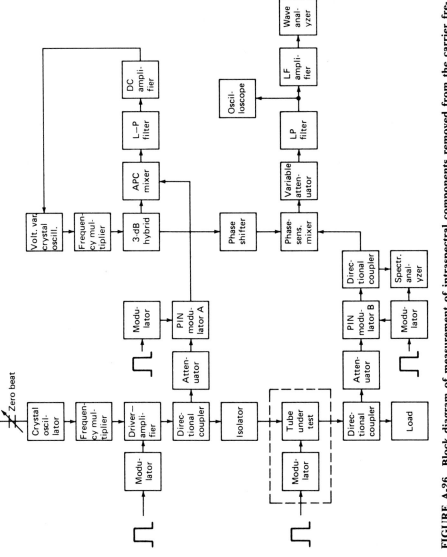

FIGURE A-26 Block diagram of measurement of intraspectral components removed from the carrier frequency. [13]

cases, the dynamic range is limited by the characteristics of the analyzer used rather than by the mixer intermodulation products.

For measurement of the spectrum far from the carrier, it is possible to utilize a bandpass filter at the carrier frequency, in order to permit conventional spectrum analyzers to be utilized for analysis of these noise components without undue limitations in system measurement sensitivity due to their limited dynamic range.

For measurements where a spectrum analyzer or wave analyzer of

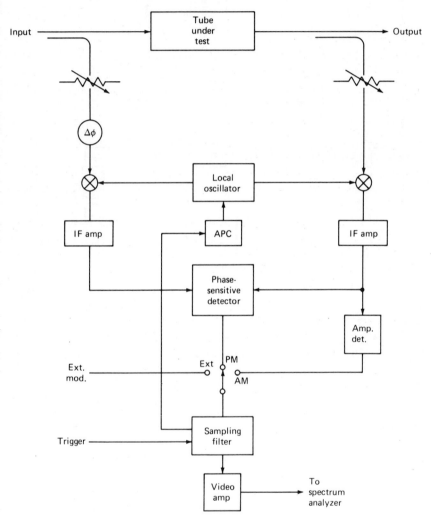

FIGURE A-27 Block diagram of intraspectral-noise measurement equipment using a sampling filter. [11]

the required dynamic range is not available, sampling filters may be utilized in order to reduce the dynamic-range requirements of the spectrum analyzer [11]. A simplified block diagram of such a system is shown in Figure A-27. Dynamic ranges in the region of 125 dB relative to the carrier in the range from 200 Hz to 10 kHz from the carrier have been realized by using a wave analyzer with approximately 80 dB of dynamic range. The use of the sampling filter imposes a $(\sin x)x$ weighting function upon the noise spectrum, which must be corrected for when such measurements are interpreted.

REFERENCES

1. Ashley, R. J., et al., "The Measurement of Noise in Microwave Transmitters," *IEEE Trans. Microwave Theory and Techniques*, vol. MTT-25, no. 4, April 1977, pp. 294–318.

2. Engen, G. F., "A Refined X-Band Microwave Microcalorimeter," *Journal of Research*, National Bureau of Standards, vol. 63C, no. 1, July–September 1959, pp. 77–82.

3. Fischer, M. C., "Analyze Noise Spectra with Tailored Test Gear," *Microwaves*, July 1979, p. 66.

4. Ginzton, E. L., *Microwave Measurements*, McGraw-Hill, New York, 1957.

5. Glasoe, G. N., and J. V. Lebacqz, *Pulse Generators*, MIT Rad. Lab. series, vol. 5, McGraw-Hill, New York, 1948. (Also available in Dover and Boston Technical Publishers editions.)

6. Henning, R. E., "Peak Power Measurement Technique," *Sperry Engineering Review*, May–June 1955, pp. 10–15.

7. Hewlett-Packard, "Fundamentals of RF and Microwave Power Measurements," Application Note 64–1, Palo Alto, Calif., August 1977.

8. Hewlett-Packard, "Spectrum Analysis: Pulsed RF," Application Note 150–2, November 1971.

9. Jackson, W. H., "A Thin-Film/Semiconductor Thermocouple for Microwave Power Measurements," *Hewlett-Packard Journal*, vol. 26, no. 1, September 1974, pp. 16–18.

10. Leibowitz, B., "Peak Pulse Power Measurements," *Cathode Press*, vol. 24, no. 2, 1967, pp. 30–36.

11. Marlow, P., and R. F. Sunderland, "Design of High-Stability Transmitters for Pulse Doppler Radars and Measurement of their Spectral Purity," in *Proc. Radar-77 Intern. Conf.*, IEEE Conference Publication No. 155, 1977, pp. 564–568.

12. Montgomery, C. G., *Technique of Microwave Measurements*, MIT Rad. Lab. series, Vol. 11, McGraw-Hill, New York, 1948.

13. Riedl, G., "Noise Measurements on Pulsed High-Power M/W Amplifiers," *Microwave Journal*, vol. 17, no. 8, August 1974, pp. 29–33.

14. Szente, P. A., S. Adam, and R. B. Riley, "Low-Barrier Schottky-Diode Detectors," *Microwave Journal*, vol. 19, no. 2, February 1976, pp. 42–44.

15. Weil, T. A., "Pulse Measurement Technique," in *Proc. 8th Symp. Hydrogen Thyratrons and Modulators*, May 1964, pp. 120–142.

B

COMMONLY USED UNITS AND CONVERSIONS

Term	Symbol	International (SI) units	Other commonly used units	Conversions
Magnetic flux	ϕ	Weber (Wb)	Lines (maxwells)	1 Wb = 10^8 lines
Magnetic flux density	B	Tesla (T, or Wb/m²)	Gauss (G); lines/in²	1 G = 6.45 lines/in² = 10^{-4} T
Magnetic field strength	H	Amperes per meter (A/m)	Oersted (Oe); ampere-turns/in	1 Oe = 2.02 ampere-turns/in = 79.6 A/m
Length		Meters (m)	Inches (in)	1 m = 39.37 in
Area		Square meters (m²)	Square inches (in²)	1 in² = 6.45×10^{-4} m²
Voltage	V	Volts (V)		
Current	I	Amperes (A)		
Permeability	μ	Henrys per meter (H/m) ($\mu_o = 4\pi \times 10^{-7}$ H/m)		

INDEX